PLASTICS TECHNOLOGY

Basic

Materials

and

Processes

McKNIGHT & McKNIGHT PUBLISHING COMPANY · BLOOMINGTON, ILLINOIS

Robert S. Swanson, Ph.D.

Dean, School of Applied Science
and Technology

Stout State University

Menomonie, Wisconsin

PLASTICS TECHNOLOGY

Basic

Materials

and

Processes

foreword

Plastics are relatively new on the industrial scene if we judge them against wood, metals, ceramics, or leather. However, in the short time they have been available, the consumer has had ample opportunity to become familiar with literally thousands of articles made of synthetic materials. This book is meant to serve as a beginning in the study of this rapidly developing industry.

It includes information on the materials of the industry and the processes by which the raw materials are converted into finished products. It offers explanations of how to work with plastics, as well as providing sample problems and products that call for applications of knowledge and skill. A list of resource materials allows expanded or specialized study. At the end of each chapter is a list of questions that may be used for review and application.

The materials of the plastics industry are defined and discussed in a semi-technical sense. The hundreds of formulations and trade names are grouped according to sixteen basic families, and the general properties and uses of each family are cited. Note that names spelled with a capital letter are registered trade marks — Formica or Fiberglas for example. Generic names are not capitalized — melamine or fiber glass.

The many industrial processes used to transform plastics into the thousands of consumer and industrial articles are explained by giving the basic principles on which they operate. Many illustrations show typical products and the industrial equipment used in their manufacture. Numerous tables summarize the basic concepts, data, and information. The *List of Tables* in the front of the book makes these summaries easy to locate.

The *Study Questions* at the end of each chapter are designed to aid in learning the important information given in each section. The *Apply Your Knowledge* sections go beyond the specific information given. These require applications of the given facts and suggest some further investigation of the vast array of plastics around us.

The *how-to* units list general procedures only. Emphasized are experimental, laboratory, and school shop work rather than

5

mass production; the operations explained are not handicraft in nature, however. They are applications and modifications of industrial practice. The equipment illustrated and referred to is small, versatile, and of a type suitable for the school or model shop. Each unit gives simple step-by-step procedures. The *List of Procedural Units* in the front of the book allows easy reference to these procedures.

Plans for sample products are included. All processes described in the *how-to* sections can be used in making the projects. It is hoped that those shown will suggest a wide range of other ideas; the scope of this field is limited only by the imagination and ingenuity of the student.

Any field that is as broad and rapidly developing as is the field of plastics cannot be covered in depth in one book. For this reason, a number of resource references are included; these listings of books, pamphlets, trade publications, magazines, and films will enable the interested reader to go far beyond the basic coverage of this text.

Meet the Author

The development of methods for teaching the most representative materials and processes of modern industry has long been a major concern of Robert S. Swanson. One of the first pieces of equipment to result from his research was a laboratory plastics-forming press using both mechanical and air pressure. After developing four models with the assistance of his students, the machine was refined commercially and manufactured as a part of the Di-Acro line. Today laboratory-sized equipment has been developed for all important processes and is found in many schools. Two instructional films for plastics have also grown out of Dr. Swanson's pioneering work.

Robert S. Swanson received his B.S. degree in 1949 and his M.S. degree in 1950, both from Stout State University. In 1955, he received his Ph.D. degree from the University of Minnesota. He began teaching as an instructor of general shop and woodworking at Stout in 1949, having been a member of the carpenter's union since 1946. In 1957, he became Head of the Department of Wood Technics, and since has developed a new, well-equipped plastics laboratory at his institution. In 1963, he became Dean of the School of Applied Science and Technology. He has been active in professional organizations, and was President of the American Industrial Arts Association in 1965. Currently he is involved in a major research project to identify the teachable basic concepts of technology which grow out of all modern materials, tools, and processes.

This book incorporates the teaching and processing procedures developed and tested by Dr. Swanson during a period of more than fifteen years. The author can be seen at work in Fig. 15-44 on page 155.

acknowledgments

The breadth of the plastics industry necessitated the collection of materials for this text from a variety of sources. Many industrial firms supplied technical assistance and photographs of equipment and processes. The author wishes to express his appreciation to the following companies who supplied materials used in this book.

Adamson United Co.
Akron, Ohio

Akron Presform Mold Co.
Cuyahoga Falls, Ohio

American Cyanamid Co.
New York, N. Y.

Auto-Blow Corp.
Bridgeport, Conn.

Cadillac Plastic and Chemical Co.
Detroit, Mich.

Catalin Corporation of America
New York, N. Y.

Celanese Corporation of America
New York, N. Y.

Cerro Sales Corp.
New York, N. Y.

Comet Industries, Inc.
Franklin Park, Ill.

Conapac Corp.
New York, N. Y.

The Dake Press Co.
Grand Haven, Mich.

Detroit Mold Engineering Co.
Detroit, Mich.

Devcon Corp.
Danvers, Mass.

The Di-Acro Corp.
Lake City, Minn.

DoAll Co.
DesPlaines, Ill.

Dow Chemical Co.
Midland, Mich.

Dow Corning Corp.
Midland, Mich.

E. I. du Pont, de Nemours Co.
Wilmington, Del.

Durez Plastics Division
Hooker Chemical Corp.
Tonawanda, N. Y.

Eastman Chemical Products Inc.
Division of Eastman Kodak
Kingsport, Tenn.

Egan, Frank W. and Co.
Somerville, N. J.

French Oil Mill Machinery Co.
Piqua, Ohio

Logan Engineering Co.
Chicago, Ill.

Marbon Chemical
Division of Borg-Warner
Washington, W. Va.

Modern Plastic Machinery Corp.
Clinton, N. J.

Molded Fiber Glass Co.
Ashtabula, Ohio

Monsanto Chemical Co.
Springfield, Mass.

Nicholson File Co.
Providence, R. I.

Nopco Chemical Co.
Newark, N. J.

Northwest Plastics Co.
St. Paul, Minn.

Rand Development Corp.
Cleveland, Ohio

Reed Prentice
Division of Package Machinery Co.
East Longmeadow, Mass.

Rohm and Haas
Philadelphia, Pa.

Seelye Plastic-Fab Inc.
Minneapolis, Minn.

Shell Lake Boat Co.
Shell Lake, Wis.

Society of the Plastics Industry, Inc.
New York, N. Y.

Union Carbide Plastics Co.
Division of Union Carbide Corp.
New York, N. Y.

United States Gypsum Co.
Chicago, Ill.

United States Rubber Co.
New York, N. Y.

Van Dorn Iron Works Co.
Cleveland, Ohio

Weldotron Corp.
Newark, N. J.

Wheelabrator Corp.
Mishawaka, Ind.

Special mention must be made of the assistance offered by several of the author's colleagues at Stout State University. Dr. David P. Barnard, head of the Audio-Visual Center, and his staff prepared many of the photographs of operating procedures. Mr. Kenneth Erickson, Industrial Graphics Department, made the drawings of processes and products.

Dr. John A. Jarvis, Dean of Instruction, has for the past fourteen years offered considerable aid and encouragement in the development of the total plastics program at Stout State University of which this book is a part.

Finally, the encouragement and released time afforded by the author's family have been indispensable.

Robert S. Swanson

contents

list of tables

list of procedural units

What comes to mind as you think of plastics? A shower curtain? A floor tile? An airplane enclosure? A toy? A tooth brush handle? A fiber glass boat? A white glue? An Orlon suit? All of these products, different as they seem, may be made from plastics.

This part of the book is concerned with a definition of plastics, their classification, ingredients, the forms in which they are available, the properties which should be considered, a listing and description of the individual members of the family of plastics, and a summary of the trade names that are applied to the many commercial varieties of plastics.

PART I

materials of the plastics industry

CHAPTER ONE ## *what are plastics?*

First of all, *plastics* is the name of a family of *synthetic* materials which have large molecules made up of chains of atoms. They are soft and moldable during manufacture, but eventually solidify. This excludes such *natural* moldable materials as wax or clay which also may be soft or plastic at times.

Plastics come in many different forms. They may appear in products as unlike as boats or toasters. They are found as film and sheeting, fibers and filaments, liquids and adhesives, or molding pellets and powders. Plastics are combined in various ways so that often the range of properties among the various formulations within a given family may be greater than the range of basic properties among different plastics.

The official definition of plastics accepted by the Society of Plastics Engineers (SPE) and the Society of the Plastics Industry (SPI) is "a large and varied group of materials which consist of or contain as an essential ingredient a substance of high molecular weight which, while solid in the finished state, at some stage of its manufacture is soft enough to be formed into various shapes—most usually through the application (either singly or together) of heat and pressure."

Classification of Plastics

The very large number of plastics available is often difficult to comprehend. The same plastic may appear in many different forms. A given plastic may be called by several different trade names. The same trade name may be applied to more than one plastic. However, each of this vast variety of materials can be placed into one of *two groups* as regards its thermal properties: *thermoplastics* and *thermosets*.

Thermoplastics

The thermoplastic plastics become soft when exposed to heat and harden when cooled no matter how often the process is repeated. By alternate heating and cooling they can be reshaped many times. They may be compared to wax in this respect. When heated they are moldable; when cooled they are rigid, but upon reheating they once again become pliable. Important members of this group are acrylics, cellulosics, Nylon, polystyrene, polyethylene, fluorocarbons, and vinyls.

Thermosets

The thermosetting plastics, thermosets, are set or cured into a permanent shape by heat and once set cannot be remelted and returned to their original state. They do not necessarily, however, retain their hardness at extreme heats. Most soften somewhat at temperatures above 350° F., but they will not return to their original flow condition. The reaction may be compared to that of boiling an egg. When heat is applied, the liquid mass is solidified and subsequent heating does not resoften the egg. Prominent members of this group of plastics are phenolics, aminos, polyesters, epoxies, and alkyds.

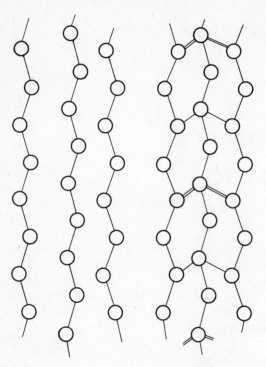

Fig. 1-1. Structure of Thermoplastics
and Thermosets

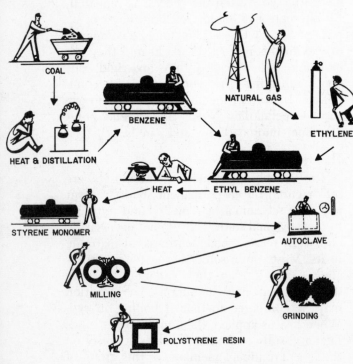

Fig. 1-2. Manufacture of Polystyrene
(Bakelite Co.)

Plastic Structure

In order to understand the reaction of plastics to heat it is necessary to understand something of their molecular structure. In the formation of plastics many atoms are combined to form molecules. Each atom is joined to the next by connecting links called *valence bonds*. Their structure is *chain-like*.

In *thermoplastics*, the atoms and molecules are joined end-to-end into a series of long chains, each chain *independent* of the others. When subjected to heat, the individual chains slip, causing *plastic flow*. When the plastic cools, the chains are once again held firmly, but with subsequent heating, slippage once again takes place. There are practical limitations to the number of heating-cooling cycles to which thermoplastics can be subjected. The result of too many cycles may be loss of color or plasticizer which affects the appearance and the properties.

The structure of *thermosets* is also chain-like and, before molding, very similar to that of thermoplastics. The curing or hardening process (usually during molding) consists of the formation of *cross-links* between adjacent molecules resulting in a *complex, interconnected network*. These cross-bonds prevent the slippage of individual chains, thus preventing plastic flow with the addition of heat. The contrasted structures of thermoplastics and thermosets are illustrated in Fig. 1-1.

How Plastics Are Made

Although plastics are synthetics, they are made from many common natural materials such as wood, air, water, petroleum, natural gas, and salt. Complex chemical reactions are used to produce a great variety of plastics by slightly modifying the processes and ingredients.

The chemist literally takes the natural materials apart by separating their basic molecules and atoms. He then recombines them in different ways with the aid of heat, pressure, and chemical action.

A simplified description of the manufacture of polystyrene illustrates the process. The

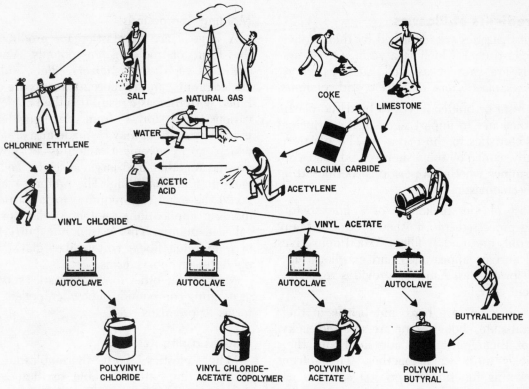

Fig. 1-3. **Manufacture of Vinyls** (Bakelite)

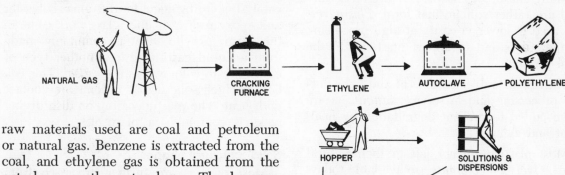

raw materials used are coal and petroleum or natural gas. Benzene is extracted from the coal, and ethylene gas is obtained from the petroleum or the natural gas. The benzene and ethylene are then linked to form ethyl benzene. The last stage involves processing the ethyl benzene with heat and pressure and then milling and grinding it to form the final result, polystyrene. Fig. 1-2 shows this process.

If ethylene gas is combined with chlorine, obtained from common salt, the result is one of the common vinyl resins, vinyl chloride. See Fig. 1-3.

Polyethylene is made from ethylene gas alone processed under heat and pressure as shown in Fig. 1-4.

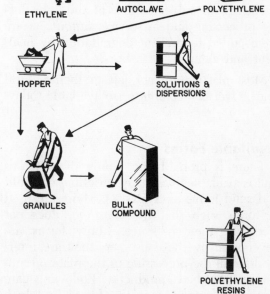

Fig. 1-4. **Manufacture of Polyethylene** (Bakelite)

Ingredients of Plastics

Most plastics are identified by their principal constituent which is a *resin*. Other materials are present as well, such as *fillers, solvents, plasticizers, stabilizers,* and *colorants*.

A *resin* or binder serves to bind the plastic together and to impart some of the principal characteristics to the material. The plastic is usually named by the resin involved. The resin determines whether a plastic is thermosetting or thermoplastic.

Most plastics make use of a *filler* before being processed into finished products. Many materials are used as fillers. Wood flour gives good surface appearance and excellent electrical properties. Asbestos provides resistance to acid and fire.

Many resins are hard and brittle in their natural state, though some are soft and tacky. All of them must be made fluid and their particles must weld together. The *solvent* serves this function. Over 300 solvents are used for various plastics.

Many plastic resins possess high viscosity and are rather stiff in final form. *Plasticizers* are used to lower viscosity at high processing temperatures and to impart plasticity to the final product.

Plastics are subjected to heat and light during processing and in service. *Stabilizers* are often added to prevent degradation by heat, light and aging.

Most plastics are not left in their natural color. Over 800 *colorants* are available today.

Available Forms

There is probably no family of materials that is available in as many variations of liquid and solid forms as is plastics. Many are used in forms such that the consumer does not recognize their presence. Many forms are never seen by the consumer; they are intermediate in the processing of the material into various finished products. Following are general descriptions of the forms in which plastics are available.

Molding Compounds

A large share of plastics are produced in the form of molding compounds. Various additives such as plasticizers, fillers, stabilizers, colorants, and reinforcing agents are combined with the basic resin. It is then made into various solid forms from fine powder to granular pellets. It may be made into *preforms* which are convenient amounts of powder pressed together into larger discs to facilitate weighing and handling. The preform may be made the exact size required for a particular molding application. Another similar form is called a *premix*. This is usually a putty form of reinforcing fibers (often fiber glass) with polyester or epoxy resins.

Many of the other forms of plastics start out as molding compounds in powder, pellets, preforms or premixes.

Liquid Casting Resins

Many plastics, both thermoplastic and thermosetting, are available as liquids for casting and reinforcing. The liquid is often a two-part system with one part being a catalyst or curing agent for the other. Polyester and epoxy resins for fiber glass work come in this form. Acrylic sheet is commonly made from a liquid casting resin. Another type of casting resin is known as a *plastisol*. This is a liquid which solidifies as it comes in contact with heat. The plastic coating on dish drying racks is commonly a plastisol.

Solid Structural Shapes

Most plastics are further processed from molding compounds and liquid casting resins into sheets, rods, and tubes of many dimensions, cross-sectional shapes, and surface finishes. In such forms, they may be machined and fabricated. Plastics to be thermoformed are first made into sheets.

Coatings

Plastic resins are similar in physical state to many natural resins used in paints, varnishes, lacquers, and other coatings. Plastics have replaced many of the natural resins as constituents of finishes. Many of the quick-drying finishes are plastics. A large share of alkyd resins go into the paint industry; phenolics make tough varnishes; cellulosics coat paper; and epoxy resins make excellent metal coatings, to name a few.

Adhesives

In the field of adhesives, plastic resins have replaced many natural materials and have solved joining problems impossible for previous adhesives. Some plastic adhesives come as dry powder to which water is added; urea wood glues are of this type. Others are liquids, either solutions or emulsions; "white" wood glues are polyvinyl acetate emulsions. Some are two-component systems, consisting of a dry powder which is added to a liquid as in resorcinol resin glues. Some adhesives are in the form of films which are laid between two pieces of wood or metal to be laminated. Some are on cloth or paper in the form of pressure-sensitive tapes.

Expanded or Expandable

A number of plastics, both thermoplastic and thermosetting, are available in expanded or expandable form. These are light in weight and appear to be full of bubbles or air spaces. More plastics are appearing in these forms each year.

Expanded plastics are low-density cellular materials of both interconnecting and non-interconnecting types. The former consists of continuous cellular structure and is referred to as open-cell material. The structure of the latter is a series of small bubbles fused together and is called closed-cell material. Expanded or *foamed* plastics appear in both rigid and flexible forms. A common rigid foam is made from polystyrene under the trade name of "Styrofoam." It is seen in displays and decorations but also has many insulating, buoyancy, and shock-resistant uses. Vinyl and urethane foams in flexible form are replacing foam rubber in many cushion applications.

Expandable plastics are materials ready to be expanded or *foamed*. They may be in the form of tiny gas-filled bubbles which expand and fuse together with heat. Other expandable plastics are thoroughly mixed with an inert gas such as carbon dioxide or nitrogen under pressure much like shaving cream in spray cans. Others come as two separate liquids. When poured together, a chemical reaction takes place which causes the material to foam. It solidifies in the foamed form.

Laminates

Laminate is a general term referring to a material made up of a number of sheets or webs of paper, fabric, fibrous glass, or aluminum. This material is first impregnated or coated with a plastic resin and then bonded under heat and pressure to form sheets or panels of various types. The countertop materials, Formica, Micarta, and Texolite, are examples of high-pressure laminates. Corrugated fiber glass reinforced panels for sun porch roofs are common architectural materials. While the term *fiber glass laminated plastics* is commonly shortened to "fiber glass," it must be remembered that these are made mostly of a plastic material with some glass fibers added for reinforcement.

Fibers and Filaments

Some plastics are extruded into continuous filaments. As filaments, polystyrene is used as bristles for brooms, and nylon is the popular monofilament line for spinning-type fishing equipment. Filaments are often woven into fabrics, and combined sometimes with natural fibers such as cotton or wool. Many new "wash and wear" fabrics appear on the market each year. Orlon (Du Pont acrylic fiber) and Dacron (Du Pont polyester fiber) are two well-established materials.

Properties of Plastics

The general properties of many materials are understood by the layman. Most people know that wood burns and that most metals do not, that iron rusts and glass does not, that rubber is elastic and paper tears when stretched. The properties of plastics are not as commonly known and appreciated. The same person who would not be surprised that a drinking glass breaks if dropped on the floor often complains of an inferior product if a plastic toy is smashed when stepped on.

Plastics is the designation of a large group of materials. Various members of the group have widely varying properties just as various members of the metals family have different properties. There are some general properties that are quite characteristic of the plastics family, however. These have been divided into physical, electrical, thermal and chemical properties.

Physical Properties

Weight: Most plastics are relatively light in weight. A few, such as polyethelene, will float in water. The heaviest, the fluorocarbons, have specific gravities of about 2.3 or a little more than twice as heavy as water. This compares with 7.7 for iron and 2.67 for aluminum. Many applications make use of this extremely advantageous property of plastics.

Hardness: Hardness is a very general term and usually represents a combination of more or less related properties. The engineering tests applied to determine and report hardness are of two types: (1) *fracture hardness,* which is the resistance to breaking the surface with a given load concentrated on a point. Scratch resistance is associated with this type of hardness. (2) *deformation hardness,* which is a measure of how much the surface deforms when a weight of a certain size concentrated on a specified area is dropped from a given height. Commonly this property is reported in terms of a number on one of several scales such as Rockwell or Brinell. Fig. 1-5 gives a comparison of values on several common scales used. These values are only approximate; some of the scales are not directly comparable.

Plastics are not very hard. The hardest types compare with brass and aluminum. Generally thermosets are harder than thermoplastics. The temperature of the material greatly affects this property; elevated temperatures soften most plastics, even thermosets, considerably.

Tensile Strength: Tensile strength is the ability of a material to resist a pulling force. In this property there is great variety among plastics. Polyesters reinforced with fiber glass achieve tensile strengths up to 100,000 pounds per square inch (psi), as compared with 25,000 psi for aluminum and 100,000 psi for steel. Many plastics exhibit values of 5,000 to 10,000 psi.

Indiscriminate application of tensile strength values obtained from a table is unwise. Since temperature has a great effect upon this property, the temperature at which the test was conducted must be investigated.

Another property which must be considered along with tensile strength is elongation, the amount a material stretches before breaking. Some plastics, such as polyethylene, stretch to five times their original length before breaking in a tensile test. Natural rubber elongates 300 to 400% before breaking, and steel elongates only 0.1% before breaking.

Compressive Strength: Compressive strength is the ability of a material to resist crushing when a squeezing force is applied to it. There is great variety among plastics in this property. Polyesters, reinforced with glass rovings, resist forces of 70,000 psi as compared to 12,000 psi for aluminum and 50,000 psi for steel. Some of the vinyl plastics exhibit compressive strengths of less than 1000 psi. Typical values are between 20,000 and 25,000 psi. Generally, thermosets have greater resistance to compressive forces than thermoplastics. Again, temperature of the material affects this property greatly.

Impact Strength: Impact strength is the ability of a material to resist sharp blows or shocks. It is a measure of the toughness of the plastic. Some fiber glass reinforced plastics such as epoxies and polyesters possess higher impact strengths than steel. Some flexible vinyl materials and polyethelene possess extremely high impact strengths for plastic materials. Special formulations of many plastics are available that are especially high in impact strength.

Creep and Cold Flow: When a material is subjected to a stress it will change dimension which is recovered after the stress is removed. However, if the stress is continuous, even

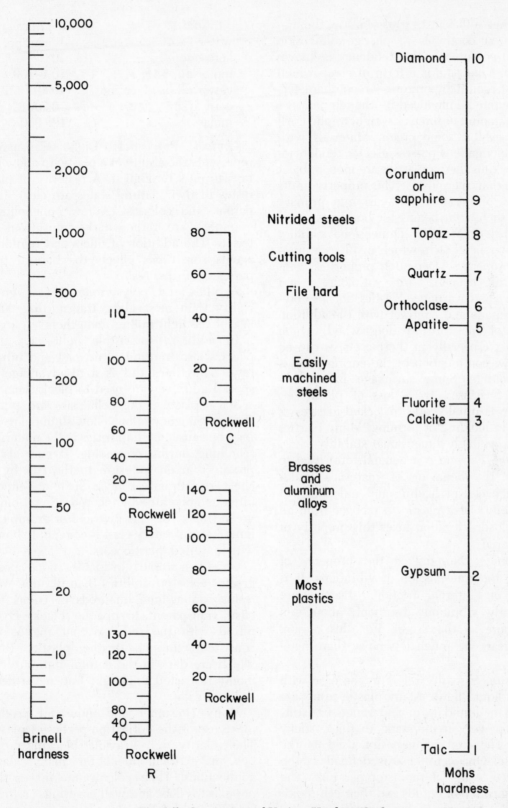

Fig. 1-5. Comparison of Various Hardness Scales

though not sufficient to cause failure, the material often continues to change dimension (stretch, compress). This tendency is known as *creep*. *Cold flow* is a form of creep which occurs at room temperature. Creep characteristics are much influenced by the temperature and the amount of force or weight applied. All plastics exhibit some creep. Materials with greater elongations possess greater tendencies to creep; thus thermoplastics are more subject to creep than thermosets. This property limits the use of plastics for carrying primary stresses such as in beams for buildings.

Dimensional Stability: Dimensional stability is a very general term which involves a number of properties. Two such properties commonly of concern are shrinkage (and swelling) and warpage. Plastics do not commonly expand and contract with the addition or loss of moisture as does wood. Much shrinkage, especially in thermosets, is caused by a slow continuation of the curing process after molding. Some shrinkage in thermoplastics is caused by a loss of plasticizer. Warpage is usually due to locked-in stresses created in molding or forming. Many plastics exhibit very high dimensional stability.

Fatigue: Fatigue is a general term used to describe the behavior of materials under constant cycles of loading and unloading. It is the ability of a plastic to recover from an applied load. Vibration taxes this property of the material.

Damping: Damping is the property of resisting the transmission of vibrations. It is a kind of "internal friction." Plastics are particularly vibration absorbent, about ten times more so than steel. For this reason, plastic gears are much less noisy than metal ones.

Viscosity: Viscosity refers to the ease with which a liquid flows. Many plastic resins are supplied in liquid form and range in "stiffness" from very free-flowing to thick, sticky masses. The unit of viscosity used is the centipoise. One centipoise is defined as the viscosity of water at room temperature. The following common liquids and their centipoise values give some basis for comparison:

Liquid	Viscosity
water	1 centipoise
kerosene	10
motor oil, SAE	10 – 100
castor oil or glycerine	1000
corn syrup	10,000
molasses	100,000

Optical Properties: Light transparency represents the ability of a plastic to allow light rays to pass through it. A majority of plastic resins in their natural states are clear, transparent, and colorless. A few (phenolics for example) are rather dark, translucent materials. The addition of fillers and reinforcing agents sometimes affects the natural transparency of the resin.

Acrylics and polystyrene possess greater clarity than most glass, transmitting 90% to 92% of the light falling upon them.

In addition to visible light rays, most plastics also transmit ultraviolet and infrared rays. Sometimes this is a disadvantage and special additives are used to block them out.

Some plastics, the cellulosics are typical, show a tendency to be yellowish in color. This may be caused by impurities in the material or scorching during processing. It may also be produced upon exposure to the sun by the effect of ultraviolet rays. Such an effect is often compensated by incorporating a blue or green tint within the plastic. For example the inner layer of safety glass is commonly bonded with a tinted plastic core.

Of all materials available, none possess greater color possibilities than plastics. Many resins can assume hundreds of colors from clear transparent to opaque black. Dye is mixed with the resin so that the color is consistent throughout the plastic. Resins which are dark in the natural state are commonly restricted to opaque but, nevertheless, brilliant colors.

Many consumer and industrial products make use of the optical properties of plastics. Their clarity and ultraviolet blocking properties make them ideal for many glazing applications. Their color range makes them popular for floor and wall coverings as well as for toys and kitchen utensils.

Electrical Properties

Dielectric Strength: Dielectric strength represents the electrical insulating value of a plastic. It specifies the maximum voltage required to cause a current to flow through a given thickness (usually .001"). Materials with high dielectric strengths are said to be good electrical insulators.

Nearly all plastics, when dry, are excellent insulators. Some have been developed which retain their insulating values even after long immersion in water. On the other hand some have been developed that actually carry current; they are conductors.

Dielectric strength is generally lowered with an increase in temperature or a load placed on the plastic.

Dielectric Constant: Dielectric constant is a measure of the material's usefulness as the insulating element in a capacitor. It is defined as the ratio of the capacitance of two electrodes separated solely by the material, to their capacitance when the electrodes are separated by air or a vacuum. The ratio varies for different frequencies of alternating current.

The dielectric constants of most plastics are very high. Using air as the base value of 1.0, most plastics range between 2.5 and 7.0 as compared with a range of 2.8 to 9.9 for glass, 4.6 to 8.0 for mica, and 2.8 to 3.8 for paraffined paper.

Oriented polyester films are often used as insulators in capacitors because of their high dielectric constant. They also possess other desirable characteristics such as high dielectric strength and high temperature resistance.

Dissipation (Power) Factor: This property is a measure of the electric power lost in a plastic insulator. In an insulating material, the dissipation factor is the ratio of the total power loss (watts) in the material to the product of the voltage and current in a capacitor in which the material is the insulator. This factor varies with current frequency.

The electrical power which is lost in the insulator results in increased temperature of the insulator. Plastics with a high dissipation factor will tend to heat up more when used as insulators. One important application is made of this property in the electronic heat sealing of vegetable bags. Polyethylene and polystyrene have very low dissipation factors and cannot be heat sealed electronically; the cellulosics have a high power factor and are readily sealed in this manner.

Typical values for polystyrene are .00015. For certain fluorocarbons the value is as low as .0003, and for the cellulosics from .005 to .12. Quartz has a dissipation factor of .00009 and electrical glass about .05.

Arc Resistance: Arc resistance is a measure of the ability of an insulator to resist the action of an electric arc tending to burn a conducting path across the surface of the material. It is usually measured in terms of the number of seconds it takes a given electrical current to render the surface of the material conductive because of carbonization by the arc flame.

Among the best plastics in this property are the acrylics which do not carbonize at all. Some plastics, such as certain phenolic formulations, have a tendency to "track," that is, to allow a current to pass along their surface.

Consideration of this property is important in applications where there is likely to be momentary flashover. Typical examples are various types of switches and circuit breakers. No organic plastic has exceptional arc resistance and where arcing is likely to be severe other materials are probably better suited.

Thermal Properties

Plastics fall in the group of heat insulators; that is, they have very low thermal conductivities. Copper transmits over 2000 times as much heat as most plastics, cast iron 250 times as much, asbestos four times as much, and wood about twice as much.

This property makes most plastics pleasant to the touch. A plastic handle on a hot pan transmits relatively little heat from the pan to the hand. A plastic refrigerator tray transmits little heat from the hand to the contents of the tray.

Specific Heat: Specific heat is an indication of the amount of heat needed to raise the temperature of a given volume of plastic. Plastics exhibit relatively high specific heats, approximately three or four times that of iron or copper. However, because plastics are so much lighter than most metals, it takes less heat to raise the temperature of a given volume of plastic than a similar volume of metal.

This property is of concern to processors of plastics. It gives information on how much heat is required to soften plastics for forming or molding.

Thermal Conductivity (K Factor): The thermal conductivity of a material is a measure of its ability to conduct heat. It is expressed as the quantity of heat that will pass through a given area and thickness of the material in a given period of time when the temperature difference between the two faces is one degree. There are two sets of units used in reporting this value and it is important to understand the particular system in use. One common system is to report the number of British thermal units (Btu) of heat conducted through a piece of the material one foot thick and one foot square in one hour when the temperature difference between the faces is one degree Fahrenheit (Btu/hour/square foot/°F/foot). This system is used here. Another system is based on calories, seconds, centimeters, and temperature in Centigrade (cal/sec/sq. cm/°C/cm).

Materials with low "K" values are good insulators. Most plastics are good insulators. Outstanding in the field are the foamed plastics. Rigid urethane foams exhibit K values from .01 to .03, and polystyrene foams approximate .02. The lower density foams are better insulators than the higher densities. Copper, a good conductor, has a K value of 226, and wood-composition boards like those used in ceiling tiles have values of .3 to .6.

Thermal Expansion: This property represents the increase in size, length, area, or volume of plastic per unit temperature rise. Thermal expansion values for most plastics are relatively large. Plastics change in dimension with changes in temperature to a greater extent than do most materials. Even phenolics, which have relatively low thermal expansion values for plastics, expand and contract with changes in temperature about five times as much as mild steel and three times as much as brass. Cellulosics, polyethylene, and some vinyls expand three or four times as much as phenolics. Of course the actual change is still rather slight, about .00015″ per inch per °C. for cellulosics.

This property must be considered very carefully where close tolerances are required in parts. A molded part, when removed from the mold, may be many degrees above room temperature and upon cooling will not be the same dimension as when it was ejected from the mold. This property is used to advantage in making *shrink fits* on various knob mountings, for instance.

Heat Resistance: This property is usually specified as the maximum temperature at which a plastic can be held for a period of time without loss of certain properties such as tensile or compressive strength, color or clarity, or electrical insulating values. This makes it a very general property, and the particular property to be maintained must be specified.

Generally, plastics are low in heat resistance. A few reinforced thermosets, the silicones and epoxies, will withstand temperatures up to 400° F. Certain formulations of the fluorocarbons will resist temperatures of 400° to 500° F. but will not withstand much stress at that point. Thermosets can be safely held at temperatures between 250° and 400° F. Some phenolics have been submitted to temperatures as high as 5000° F. for a few seconds in jet engines. Ordinarily, thermoplastics should not be submitted to temperatures above that of boiling water and many will not withstand even that.

Usually plastics are ruled out where high heat resistance is needed. This property becomes an advantage in certain applications, however. For instance, heat sealing of polyethelene vegetable bags is made possible by the low heat resistance of the plastic. On other occasions, even though the plastic is somewhat deficient in this property, other properties make it advantageous. In missile nose-cones, the problem is one of protecting the inside of the missile from extremely high temperatures for a few seconds. The most important properties needed here are low thermal conductivity and resistance to thermal shock and these properties are obtained in silica-fiber-reinforced phenolics.

Fire Resistance: The properties commonly considered in connection with fire resistance of plastics are: (1) Flammability, the temperature at which the plastic bursts into flame, and (2) Burning rate, the speed at which the plastic burns.

Many plastics can be ignited with an open flame. Few would burst into flame from elevated temperatures alone; they would melt and char instead. The melamines and fluorocarbons will not burn at all and many others are *self-extinguishing*; that is, they will burn only as long as a flame is in direct contact with them. One exception is cellulose nitrate (used in early motion-picture film and celluloid) which burns very rapidly. Other members of the cellulosic family burn very slowly and cellulose acetate (safety film) is self-extinguishing.

Few plastics are used where they come into direct contact with fire. Many plastics are used under less severe heat conditions such as for ash trays and counter tops where hot pans are to be set.

Resistance to Cold: This property is a measure of the ability of a plastic to maintain certain properties such as impact and tensile strength at low temperatures.

Plastics, as a family of materials, have good resistance to cold. Polyethylene may be used in food packaging at temperatures of $-60°$ F.; melamines and ureas withstand temperatures of $-70°$ F.; some of the fluorocarbons have been tested at $-320°$ F.

The refrigeration industry makes extensive use of plastics. Refrigerators have many plastic parts. The plastics' good resistance to cold plus their low thermal conductivity make them excellent low-temperature materials. A large portion of the freezer packaging industry is a plastics industry.

Chemical Properties

Most considerations of chemical properties of plastics consist of "resistance ratings" to various chemicals. The tests may be concerned with a gain or loss in weight or dimension, a change in certain physical properties, or merely the plastic's ability to endure contact with the chemical. It should be remembered that special formations of many plastics are available to provide resistance to many chemicals.

Resistance to Acids: Most plastics are extremely resistant to weak acids. Almost none are affected by fruit juices, vinegar, etc. Many are resistant to strong mineral acids, but the effect of strong oxidizing acids varies from slight softening to actual decomposition of some, such as cellulosics and some formulations of phenolics.

The fluorocarbons are probably the most resistant of all plastics to the effects of acids. They are used for piping all types of chemicals and seem to suffer no ill effects from any.

Resistance to Alkalies: Most plastics are very resistant to weak alkalies, but only about half of them resist strong alkalies completely. Exceptional plastics in this respect are the styrenes, polyethylenes, and fluorocarbons. The cellulosic, melamine, and casein plastics are decomposed by many strong bases.

Resistance to Other Chemicals: Most plastics are resistant to common vegetable and mineral oils and greases. Some are affected by gasoline and kerosene. Few are affected by photographic solutions. Most have good resistance to foods and drinks, although some are stained by them. Few cosmetics have adverse effects on plastics and most drugs in liquid and solid form will not harm them. Most plastics are unaffected by soap and detergents; however many thermoplastics are harmed by strong cleaning fluids such as carbon tetrachloride. Almost all plastics are impervious to the effects of moisture and actual immersion in water.

Thus it is important to select a plastic material carefully if it must withstand volatile solvents, fumes, strong chemicals, or be resistant to weathering.

Members of Plastics Family

Under the general heading of metals come many individual materials such as iron, copper, zinc, and tin. Such members as birch, pine, oak, and cherry, belong to the group of materials called woods. Similarly, the family of plastics is made up of a number of individual but related materials such as acrylic, styrene, phenolic, and vinyl.

Metals are combined or alloyed to produce new materials having properties different from any of the components. For example, brass is an alloy of copper and zinc. Plastics too are alloyed or copolymerized to form new materials. A copolymer of styrene and acrylonitrile is combined with a blend of butadiene acrylonitrile rubber to produce an extremely high-impact material often referred to as ABS plastic (acrylonitrile-butadiene-styrene).

To summarize, the individual members of the plastics family are often classified as *thermoplastic* and *thermoset*. Included in the class of thermoplastics are acetal, acrylic, cellulosic, fluorocarbon, polyamide, polyolefin, styrene, and vinyl. The common members of the class of thermosets are amino, casein, epoxy, phenolic, polyester, silicone, and urethane.

The next two chapters deal in some detail with these individual materials, describing their outstanding properties and uses.

Study Questions

1. What is the "official" definition of plastics? Phrase this in your own words.
2. What are the two classifications of plastics in terms of the way heat affects them? Name a plastic from each group.
3. What does a thermoset look like "inside" and how does this make it react to heat as it does?
4. What does a thermoplastic look like "inside" and how does this make it react to heat as it does?
5. What are the general ingredients of most plastics? What does each ingredient do?
6. List the forms in which plastics can be found. Give an example where each could be used.
7. What are the four general groups of properties that should be considered when studying a plastic?
8. How does the weight of plastics compare with that of metal? of wood?
9. Are plastics generally hard or soft as compared to most metals?
10. How do most plastics compare with steel in their resistance to being pulled apart?
11. How do plastics compare with steel in resisting a crushing or squeezing force?
12. Name a plastic which resists sharp blows well.
13. What is creep? cold flow?
14. What is likely to cause a plastic to warp?
15. What is fatigue as applied to plastics?
16. Why are plastic gears generally more quiet than steel gears? What property is involved?
17. Name a plastic that is very clear.
18. Are plastics generally good or poor insulators?
19. Why is it difficult to seal polyethylene electronically?
20. What is arc resistance? Where is it important?
21. Are plastics generally good or poor conductors of heat?
22. What use do processors make of a knowledge of the specific heat of a plastic?
23. What term is used to indicate the heat insulating value of a plastic?
24. What is the effect of heat on the size of a plastic?
25. What is the maximum temperature that most plastics will resist?
26. What does it mean when we say that a plastic is self-extinguishing?
27. How do most plastics react to freezing temperatures?
28. How do plastics commonly react to acids?
29. How do plastics commonly react to alkalies?
30. What is the effect of common foods, liquids, and household chemicals on plastics?

Apply Your Knowledge

1. Why do you suppose this group of materials was called plastics in the first place?
2. What is a basic difference between plastics and wood or metal?
3. Name a material that is not a plastic but acts like a thermoset when subjected to heat or cold.
4. Name a material that is not a plastic but acts like thermoplastic when subjected to heat and cold?
5. Concrete is made up of sand, cement, gravel, and water. Compare each of these to one of the ingredients of plastics.
6. Bring to class as many different forms of plastics as you can.
7. Why is it so difficult to give a general description of the properties of plastics?
8. Give an example of a product where its physical properties would be of great importance. Its electrical properties, its thermal properties, its chemical properties.
9. If you were to try to melt a plastic by causing an electrical current to pass through it, what property would you be most interested in?
10. Why are the handles of many cooking pans made from plastics?
11. Even if plastics would not melt they would not be very good for frying pans. Why?
12. If you were installing ceiling tile in a cottage to keep it cool in the summer would you look for a material with a high or a low K factor? Would most plastics be pretty good for this purpose?
13. To what extent are most plastics a fire hazard? What other common material is similar to most plastics in terms of fire resistance?
14. What combination of properties makes plastics ideal for refrigerator trays?
15. Write down each of the properties listed in this chapter. After each, list one material that is much better than plastics in this property and one that is inferior to plastics in this property. Also after each, name a product in which the property would be of great importance.
16. In certain situations some properties of materials are much more important than others. After each of the items listed below name three properties that a designer and a manufacturer would have to consider carefully in selecting the material to use in making the product: fishing rod, automobile seat covers, kitchen counter top, plastic drinking glass, raincoat, canoe.
17. In which form would you be most likely to find the plastic in the following applications?

    a factory making caps for tooth paste tubes
    a factory making fiber glass boats
    fishing line
    a sweater
    a kitchen counter top
    a man painting a house with plastic paint
    a factory where wood is being glued with white glue
    Styrofoam Christmas decorations
    an Orlon suit

CHAPTER TWO

the thermoplastic family

The various plastics described in this chapter are different in many ways, but they all have one property in common — they are thermoplastic. Each material is described generally by listing its outstanding physical, electrical, thermal, and chemical properties and by illustrating some of the typical uses made of it. To enable easy comparison, Table 1 at the end of the chapter summarizes the properties of the group (see page 43).

Plastics included are acetal, acrylic, cellulosic, fluorocarbon, polyamide, polyolefin, styrene, and vinyl.

Acetal Plastics

The acetal (AS-se-tal) plastics are among the most recently developed members of the plastics family. Delrin, a Du Pont development, went into commercial production in 1959. Extensive laboratory and field tests prior to commercial introduction indicate the possibility of its replacing and supplementing metals in many applications.

Description of Properties

Acetals with a specific gravity of 1.4 are about medium in weight for plastics. They exhibit high tensile strength and compressive strength with no true yield point. Dimensional stability is excellent with only slight changes resulting from high humidity and immersion in water. Few plastics surpass them in abrasion resistance. They have a very low coefficient of friction which is not increased at temperatures up to 250° F. The dynamic and static friction are equal so that the "slip and stick" property is not observed. This plastic is the toughest and most resilient of all thermoplastics.

Acetal moldings are excellent electrical insulators. The important feature for many applications is that this property is maintained at relatively high temperatures and in humid conditions. Arc resistance is good but the material will eventually burn if subjected to arcing for a long enough time.

Acetals are thermoplastics which melt at 347° F. Their service range without appreciable loss of properties is from 185° to 250° F. At 200°, tensile strength is reduced from 10,000 psi to 6000 psi. Low temperature resistance is good.

The outstanding chemical property of this resin which places it above most thermoplastics is its extremely high resistance to solvents of all types. Most thermoplastics are affected by ketones and aromatic hydrocarbons, but acetals are almost impervious to them at room temperatures. This property makes solvent cementing impossible but provides excellent resistance to staining by beverages, foods, oils, and greases. Resistance to strong acids and alkalies is poor, and many mild acids and alkalies affect the material.

Acetal molding powder is naturally opaque white but can be made to assume a wide range of translucent to opaque colors. It has good outdoor properties, but prolonged exposure to sunlight causes some chalking.

Typical Applications

The metal-like properties of acetals such as stiffness and abrasion resistance without susceptibility to corrosion make them attractive substitutes for metal in such applications as zippers. They maintain easy operation even in very humid conditions or where they come into contact with salt spray.

Acetal moldings will take and hold screws much like metal and are thus easy to fasten with such quick-assembly devices as self-tapping screws. This, coupled with lightness of weight, makes them attractive materials for various types of housings.

Lightness of weight, toughness, and corrosion resistance make them ideal for aerosol containers for various types of sprays.

High heat and corrosion resistance make them useful for shower heads and other plumbing fixtures. See Fig. 2-1.

The coupling of low coefficient of friction and resistance to most solvents has specified their use in bearings and rollers for conveyor systems or for use in such household items as the egg beater shown in Fig. 2-2.

Acrylic Plastics

The acrylic (a-KRIL-ic) plastics are among the most familiar plastics to the average consumer. The tradenames, *Plexiglas* and *Lucite*, are synonymous with plastics. Stemming from basic work by Dr. Otto Rohm in Germany in 1901, these plastics were first used as a bonding agent for safety glass in 1931, and introduced as clear sheet in 1936, and as molding powders in 1937. World War II provided impetus to their development as aircraft enclosures.

Description of Properties

Acrylic plastics with a specific gravity of 1.2 are about average in weight for thermoplastics. They are exceptionally rigid and have high impact strength which is enhanced by forming to curved shapes. The surface is not particularly scratch resistant and care must be used in cleaning to avoid abrasion. They are dimensionally very stable over a wide temperature range.

Acrylics are nonconductors of direct current and of AC at power frequencies. They are unsuitable for high frequency insulation, however. They have excellent arc resistance.

Within the group of thermoplastics, the acrylics have good resistance to heat. They withstand deformation and loss of physical properties up to about 200° F. Special types can stand even higher temperatures. Low temperatures have no adverse effects on the plastic. These plastics are somewhat unusual in that they can maintain a rubbery condition when heated over a rather wide temperature

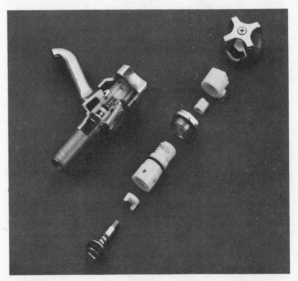

Fig. 2-1. Delrin Acetal Plastic Faucet (Du Pont)

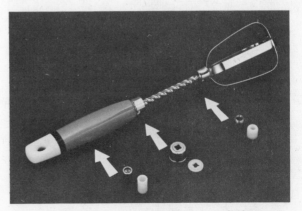

Fig. 2-2. Three Uses of Delrin Acetal Plastic (Du Pont)

range. This makes them especially fine materials for thermoforming. They exhibit great "plastic memory", i. e. the ability to return to their original form. An open flame will ignite acrylics and cause them to burn similar to wood.

Chemically, acrylics are unaffected by alkalies and weak acids. Oxidizing acids will attack them, however. There is little or no effect from household chemicals such as bleaching compounds, window cleaners, vinegar, animal and vegetable oils, waxes and foods. They are attacked by perfume, high octane gasoline, acetone, lacquer thinner and cleaning fluids such as carbon tetrachloride. They absorb very little water even with prolonged immersion and exhibit no swelling.

Acrylics are superior for outdoor applications. Prolonged exposure to sunlight and weather have little or no effect on any of their physical properties. High optical clarity is another of the strong points of acrylic plastics; no other plastic exceeds them in this respect. Color possibilities are unlimited in transparent, translucent, and opaque hues.

Fig. 2-3. Acrylics in Advertising (Rohm & Haas)

Typical Applications

The relatively high cost of acrylic plastics makes it essential that manufacturers exploit the unique properties of this group of materials. It is unlikely that an acrylic will be used where its properties are not outstanding.

Their high transparency, lightness of weight, and resistance to weathering are factors in their selection for aircraft enclosures.

Their exceptional outdoor properties make them principal materials of the outdoor advertising industry, as shown in Fig. 2-3.

Their toughness and shatter resistance cause them to be the material used for almost all automobile tail lights.

Their optical clarity and complete compatibility with human tissue have made them the principal material for contact lenses.

Their lustrous finish, scratch resistance, and ease of cleaning have made them popular for toilet articles.

Their shatter resistance and lack of tendency to "haze" cause them to be used as television screens.

Their resistance to various cleaners, lack of discoloration and ease of decorating cause their use in all types of dials, control panels, faucet handles, and medallions. A parking lot fence, Fig. 2-4, uses panels of acrylic plastics reinforced with glass fibers.

Their dimensional stability is exploited in precisely calibrated drafting instruments.

Fig. 2-4. Decorative Fiberglas Acrylic Panels
(Du Pont)

Their lack of odor or taste makes them popular for juice dispensers and other food service equipment.

Their resistance to the effects of weather has been emphasized in advertising of acrylic-resin paints.

Cellulosic Plastics

The discovery of one of the cellulosic (sell-you-LOES-ic) plastics, *cellulose nitrate*, (celluloid), is commonly noted as the beginning of the plastics industry. It was patented by the Hyatt brothers in 1869 in the United States as a substitute for ivory in billiard balls. This family of plastics is the least synthetic of all plastics, employing cellulose fibers from wood or cotton. The use of cellulose plastics in movie film was in part responsible for the rapid growth of both the movie and the plastics industries.

There are five basic resins in the cellulosic family; *cellulose acetate, cellulose nitrate, cellulose acetate butyrate, ethyl cellulose,* and *cellulose propionate.*

Description of Properties

The cellulosics are lightweight plastics with specific gravities of 1.15 to 1.39. They possess relatively high tensile, compressive, and impact strengths. Cellulose nitrate is the toughest of all thermoplastics. All the resins of this family have good abrasion resistance for plastics. The natural resins have a sparkling clarity and can assume an unlimited range of colors. Generally, with the exception of cellulose acetate butyrate, they are not outdoor materials and tend to yellow and crack upon prolonged exposure to sunlight. Cellulose acetate butyrate has a slight odor when confined indoors; this is not noticeable in outdoor applications.

Cellulosics possess average electrical properties for plastics. They offer good resistance to high and low frequency currents. They have high dielectric constants and low power-loss factors.

Cellulosics are thermoplastic and possess average heat resistance for this group of plastics. Cellulose nitrate is the poorest in this respect but others of the family should not be subjected to temperatures above the 140° to 200° F. range. All members of the cellulose family withstand low temperatures without appreciable loss of properties. The exceptional properties of cellulose nitrate are often negated by the fact that it burns very rapidly; other cellulosics burn slowly and some are self-extinguishing.

All cellulosics resist weak acids and alkalies well, but all except ethyl cellulose are affected adversely by strong acids and alkalies. They are resistant to common household chemicals contained in foods and liquids. Lacquer thinner, acetone, nail polish, and some alcohols affect them. Cellulosics are more water absorbent than any other group of plastics, with cellulose acetate the poorest of the group. Compared to other materials such as wood, plastics still absorb relatively little water.

Typical Applications

The toughness and flexibility of cellulose nitrate make it an ideal component for lacquers. These properties also suit its use for such common items as the body and cap of pens and pencils. Its flammability limits its use in many other applications.

Fig. 2-5. Ball Point Pen Molded from Cellulose Propionate (Celanese)

The lustrous surface finish and ease of forming make cellulose acetate ideal for numerous indoor display racks and packages.

The ease of molding, ability to be colored throughout, and toughness have recently made cellulose acetate competitive with wood for heels on ladies' shoes. Similar properties of cellulose propionate are shown by the pen in Fig. 2-5.

The high tensile strength, even when wet, of cellulose acetate monofilaments woven into fabrics have made the "acetates" very important synthetic fibers.

Good resistance to soaps and abrasion make cellulose acetate a most common material for tooth brush handles and other toilet articles.

Exceptional weathering properties, lightness of weight, and brilliance of color cause the use of cellulose acetate butyrate in much outdoor display and advertising.

Toughness, ease of molding, and low thermal conductivity make cellulose acetate butyrate ideal for steering wheels, typewriter keys, and eyeglass frames. See Figs. 2-6 and 2-7.

Fluorocarbon Plastics

While many plastics have superior individual properties, none surpasses the combination of favorable properties of the fluorocarbons. There are two principal formulations of this family, tetrafluorethylene (TFE) and chlorotrifluorethylene (CFE). Developed in 1943, these plastics are relatively high in cost and their use is presently limited to industrial applications which exploit their exceptional combination of properties.

Description of Properties

The fluorocarbons are among the heaviest of all plastics with specific gravities of 2.1 and 2.3. Their tensile and compressive strengths are average for plastics but impact strength is exceptional. They may be formulated as rigid hard materials or as flexible tubing. Mechanical strength is maintained even at elevated temperatures. For example, molded bars held at 480° F. for a month showed almost no loss of tensile strength. Their coefficient of friction is exceptionally low, comparable to that of two pieces of ice rubbed together. Static friction is lower than dynamic friction which eliminates the "slip-stick" tendency.

The fluorocarbons have outstanding electrical insulating properties which remain essentially constant regardless of temperature, frequency, and humidity. The electrical and related properties are particularly useful where any of these conditions is involved: high

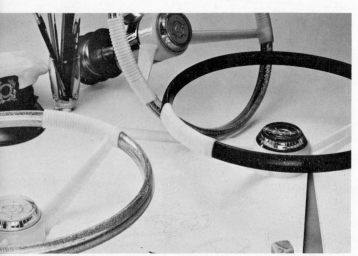

Fig. 2-6. **Steering Wheels of Cellulose Acetate Butyrate** (SPI)

Fig. 2-7. **"1500" Telephone Series Molded from Cellulose Acetate Butyrate** (Eastman)

frequencies, high temperatures, long exposure to even slightly elevated temperatures, flexing or impact conditions at low temperatures, and moist or corrosive atmospheres.

Although thermoplastic, the fluorocarbons can be used continuously at temperatures as high as 500° F. and at higher temperatures for shorter intervals. Increased pressure raises the melting point even further; for instance, in one application, a gasket withstood 930° F. under 15,000 psi. Flexibility is maintained at temperatures as low as that of liquid nitrogen (−320° F.). Fluorocarbons will not burn.

This family of resins is inert to nearly all chemicals and solvents used commercially. They are completely unaffected by boiling hydrocarbons, ketones, esters, alcohols, aqua regia, hydrofluoric acid, nitric acid, or sulfuric acid. Alkalies of all concentrations have no effect on them. Under certain conditions fluorine and molten alkali metals do attack them. They have a zero water absorption rate.

Weather, sunlight, and changes in temperature do not deteriorate fluorocarbons. One member (CFE) is transparent to translucent, while the other (TFE) is opaque and naturally white. They can be colored but coloring is often done for identification rather than appearance. However, their increased use for consumer products may change this.

Typical Applications

The high cost of fluorocarbon resins usually demands that they be used only in applications requiring their outstanding combination of properties.

Their heat resistance makes them ideal for wire insulation where soldering melts, softens, or chars other wire coatings.

Their outstanding dielectric properties are aids to miniaturization where thinner layers of insulation can be used, reducing coil size.

Chemical properties are exploited in completely corrosion-proof pipe systems. Pipe and fittings lined with TFE resins withstand practically all chemicals and solvents. There is no buildup of deposits. Fig. 2-8 illustrates some typical uses of Teflon.

The exceptionally low coefficient of friction is exploited in all types of bearings. They do not require lubrication and are thus useful in mixers where lubricants might contaminate foods.

Heavy-duty application of Teflon fluorocarbons is found in flexible bellows that resist wear and attack by chemicals; see Fig. 2-9.

The low coefficient of friction makes them an ideal coating for the skiis on Air Force polar troop carriers. In addition to offering a slick surface, their antistick properties prevent snow, ice, or dirt from building up.

Fig. 2-8. "Teflon" Fluorocarbons in Valves, Insulation, and Bearings (Du Pont)

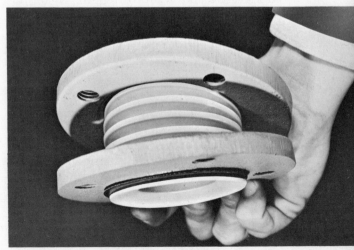

Fig. 2-9. Flexible Bellows of "Teflon" Fluorocarbon (Du Pont)

Non-adhesive properties make TFE ideal for hoses to convey hot glue in a shoe cementing machine. There is no tendency for glue to stick to the hose walls and cause eventual stoppage. Some cooking kettles and frying pans are coated with Teflon to reduce sticking and need for grease when frying.

Polyamide Plastics — Nylon

Never has a more effective job of public relations been accomplished than in the introduction by Du Pont of Nylon in 1938 as a substitute for silk in hosiery. So complete was the acceptance of this material that it has almost totally replaced silk in this application. The high regard of the public for nylon is illustrated by the salesman's answer to a question about the material contained in a set of automobile seat covers. "Oh no," he replied, "they are not plastic; they're nylon." The applications of this important plastic have expanded to many phases of industry. The name *nylon* has come to be also used interchangeably with the class name, polyamide (polly-AM-ide).

Description of Properties

Nylons are among the lighter plastics with specific gravities of 1.09 to 1.14. They exhibit medium to high tensile strength, and average compressive and flexural strength. Nylons are exceptionally tough and wear resistant materials. Some forms elongate as much as 300% before breaking. One of the outstanding properties of nylons is their extremely low coefficient of friction. Damping capacity is very good. These resins are naturally translucent and can assume many colors. In thin filaments, these plastics appear transparent. Special formulations withstand outdoor use, but they are not generally considered outdoor materials. Nylons exhibit more mold shrinkage than average.

The electrical properties of nylon are acceptable for most applications. They are relatively poor insulators for high frequency currents. Ordinarily, it is their other properties that specify their use in electrical installations.

Nylons are thermoplastic but have greater resistance to heat than many thermosets. They can safely be immersed in boiling water. Glass-filled compounds can be subjected to temperatures as high as 400° F. This extreme heat resistance presents some problems in molding. Freezing temperatures have little effect on their properties.

Chemically, nylons resist weak acids and either weak or strong alkalies. They are attacked by strong acids. They have excellent resistance to all household solvents, petroleum oils and greases, brine solutions, gasoline, and alcohol. Nylons have a tendency to absorb water and must be dried before molding. They are rather easily stained by foods and liquids such as coffee and tea.

Typical Applications

Nylons are expensive plastics and more difficult to mold than most. For these reasons, they are unlikely to be used unless the application requires their peculiar combination of properties.

Their low friction, high strength, and good damping qualities specify their use for quiet-running lubrication-free gears and bearings. Food and textile processing equipment is more sanitary and stain-free if no gear lubricant is used. Many kitchen appliances such as mixers and clocks run much more quietly with nylon gears. Because of their good damping characteristics less close fits are acceptable than with metal gears.

Their high tensile strength and ease of cleaning make them popular fabrics for clothing and other uses.

Their lightness and toughness make them important fabrics for parachutes.

Their exceptional resilience and wear resistance make them common materials for softface hammers and dies. Tough and unbreakable yet light and resistant to chemical attack the shower head shown in Fig. 2-10 is a popular application.

Their corrosion resistance is important in valves and piping for carrying petroleum products and other chemicals. Nylon impellers are used in the pump for spraying chemicals shown in Fig. 2-11.

Their strength and flexibility are important in high-pressure aerosol bottles.

Polyolefin Plastics —

Polyethylene and Polypropylene

Polyethylene (polly-ETH-el-een) is one of the simplest plastics, chemically, but is also one of the most recently discovered. It was first formulated in 1933 and commercially produced in England in 1934. Its important military applications led the United States government to encourage two American companies to produce it in 1943. Since World War II it has assumed a significant place in the consumer market.

An even more recent addition to the polyolefin (polly-OEL-e-fin) family is polypropylene (polly-PRO-pel-een). It is superior to polyethylene in many properties and because of the availability of the chief component of its manufacture, propylene, it promises to be, as it is developed, a serious competitor for polyethylene.

Description of Properties

Polyethylene: Polyethylene is among the lightest of plastics with a specific gravity of .92. In very thin sections, it is flexible but as a thick material, quite rigid. It has rather low tensile and compressive strength for a plastic, but due to the fact that it stretches as much as 500% before breaking, it is difficult to tear. It exhibits exceptionally high "folding" endurance. It has a waxy feel and water will not adhere to it.

The electrical properties of the plastic are good. It has high resistance to both high and low frequency currents. Its power factor and dielectric constant are both low.

Polyethylene is a thermoplastic and, as such, is not particularly heat resistant. Some formulations will resist the heat of boiling water but more commonly its continuous service temperature should not exceed 170° or 180° F. Temperatures as low as —60° F. have little or no effect upon its strength and flexibility. It burns about like wax in an open flame.

Polyethylene has good resistance to weak acids and all alkalies. It is attacked slowly by oxidizing acids. It has poor resistance to most oils and greases; it is attacked by kerosene and gasoline, especially at higher temperatures. Although it is very resistant to the passage of moisture, it readily allows many gases and odors to penetrate it.

Polyethylene is fairly transparent in film form but looks milky white in thicker sheets. Its color possibilities are unlimited. It can be stored indefinitely without loss of properties. Sunlight causes surface crazing and the material is not recommended for outdoor uses although black polyethylene is quite resistant to the effects of the sun.

Fig. 2-10. Nylon Shower Head (Du Pont)

Fig. 2-11. Pump Using Nylon Impellers (Du Pont)

Polypropylene: The properties of polypropylene are similar to those of polyethylene but it is generally more heat resistant and has greater strength in spite of the fact that it is lighter in weight with a specific gravity of .90. Products made of this material can be sterilized and used continuously at temperatures of 300° F. It melts at 320° to 340° F. It surpasses polyethylene in tensile, compressive, and impact strength. In fiber form it has a tensile strength of 110,000 psi as compared to 80,000 for polyethylene and nylon and 35,000 for rayon. Its wet strength is equal to its dry strength.

Like polyethylene, it is highly resistant to most chemicals, impervious to most vapors and has excellent electrical properties.

Typical Applications

Examined individually, most of the properties of the polyolefins do not seem particularly impressive. It is the unusual combination of properties that makes them so applicable for a variety of uses.

One of the largest markets for polyethylene is in packaging all types of produce and merchandise. In the packaging of fresh fruits it is essential that moisture loss be kept low. Many plastics can prevent moisture loss, some better than polyethylene, but most fresh fruits must also "breathe", that is, take on oxygen

and give off carbon dioxide. The inability of polyethylene to stop permeation of gases makes it ideal in allowing this needed respiration. Similarly, packaged meats require some oxygen to take on an attractive red color. Other plastics used for meat packages have been unsuccessful because they do not allow oxygen to penetrate and the packaged product is unattractive to the consumer. Most packages are heat sealed; the low resistance of polyethylene makes such sealing possible.

Their excellent resistance to deteriorating effects of aging make them ideal building vapor barriers. Some tests have shown an actual increase in physical properties over a period of five years.

Their flexibility and break-resistance are commonly known in applications for toys, drinking glasses, and other kitchen ware. See Fig. 2-12.

Their resistance to many chemicals combined with flexibility over a range of temperatures makes them most commonly used for the "squeeze bottle" of recent fame.

Their resistance to the adhesion of water plus good properties at low temperatures make them ideal materials for nonsticking ice cube trays.

Though not the cheapest plastics on the basis of cost per pound, the polyolefins, because of their extremely light weight, yield greater amounts of film per pound than other resins. This makes them very inexpensive packaging materials. See Fig. 2-13. The coating is commonly extruded directly onto packaging papers making them waterproof and grease-resistant.

Their noiselessness and corrosion resistance make them ideal materials for kitchen containers for flour, salt, and spices, as well as molded pails, pans and kitchen wares.

In many of their electrical properties they are not outstanding. Yet here again, it is the combination of properties such as low water absorption, light weight, flexibility over a wide temperature range, coupled with one of the lowest known dielectric-loss factors, that makes the polyolefins ideal insulating coverings for high frequency electric cables.

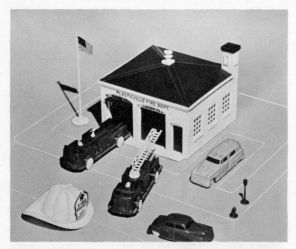

Fig. 2-12. Colorful, Unbreakable Polyethylene Toys (Catalin)

Styrene Plastics

Although basic chemical work leading to the discovery of styrene began in the 1830's, styrene was not produced commercially until a hundred years later and achieved a high volume production only after World War II. Today, the various formulations of styrene plastics rank second among plastics in volume produced.

Description of Properties

Any description of properties of the styrene plastics must distinguish between at least two general groupings. The first group includes general purpose polystyrene and its special formulations such as heat-resistant, light-stabilized, and glass-reinforced types. The second group is referred to as styrene alloys or rubber blends.

General Purpose Styrene: These materials are the lightest of all rigid plastics with specific gravities ranging from .98 to 1.1. They are fairly hard and rigid but tend to be brittle. They are not recommended for uses which are subject to severe impact or flexing. Their abrasion resistance leaves much to be desired. They exhibit excellent dimensional stability with mold shrinkage as little as 0.3%. Changes in temperature and humidity do not cause warpage.

All styrenes are excellent electrical insulators, comparable to fused quartz within the plastic's effective temperature range. They have a strong tendency to store an electrostatic charge and attract dust and lint. Various cleaners and waxes minimize this tendency.

Like all thermoplastics, the styrenes are not particularly heat resistant. General purpose polystyrene loses practically all strength above 180° F.; heat-resistant formulations will resist the temperature of boiling water. Low temperature properties are outstanding; sub-zero temperatures cause little or no loss of physical properties. Styrene plastics are ignited by an open flame but burn very slowly.

Chemically, the styrenes are unaffected by alkalies and weak acids. Oxidizing acids attack them. Most chemicals contained in foods, drinks, oils and alcohols, will not harm them. Liquids such as gasoline, turpentine, cleaning fluids, and nail polish have harmful effects. The plastic has practically no tendency to absorb water, but will allow the passage of water vapor and other gases. The material is tasteless, odorless, and non-toxic.

Polystyrene is not an outdoor material. With the exception of light-stabilized styrene, exposure to sunlight causes fading and eventually produces checks and cracks. In its natural state, polystyrene is optically clear. It can be colored with a variety of hues from clear transparent to opaque black.

Styrene Alloys or Rubber Blends: One of the shortcomings of styrene has always been

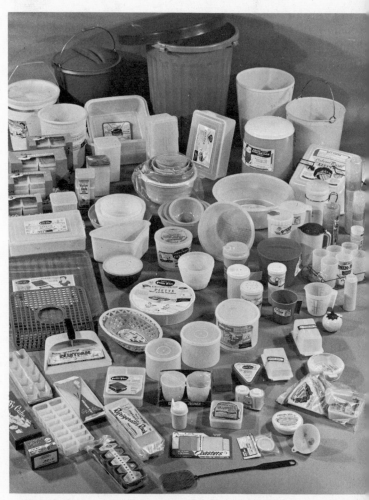

Fig. 2-13. The Packaging Field Extensively Uses Polyethylene (Du Pont)

its brittleness and lack of toughness. Even with these limitations it has been widely accepted in consumer products. It was found in the late 1940's that it could be blended with certain synthetic rubbers to produce materials which retained many of the properties of the plastic but added many desirable properties of rubber. ABS (acrylonitrile-butadiene-styrene) was described on page 28.

Among the important property improvements are tremendously increased impact

Fig. 2-14. Brush with Styrene Monofilament Bristles (Union Carbide)

Fig. 2-15. ABS Plastics Are Tough and Colorful
(Union Carbide)

strength, heat distortion temperatures up to 210° F., increased hardness, and greater chemical resistance.

Styrene alloys are not transparent but will take a wide range of translucent and opaque colors. They cost about one-third more than polystyrene and are somewhat more difficult to process.

All in all, their improved properties are resulting in an ever-expanding production.

Typical Applications

Styrene plastics are to be found in consumer products of all types. Each exploits one or more of their outstanding properties.

Their low cost, brilliant colors, and ease of molding make them ideal for toys, premiums, novelties, and toilet articles. Practically all plastic models to be assembled are made from styrene.

Their excellent low temperature properties are advantageous in refrigerator door liners, frozen food containers, and crisper trays. Many rigid disposable frozen food containers are of this type.

The toughness of their alloys specifies their use in carrying cases for typewriters and dictating machines, portable radio housings and automobile dash boards.

Their lustrous finish and moisture resistance are exploited in wall tile for kitchens and bathrooms.

Unaffected by moisture and dirt, a brush with styrene monofilament bristles, Fig. 2-14, is easy to clean.

Their resistance to soap, water, and detergents causes manufacturers of automatic washers to use them for lint traps and door liners.

The outstanding light diffusing qualities of the light stabilized type make it a good low cost light fixture material.

Their toughness, lack of taste and odor, and ease of washing are factors in their selection for serving trays on air liners. See Fig. 2-15.

They are important in latex or rubber-base paints where their resistance to alkalies makes it possible to paint over recently plastered walls and produce a quick drying, washable surface.

The chemical resistance of special types makes them ideal for battery cases and piping for oils and other chemicals.

Their brilliant clarity and rigidity even in thin sections make them ideal for packaging various consumer products to protect, display, and store them.

The buoyancy and water resistance of expanded styrene is exploited in flotation materials. This type also serves as a lightweight, easily handled insulation material as shown in Fig. 2-16.

Vinyl Plastics

The family of vinyl (VINE-el) plastics has been known for seventy-five to one hundred years. The pure resins are rather hard and brittle and commercial exploitation of them came only when suitable plasticizers were found to soften them enough for processing. Commercial production began in Germany in 1925. The vinyls were first used on a large scale in the United States in 1933 as a lacquer for lining tin cans.

Description of Properties

A general description of the properties of vinyl plastics is difficult because there are at least seven different plastics in this group. In addition they may be produced in either flexible or rigid form, with a consequent variation in properties. For that reason only properties rather common to the entire group will be discussed; unique properties of the individual materials will be listed separately.

Vinyls are light to medium in weight with specific gravities from 1.1 to 1.65. Flexible vinyls have almost no compressive strength, and medium tensile strength. They stretch considerably, however, and are difficult to tear. Rigid vinyls exhibit very little elongation but have average compressive and tensile strength. All types are mildly abrasion resistant. The natural resins are transparent so these plastics are available in a wide range of colors. Some types are suitable for outdoor use although this is not a strong feature of the entire group.

Vinyls offer high resistance to the passage of high and low frequency currents. They have average dielectric constants for plastics and low power-loss factors. They may be sealed by dielectric heating.

Chemically, vinyls are resistant to weak acids and all alkalies. Oxidizing acids cause swelling. Rigid vinyls are generally superior to flexible materials in this respect. Vinyls have little tendency to absorb water and are impervious to oils, foods, gasoline, and many household chemicals. Nail polish, lacquer thinner, moth repellents, carbon tetrachloride, ammonia, and acetone have adverse effects.

Vinyls are thermoplastic and not very heat resistant. Most members of the group will not withstand temperatures above 130° F. for any length of time. This makes them easy to heat seal. All types, especially flexible vinyls, maintain their properties exceptionally well at low temperatures. Rigid vinyls have excellent plastic memory. Vinyls will burn in an open flame but most are self-extinguishing.

Fig. 2-16. Lightweight, Insulating, "Styrofoam" (Dow)

Fig. 2-17. Luminous Ceilings of Rigid Vinyl Sheeting (Union Carbide)

Typical Applications

The adhesive properties plus its ability to emulsify make polyvinyl acetate an ideal adhesive for a variety of materials. "White glues" are of this type.

The high transparency, elasticity, and adhesiveness of polyvinyl acetals (AS-se-tals) specify their use as an interlayer in safety glass. Luminous ceilings of rigid vinyl sheeting provide glarefree light for showrooms as seen in Fig. 2-17.

The chemical resistance, toughness, and flexibility of polyvinyl alcohol resins are utilized in hosing to carry all types of chemicals. Molded vinyl parts such as those in Fig. 2-18 are tough and long lasting.

The smooth but nonskid surface, resistance to various solvents, ease of cleaning, and non-adherence of dirt make the polyvinyl chlorides, often asbestos filled, ideal floor tile materials even over concrete floors.

The toughness, flexibility, clarity, and ease of printing make polyvinyl chloride a good packaging and inflatable toy material. Vinyl foam has entered the cushioning field as illustrated in Fig. 2-19.

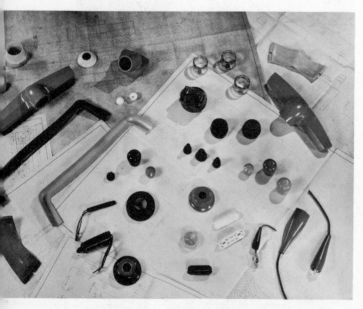

Fig. 2-18. Variety of Molded Vinyl Parts (Union Carbide)

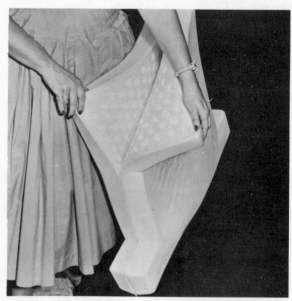

Fig. 2-19. Vinyl Foam Cushioning (Union Carbide)

The high tensile strength, resistance to dirt, and ease of coloring make the monofilament of polyvinylidene chloride (Saran) a popular material for woven fabrics in upholstery, draperies, and window screening.

The flexibility, water and tear resistance, and resistance to wearing at folds have opened the rainwear market to polyvinyl chloride acetate.

TABLE 1
PROPERTIES OF THERMOPLASTICS

	ACETALS	ACRYLICS	CELLU-LOSICS	FLUORO-CARBONS	POLY-AMIDES	POLY-OLEFINS	STYRENES	VINYLS
Specific Gravity	1.4	1.17–1.20	1.15–1.40	2.1–2.2	1.09–1.14	.91–.97	.98–1.1	1.2–1.55
Tensile Strength (1000's psi)	10	7–14.5	1.9–8.5	6.5–9.9	7.0–11.0	1.5–5.5	3.5–12.0	1.5–9.0
Compressive Strength (1000's psi)	18	12–18	13–36	1.7–80.0	7.2–13.0	2.5–10.0	4.8–16.0	1.0–13.0
Impact Strength	Excellent	Excellent	Good	Excellent	Excellent	Excellent	Good	Good
Clarity[1]	Trl–O	T–O	T–O	Trl–O	Trl–O	Trl–O	T–O	T–O
Electrical Resistance	Excellent	Good	Good	Excellent	Excellent	Excellent	Good	Good
Heat Distortion Point (Degrees F.)	338	150–210	115–250	250	300–360	105–230	165–225	100–165
Maximum Service Temp. (Degrees F.)	185–250	140–200	115–200	390–550	175–400	212–320	140–250	115–200
Low Temperature Properties	Good	Good	Good	Excellent	Good	Good	Excellent	Good
Burning Rate[2]	S	S	S to SE	None	S to SE	S	S	S to SE
Water Absorption Rate	Low	Low	High for plastic	None	None	Low	None	Low
Effect of: Weak Acids	Attacked by some	Little	Little	None	Little	Little	None	Little
Strong Acids	Attacked	Attacked by some	Decompose	None	Attacked	Slowly attacked	Attacked by some	Attacked by some
Weak Alkalies	Attacked by some	Little	Little	None	None	Little	None	Little
Strong Alkalies	Attacked	Attacked by some	Decompose	None	None	Little	None	Little
Solvents	None	Soluble in some	Soluble in many	None	Little	Soluble in some	Soluble in some	Little
Outdoor Conditions (Sunlight)	Little, "chalks"	None	Little	None	Slight discolor	Crazes discolor	Discolor	Little

[1]T — transparent, Trl — translucent, O — Opaque   [2]S — slow, SE — self-extinguishing

Study Questions

1. Make a list of the plastics belonging to the family of thermoplastics.
2. After each plastic list two or three of its outstanding properties.
3. After each plastic list two or three properties which are not very good.
4. After each plastic list several of its uses.

Apply Your Knowledge

1. Bring to class as many common plastic articles as you can find and label them with the name of the plastic of which they are made.
2. Clip pictures from catalogs, newspapers, or magazines showing and describing products made from the various materials explained in this chapter.
3. Make a display board of as many different plastic articles as you can find with a label telling what plastic was used for each and why this was (or was not) a good choice of material.
4. Secure samples of plastic raw materials from companies manufacturing plastics articles.
5. Predict some articles for which the various plastics might be used in the future because of their unusual properties. List the name of the plastic and why you think it would be good for the use you named.
6. Find as many forms of the same plastic as you can. For example, styrene can be found as sheets, rods, tubes, foam, broom bristles, etc.
7. Visit a plastic plant in your area. Secure a small quantity of the raw material used and a sample product they are making from it if possible.
8. Find a magazine article describing a new use to which a plastic has been put. Report on it to the class.

CHAPTER THREE ## the thermoset family

The various plastics described in this chapter are different in many ways but they all are thermosetting. Each material is described generally by listing its outstanding physical, electrical, thermal, and chemical properties and by illustrating some of the typical uses made of it. Table 2 at the end of the chapter summarizes the properties of the group to enable easy comparison (see page 54).

Plastics included are amino, casein, epoxy, phenolic, polyester, silicone, and urethane.

Amino Plastics
Urea and Melamine

Three applications of the amino (a-ME-no) plastics are very familiar to most consumers. Urea (you-REE-a) resins in powder form are popular glues for wood and are often sold as *plastic resin* glues. Melamine (MEL-a-meen) is the most common plastic used in dishware, and is often sold as Melmac. Countertop materials with such names as Formica and Texolite are melamine plastics. Urea was first developed in 1929 and melamine ten years later.

Description of Properties

Amino plastics are a little heavier than the average for plastics, with specific gravities ranging from 1.47 to 1.55. They possess average tensile strength and exceptional compressive and flexural strength. They resist breakage very well but should not be subjected to sharp blows. They possess hard surface finishes. The aminos are not outdoor materials; they tend to fade and lose strength with prolonged exposure to sunlight. The resins are translucent and can be colored with a wide range of translucent to opaque dyes from light pastel to dark. They possess excellent light diffusing properties.

Amino plastics have good electrical properties. They are good insulators for low frequency currents but are not particularly well suited to high frequency insulation. They possess high dielectric constants and low power-loss factors. They exhibit very high resistance to arcing and are often used in place of phenolics in cases where arcing is likely to occur.

The aminos are thermosetting plastics with good heat resistance. If asbestos filled, they withstand continuous temperatures from 210° to 400° F. Neither plastic will burn but both will char and discolor in the presence of excessive heat. Temperatures as low as —70° F. have no adverse effects. They possess relatively high thermal conductivities for plastic materials, but are, of course, still much lower than metals.

Chemically, this group resists the action of weak acids and alkalies. Strong acids and alkalies have a tendency to decompose them. They are exceptionally impervious to attack by detergents, strong cleaning fluids, oils, greases, gasoline, lacquer thinner, and kerosene. Both have a greater than average tendency among plastics to absorb water.

They are rather easily stained by some foods and drinks such as coffee and tea. Generally, melamine is more chemically resistant than urea.

Typical Applications

The excellent abrasion resistance, smoothness, and resistance to heat and chemicals make amino plastics ideal countertop materials for kitchens, bathrooms, and store counters.

Their excellent strength, attractive colors, resistance to detergents and hot water make them the most popular plastics for dishware on the market today. See Fig. 3-1.

Their excellent adhesive powers and resistance to moisture make urea resins the most used bonding agent for plywood and partical boards.

The good electrical properties and excellent arc resistance make them ideal in many types of switchgear.

Their ability to diffuse rather than absorb light enables their use as diffusers for indirect lighting.

Their resistance to chemicals plus their compatibility with other resins, such as alkyds, make them useful constituents of surface coatings for stoves and refrigerators.

Their ability to combine with cellulose causes their use as sizings for paper and fabrics producing wrinkle and dirt resistant materials with high wet strength.

Fig. 3-1. Melamine Plastics Are Common in Dinnerware (SPI)

Casein Plastics

Casein (ka-SEEN) gained early prominence as a component for water-resistant adhesives. It was used in bonding water-resistant plywood about the time of World War I. Casein resins were first developed in Europe and brought to the United States about 1900. Lack of certain physical properties has relegated them to rather limited use.

Description of Properties

Casein plastics are about average in weight for plastics with a specific gravity of 1.35. Casein moldings exhibit high impact strength and resist compressive and flexural forces very well. The resins are transparent and can assume a wide variety of colors from transparent to opaque. Many are formulated in variegated colors. Colors often fade in bright sunlight and the material loses many physical properties upon prolonged exposure to outdoor conditions.

The electrical properties of these materials are about average for plastics, but they are not used for electrical applications because of poor moisture resistance.

Casein resins are thermosetting with average thermal properties for materials of this classification. They resist temperatures of 275° F. continuously but become brittle at temperatures below freezing. Exposure to an open flame will cause them to burn slowly.

The caseins are below average in chemical resistance. While they resist weak acids they are susceptible to attack by strong acids and all alkalies. They have only fair resistance to most solvents. Their major shortcoming is their failure to resist moisture. Even high humidity will cause them to swell. Immersion in water for long periods will cause them to swell, soften, and break easily.

Typical Applications

Their brilliance of color and high surface finish make them usable for many novelty items.

Their flexural strength and smooth surface cause them to be used in knitting needles.

Their toughness and ease of processing make them a common material for buttons, dress buckles, or novelties as shown in Fig. 3-2.

Epoxy Plastics

The epoxy (ep-OX-ee) plastics are among the newest plastics commercially available. Though simple epoxies have been known chemically for about one hundred years, it is only since 1947 that they have assumed commercial significance. Their first application as a metal-to-metal adhesive has now spread to a wide variety of uses.

Description of Properties

Epoxy resins are medium-weight plastics with specific gravities of 1.11 to 1.8. They possess relatively high tensile, compressive, and impact strength. In fiber glass reinforcements they possess tensile strengths as high as 65,000 psi as compared to 60,000 psi for structural steel. They are very resistant to abrasion. The most unique property of epoxies is their ability to adhere to any type of surface, no matter how dense or smooth. This property is enhanced by their ability to "wet" any surface. Aluminum-to-aluminum bonds with shear strengths of 6000 psi are typical. In addition to good adhesion they possess some flexibility which improves bond strength. Epoxies exhibit less shrinkage in curing than other thermosets, can be cured at room temperatures, and possess very low viscosities.

Epoxies have excellent electrical resistance. They have low power-loss factors and good arc resistance.

Epoxies are thermosetting and therefore somewhat heat resistant. Special formulations resist temperatures as high as 600° F., but generally their continuous service temperature falls in the 200° to 300° F. range. Low temperatures do not affect them adversely. They will burn slowly in an open flame but are self-extinguishing.

They are chemically very inert. No other thermoset offers more effective resistance to both acids and alkalies. They resist most common solvents, oils, and greases. They have a low water absorption rate.

Typical Applications

Their extremely high adhesive properties are exploited in numerous places where bonding is difficult. Aluminum honeycomb constructions in aircraft, auto body repair, china and other ceramic gluing are typical illustrations. See Fig. 3-3.

Their abrasion resistance and chemical inertness make them an important ingredient in surface coatings for appliances, gymnasium floors, and other hard-to-protect surfaces. Also

Fig. 3-2. Casein Plastics Used for Buttons and Novelties (SPI)

Fig. 3-3. Epoxies Can Do "Impossible" Repairs
(Union Carbide)

an epoxy-based coating as on the TV set in Fig. 3-4 is less expensive than electroplating.

Their unsurpassed combination of electrical resistance, low shrinkage during curing, speed of curing, and low viscosity make them unequaled as potting and encapsulating compounds for electrical components.

Their high strength when reinforced with glass fiber, ease of fabrication, and corrosion resistance have made them exceptional tooling materials for industrial fixtures, jigs and dies.

Their good resistance to chemicals and weathering is important in helicopter blades and guided missile parts. The reinforced epoxy contravene pictured in Fig. 3-5 for the 6-ton Sikorsky helicopter is still in good condition after 15 million cycles.

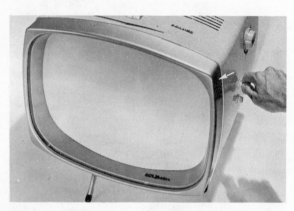

Fig. 3-4. An Appliance with an Epoxy-Based Coating
(Union Carbide)

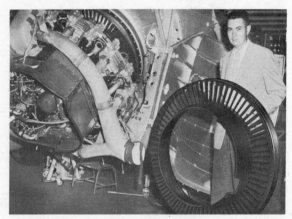

Fig. 3-5. Reinforced Epoxy Contravene for Sikorsky Helicopter (SPI)

Their ability to foam makes them usable as cores in lightweight sandwich construction.

Phenolic Plastics

Phenolics were the first plastics used for the production of any volume of consumer goods. Many of the plastic products on the market in the 1930's were made from Bakelite, named after Dr. Leo Baekeland, who obtained the basic patent on the manufacture of phenolic resins in 1909. This family of plastics, with many variations in formula, is still the backbone of the plastics molding industry.

Description of Properties

Phenolics are medium-weight plastics with specific gravities of 1.25 to 1.55. They are among the hardest of plastics. They possess only average tensile strength but have high compressive strength. They stretch very little without breaking and have low flexural strength. Phenolic resins are naturally an amber color and, especially with the addition of common fillers, are opaque. Though early phenolics were commonly dark brown or black, they can be colored with a number of bright opaque colors today. Outdoor properties are not outstanding; sunlight causes a fading of color. These plastics exhibit excellent dimensional stability over a wide range of temperature.

The electrical properties of phenolics are generally good. They are good insulators for high and low frequency currents. They have high dielectric constants and low power-loss factors. Many formulations have poor arc resistance. The surface tends to carbonize in the presence of a spark and eventually allows the passage of a current along it.

Phenolics are thermosetting plastics and somewhat heat resistant. Unmodified resins resist temperatures of only 160° to 180° F. for continuous service. Those with mineral fillers will stand temperatures as high as 400° F. without appreciable loss of physical properties. Phenolics will withstand low temperatures well. They burn slowly in an open flame; some formulations are self-extinguishing. They are poor conductors of heat.

The chemical properties of phenolics are average for plastics. Special formulations have been developed to provide resistance to attack by almost any chemical; this is usually accompanied by a loss of some other property. Unmodified resins resist weak acids and alkalies well. Oxidizing acids and strong alkalies eventually cause deterioration. Phenolics are generally resistant to water, alcohols, greases, oils, and common household chemicals.

Typical Applications

The properties of phenolics can be varied considerably by varying the chemicals combined to produce the resins or by substituting various fillers. Special formulations make it possible to produce a phenolic suitable for almost any purpose.

The balance of strength, hardness, and rigidity makes them usable for compression molded furniture drawers and television cabinets.

The high insulating value, resistance to oil and grease, and ease of molding metal inserts in place specify their use in various electrical applications such as automobile distributor caps and switch gear.

Their poor conductance of heat makes them ideal for handles for irons and cooking utensils. See Fig. 3-6.

Their high moisture, detergent, and soap resistances make them especially suited for washing machine agitators.

Their chemical resistance and low cost make them ideal for photographic developing trays and tanks.

One member of the phenolic family, resorcinol-formaldehyde, exhibits excellent adhesive powers plus the ability to cure at room temperatures. This makes it a widely used waterproof adhesive for exterior and marine plywood. Note Fig. 3-7 where acid-proof mortar incorporates phenolic resin.

Phenolics can be foamed to 300 times their original volume to produce a material weighing as little as ⅓ pound per cubic foot. In this form they are used for buoys and flotation tanks as well as for stiffeners in airplane wing sections.

The adhesive power of these plastics plus their ability to be burned away slowly with sufficient heat aided in the development of a foundry process called shell molding.

Their high strength and smooth surface make them usable for metal and plastic forming dies and molds.

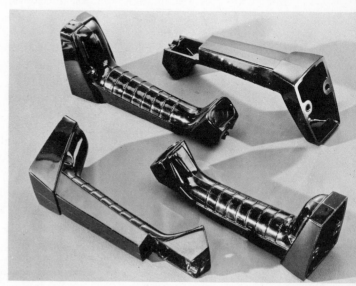

Fig. 3-6. Molded Phenolic Appliance Handles
(Durez)

Fig. 3-7. Acid-Proof Mortar Incorporating Phenolic Resin (Durez)

Polyester Plastics

The term, polyester, encompasses several plastics. It is a chemical term referring to the reaction product of an alcohol and an acid. Most polyester resins are thermosetting, but one has the structure of a thermoplastic. The names applied to the various polyesters are often confusing. One group, called alkyds, find wide use in enamels, paints, lacquers, and other surface coatings. They are also formulated as molding compounds. The thermoplastic polyester is extruded, stretched into filaments, and woven into one of our contemporary wonder fabrics, Dacron. It is also stretched bi-axially into the marvelous film, Mylar.

The group most commonly called polyesters is used as bonding agents for fibrous glass in applications simply termed "fiber glass." They first appeared in 1942, got their start in World War II military applications, and have since entered the consumer market in rather spectacular applications. The description of properties here is concerned largely with this latter group, although it generally applies to the others as well.

Description of Properties

Since a good share of the polyester resins are employed in reinforced products it is almost necessary to describe the properties of the reinforced plastics rather than of the resin alone. In some cases the property is determined almost entirely by the resin and in others by the reinforcement. Most strength properties are dependent upon how completely the resin has wetted the reinforcement.

Polyester resin itself has a specific gravity of 1.3. Depending upon the reinforcement used, the specific gravity of the reinforced member varies from 1.5 to 2.28. Glass-reinforced polyesters possess tremendous tensile, compressive, and flexural strength. Surface hardness is usually very good for a plastic. These plastics often tend to lose color upon prolonged exposure to sunlight but are otherwise not seriously affected by weathering. The resin and often the reinforcing are relatively clear and a wide variety of colors is easily obtained. These plastics exhibit some mold shrinkage, more than epoxies for instance.

Polyesters are good insulators of low-frequency currents. They possess some shortcomings as high-frequency insulators. They have medium high-dielectric constants and medium power loss factors. Their electrical applications are more often based upon other desirable properties such as strength and chemical resistance.

This group of polyesters is thermosetting and can be made to cure at room temperature. This is an advantage for hand layup of reinforced plastics. Most glass reinforced polyesters resist temperatures in the 250° to 350° F. range for extended periods. They burn slowly and most are self-extinguishing. They exhibit low thermal conductivity and offer good resistance to low temperatures.

Polyesters resist weak acids and alkalies but are affected by strong acids and bases. They are resistant to brine solutions, oils, greases, and water. Chlorinated solvents such as carbon tetrachloride are likely to attack them. The chemical inertness of glass generally adds to the chemical resistance of reinforced members.

Typical Applications

Many plastics must be molded under heat and great pressure resulting in the need for heavy, large, and expensive equipment if a product of any size is to be made. The room-temperature curing of polyester resins thus becomes an advantage in the manufacture of very large parts such as auto bodies, truck bodies and boat hulls as in Fig. 3-8.

The resilience, resistance to denting, and ease of repair make glass-reinforced polyesters ideal for auto bodies and appliance housings. As yet, the material cost prohibits large volume production, but sports car manufacturers make extensive use of this plastic.

Strength and chemical resistance make polyesters usable for chemical storage tanks.

The high strength in comparison to weight, coupled with transparency or translucency, makes these materials attractive building panels.

Fig. 3-8. Polyesters as Used in Fiberglass Boats (U.S. Rubber)

High tensile strength, flexibility, and corrosion resistance make fiber glass fishing rods popular sports equipment especially for salt water fishing.

Reinforced polyesters show usable strengths at higher temperatures than aluminum alloys.

The combination of free flow and exceptionally fast cure makes alkyd molding compounds economical to mold with low molding pressures required and rapid molding cycles.

The high dimensional stability plus high dielectric strength makes Mylar film useful for coil insulation or slot liners in motors.

High optical clarity, coupled with great tear resistance, makes Mylar an ideal base for photographic film.

It is the exceptional ability of polyester laminating resins to wet the surface of glass that makes them so useful as bonding agents in reinforced plastics applications.

The ease of working polyester resins has made them popular "do-it-yourself" materials for boat building or repair and car customizing.

Silicone Plastics

One of the inherent limitations of almost all plastics is their poor resistance to high temperatures. Even thermosets, in the main, should not be subjected to temperatures above 400° F. Silicones (SILL-i-cones) are exceptions to this generalization. Development of these resins stems back to the work of German chemists of the 1870's. Further research in England in about 1900 laid the basis for the use of silicones. Cooperative development between General Electric and Corning Glass Works made commercial production possible in the United States in the 1930's.

Description of Properties

Silicone molding compounds are rather heavy plastics with specific gravities ranging from 1.6 to 2.0. Many silicones are used in liquid form, but moldings of the resin exhibit medium to high tensile, compressive, and flexural strengths. The resins are opaque and coloring is possible. Generally, the addition of color is unnecessary because the primary uses are more often functional than decorative. Sunlight has little effect on these resins.

The electrical properties of silicones are outstanding in both liquid and solid form. They are good insulators for high and low-frequency currents and have high dielectric constants and low power-loss factors. It is the excellent retention of these properties over a wide range of temperatures that makes them so important.

Silicones are thermosetting resins with exceptional heat resistance. Glass-filled molding compounds retain their properties at temperatures as high as 900° F. and other silicone compounds have good properties at 450° to 500° F. The resins have little tendency to support combustion and burn only very slowly when finally ignited. Their thermal conductivity is relatively high for a plastic.

Chemically, the silicones are inert. They resist most acids and alkalies. They are incompatible with many organic polymers and thus make good release agents for plastics, rubber, glass, and metals. In liquid form they do not react with metals and are thus corrosion resistant.

Typical Applications

An important application of these plastics is in combination with rubber. Silicone's extreme resistance to loss of physical, electrical, and chemical properties is imparted to the rubber, producing a material with serviceable temperatures from —150° F. to 600° F.

They impart anti-foaming and nonflammability to oils and greases at elevated temperatures.

They impart wear-resistance, ability to hide small scratches, and stain-resistance to waxes and polishes for furniture and automobiles.

Their exceptional heat resistance, non-volatility, chemical inertness plus the resistance to sticking of certain formulations make them prominent mold release agents for all types of materials.

The excellent adherence properties of other silicone formulations coupled with their other typical properties make them components of pressure-sensitive adhesives such as tapes.

The ability to be foamed at moderate temperatures, coupled with high moisture and electrical resistance, makes them common potting or encapsulating materials for electrical components. Illustrated in Fig. 3-9, silicone-glass laminates used in electrical insulation have retained their properties at temperatures of 500° F.

Fig. 3-9. Electrical Insulation of Silicone-Glass Laminates (Dow Corning)

Urethane Plastics

Basic research from which urethane (YUR-e-thane) plastics developed was first carried out by Wurtz in Germany in 1848. The results of his work were little used by the plastics industry until just prior to World War II. Although urethanes are produced as hard resins, solid elastomers, and adhesives, their primary use to date has been in the form of flexible or rigid foam. The Society of the Plastics Industry has adopted the name "urethane foam" for materials that previously were called isocyanate, polyurethane, or polyester foam.

Description of Properties

Any discussion of the properties of urethanes, especially physical properties, is very difficult because the properties vary widely with foam density. Generally, urethane resins are light in weight with a specific gravity of 1.15 to 1.20. Foams weighing as little as 1.5 pounds per cubic foot have been produced. Values for compressive and tensile strengths vary considerably with density. Urethane flexible foams are more tear resistant than foam rubber but stretch less. They have some tendency to yellow with age but this seems to have nothing to do with physical properties. Sound and vibration absorption are outstanding. Ready adhesion to a wide variety of materials is another strong property of this group of plastics.

Electrical properties are excellent. The coating resins are good insulators even in humid conditions. Urethane wire coatings do not have to be cleaned off before soldering connections. Urethanes allow fine transmission of radar, radio, and x-ray waves.

Urethanes are thermosets and among the most heat resistant of the foamed plastics. They are usable over a temperature range of —50° to 250° F. with some formulations from —80° to 400° F. Most foams can be made self-extinguishing and are not ignited by a glowing cigarette. They are excellent heat insulators.

Urethanes have good chemical resistance. They are unaffected by most acids and alka-

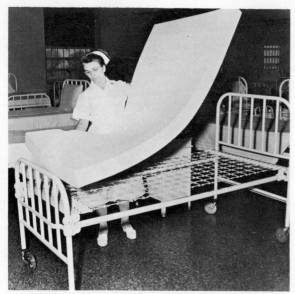

Fig. 3-10. Flexible Polyurethane Foam Mattress
(Nopco)

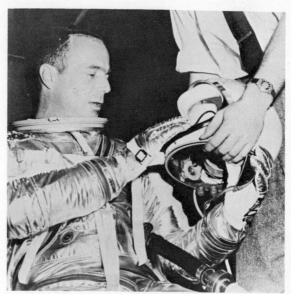

Fig. 3-11. Polyurethane Foam Liner Helmet
(Nopco)

lies. They can be made impervious to the effects of detergents and cleaning solvents. They are resistant to rot and vermin.

Typical Applications

Flexibility, coupled with tear-resistance, makes flexible urethane foams ideal for cushioning materials. Their somewhat high cost and more recent appearance have not allowed them to encroach on foam rubber as much as they probably will in the future. In Fig. 3-10, flexible polyurethane foam is used for mattresses weighing only twelve pounds.

Lightness of weight, high compressive strength, ready adhesion to aluminum, and ease of foaming in place make rigid urethane foam ideal for filling airplane wing sections to increase rigidity.

The near-perfect radar transmission properties allow them to serve in radomes of aircraft and guided missiles.

Their heat insulating properties plus tear resistance enable their use as lining materials in winter clothing. Foam liners only one-sixteenth inch thick provide sufficient warmth for even arctic temperatures.

In Fig. 3-11, a 1½-inch-thick rigid polyurethane foam liner in the astronaut's helmet protects against shock and reduces the noise level.

Exceptional resilience plus ability to bond to fibers makes flexible foams useful as rug pads.

The somewhat high cost of urethanes is often more than offset by their simple foaming qualities. For example, a refrigerator car which required six or seven days to insulate by conventional means is insulated by foaming urethane in place in five hours.

The outstanding chemical resistance of the urethane surface coatings has produced finishes for chemical equipment that holds up well in sulfuric acid plants.

Study Questions

1. Make a list of the plastics belonging to the family of thermosets.
2. After each plastic list two or three of its outstanding properties.
3. After each plastic list two or three properties which are not particularly good.
4. After each plastic list several of its uses.

TABLE 2
PROPERTIES OF THERMOSETS

	AMINOS	CASEIN	EPOXIES	PHENOLICS	POLYESTERS	SILICONES	URETHANES
Specific Gravity	1.47–1.55	1.35	1.11–1.8	1.25–1.55	1.3	1.6–2.0	1.15–1.20
Tensile Strength (1000's psi)	5.0–13.0	10.0	4.0–13.0	4.0–9.0	4.5–25.0	4.0–35.0	Varies with rigid and flexible
Compressive Strength (1000's psi)	25–45	27–53	13–28	15–50	12–34	9–15	
Impact Strength	Good	Fair	Excellent if reinforced	Good	Excellent if reinforced	Good	
Clarity[1]	Trl–0	T–0	T–0	Trl–0	T–0	0	0
Electrical Resistance	Good (low freq.)	Fair	Excellent	Good	Good (low freq.)	Excellent	Good
Heat Distortion Point (Degrees F.)	266–400	300	250–290	150–260	140–425	500–900	does not apply
Maximum Service Temp. (Degrees F.)	210–400	275	200–300	160–300	250–350	450	400
Burning Rate[2]	None SE	S	S to SE	S to none	S to SE	S to none	S to SE
Water Absorption Rate	Low	High for plastic	Very low	Low	Low	Very low	Very low
Effect of:							
Weak Acids	Little	Little	None	Little	Little	Little	Little
Strong Acids	Decompose	Decompose	Attacked by a few	Attacked	Attacked	Little	Little
Weak Alkalies	Little	Decompose	None	None	Attacked by some	Little	Little
Strong Alkalies	Attacked by some	Decompose	Little	Decompose	Attacked	Little	Little
Solvents	None	Little	Little	Little	Attacked by some	Attacked by some	Little
Outdoor Conditions (Sunlight)	Discolor	Discolor	None	Discolor	Discolor	Little	Discolor on some

[1]T — transparent, Trl — Translucent, 0 — Opaque   [2]S — slow, SE — self-extinguishing

Apply Your Knowledge

1. Bring to class common plastic articles and label them with the name of the plastic of which they are made.
2. Clip pictures from catalogs, newspapers, or magazines showing and describing products made from the thermosets.
3. Make a display of many different plastic articles labeling the plastic used for each and why this was (or was not) a good choice of material.
4. Secure samples of plastic raw materials from manufacturers of plastic articles.
5. Predict some uses to which the various plastics might be put in the future because of their unusual properties. List the name of the plastic and why you think it would be good for the use you named.
6. Find as many forms of the same plastic as you can. For example, melamine plastics are found in solid form in dishes, as powders in glues for wood, or as laminations in counter top materials.
7. Visit a plastics plant in your area.
8. Find a magazine article describing a new use for a plastic. Report on it to the class.

CHAPTER FOUR *plastics*
trade names

Plastics are known by many names. In some cases, the chemical name of the resin is used. For example, the terms polyethylene and polystyrene, are commonly known and used by the consumer.

The chemical names of some plastics are rather complicated and difficult to spell and pronounce; consequently, manufacturers have coined "catchy" names which are colorful and attractive. In some cases, a trade name conceived early in the development of the plastic has become accepted as the generic name of the group and is used by many different companies. *Nylon* is an example.

In other cases, a company name was applied to the one resin produced by that company. As production expanded and other families of resins began to be manufactured, the same trade name was applied to all the resins made by the company. For example, *Bakelite* was the name applied to the phenolic resin developed by the Bakelite Corporation. The company, now under the name of Union Carbide Plastics Company, added many different plastics, all called *Bakelite*.

Still other companies have created an individual name for each of the different plastics they manufacture. Koppers Chemical Company calls its polyethylene *Dylan*, its polystyrene *Dylene*, and its expandable polystyrene *Dylite*. In addition, there may be attached numbers indicating special formulations of the materials.

This great variety of terminology can lead to considerable confusion with the consumer. The following list of trade names and manufacturers will aid in identifying individual products. It is difficult to make such a list complete because new materials are developed and named each year. Primary emphasis is on structural plastics rather than fibers, adhesives, or coatings.

TABLE 3
TRADE NAMES AND MANUFACTURERS

Trade Name	Plastic Family	Producer
Abson	Styrene (ABS)	B. F. Goodrich and Co.
Aclar	Fluorocarbon film	Allied Chemical Corp.
Acrilan	Acrylic (acrylonitrile-vinyl chloride)	Chemstrand Div. of Monsanto Chemical Co.
Acrylite	Acrylic	American Cyanamid Co.
Alathon	Polyolefins	E. I. du Pont du Nemours Co.
Alkanex	Polyester coating materials	General Electric Co.
Ameripol	Polyethylene	Goodrich-Gulf Chemical Co.
Amester	Polyester resins	American Alkyd Industries
Araldrite	Epoxy	Ciba Products

Trade Name	Plastic Family	Producer
Armalite	Foamed plastic insulation	Armstrong Cork Co.
Arnel	Cellulose (triacetate fiber)	Celanese Corp. of America
Aropol	Polyester resin	Archer-Daniels-Midland Co.
Atlac	Polyester resin	Atlas Powder Co.
Avisco	Urea-formaldehyde	American Viscose Corp.
Avisun	Polypropylene	Avisun Corp.
Bakelite	Many resins including polyolefins, vinyl, styrene, phenolic, and epoxy	Union Carbide Plastics Co.
Beetle	Urea-formaldehyde	American Cyanamid Co.
Beckosol	Alkyd resins	Reichhold Chemicals, Inc.
Boltaflex	Vinyl sheet	Bolta Products Div. General Tire and Rubber Co.
Boltaron	Styrene (ABS)	Bolta Products Div. General Tire and Rubber Co.
Celanese	Acetates, polyethylene film, polyester resins, polyvinyl acetate emulsions	Celanese Corp. of America
Celcon	Acetal	Celanese Corp. of America
Chem-o-sol	Vinyl plastisols	Chemical Products Corporation
Chevron	Polypropylene	California Chemical Co.
Clopan	Vinyl film	Clopay Corp.
Consoweld	High-pressure laminate	Consoweld Corp.
Crest-foam	Vinyl foam	Crest Chemical Industries Corp.
Cyclolac	Styrene (ABS)	Marbon Chemical Co.
Cycolon	Styrene (ABS)	Marbon Chemical Co.
Cymac	Styrene	American Cyanamid Co.
Cymel	Melamine	American Cyanamid Co.
Cyzac	Laminating resins	American Cyanamid Co.
Dacron	Polyester fiber	E. I. du Pont de Nemours Co.
Delrin	Acetal	E. I. du Pont de Nemours Co.
Dow Corning	Silicones	Dow Corning Corp.
Durez	Phenolic and polyester resins	Durez Plastics Div. of Hooker Chemical
Dylan	Polyethylene	Koppers Chemical Co.
Dylene	Polystyrene	Koppers Chemical Co.
Dylite	Expandable polystyrene	Koppers Chemical Co.
Elastofoam	Vinyl plastisol	Union Carbide Plastics Co.
Elrex	Polyolefins and polystyrene	Rexall Drug and Chemical Co.
Epilote	Epoxy resin	Shell Chemical Co.
Epiphen	Epoxide resins	Borden Chemical Co.
Epocast	Casting, bonding, laminating resins	Furane Plastics, Inc.
Epolene	Polyethylene resins	Eastman Chemical Products, Inc.
Epon	Epoxy resins	Shell Chemical Co.
Epotuf	Epoxy resins	Reichhold Chemicals, Inc.
Epoxical	Tooling resins	U. S. Gypsum Co.
Escon	Polypropylene	Enjay Chemical Co.
Ethafoam	Polyethylene foam	Dow Chemical Co.
Ethocel	Ethyl cellulose	Dow Chemical Co.
Evenglo	Polystyrene	Koppers Co., Inc.
Evr-Kleer	Cast acrylic sheet	Cast Optics Corp.
Fairlon	Polyethylene film	Chippewa Plastics, Div. of Rexall Drug and Chemical Co.
Fiberite	Reinforced phenolic, melamine, and epoxy molding materials	The Fiberite Corp.
Formica	High-pressure laminate	Formica Corp. Subsidiary of American Cyanamid
Forticel	Cellulose propionate	Celanese Corp. of America
Fortiflex	Polyethylene	Celanese Corp. of America
Fortisan	Rayon fiber	Celanese Corp. of America

Trade Name	Plastic Family	Producer
Fortrel	Polyester fiber	Fiber Industries, Inc.
Fosta Nylon	Nylon	Foster-Grant Inc.
Fosta Tuf-flex	High-impact polystyrene	Foster-Grant Inc.
Fostalite	Light-stable polystyrene	Foster-Grant Inc.
Fostarene	Polystyrene	Foster-Grant Inc.
Genco	Many resins including acrylic, cellulose acetate butyrate, polyethylene, and styrenes	General Plastics, Inc.
Geon	Vinyl	B. F. Goodrich Co.
Gerlite	Acrylic sheeting	Gering Plastics
Ger-pak	Polyethylene film	Gering Plastics
Glykon	Polyester resins	Chemical Div., General Tire and Rubber Co.
Grex	High-density polyethylene	W. R. Grace and Co.
Halcon	Fluorocarbon	Allied Chemical Corp.
Hetrofoam	Rigid urethane foam	Durez Plastics Div., Hooker Chem.
Hetron	Polyester	Durez Plastics Div., Hooker Chem.
Hi-fax	Polyethylene	Hercules Posder Co.
Hysol	Epoxy	Hysol Corp.
Implex	Acrylic	Rohm and Haas
Kel-F	Fluorocarbon	Minnesota Mining and Mfg. Co.
Kodapak	Cellulosics	Eastman Kodak Co.
Kodel	Polyester fiber	Tennessee Eastman Co.
Kralastic	Styrene (ABS)	Naugatuck Chemical, Div. of U. S. Rubber Co.
Krene	Vinyl	Union Carbide Plastics Co.
Kynar	Fluorocarbon	Pennsalt Chemicals Corp.
Laminac	Polyester	American Cyanamid Co.
Lemac	Polyvinyl acetate	Borden Chemical Co.
Lexan	Polycarbonate	General Electric Co.
Lucite	Acrylic	E. I. du Pont de Nemours Co.
Lumarith	Cellulose acetate	Celanese Corp. of America
Lustran	Styrene (ABS)	Monsanto Chemical Co.
Lustrex	Styrene	Monsanto Chemical Co.
Marafoam	Urethane foam resins	Marblette Corp.
Maraset	Epoxy	Marblette Corp.
Marblette	Phenolic resins	Marblette Corp.
Marco	Polyester resins	Celanese Corp. of America
Marcothix	Thixotropic polyester resins	Celanese Corp. of America
Marlex	Polyolefins	Marbon Chemical Co.
Marvinol	Vinyl	U. S. Rubber Co.
Merlon	Polycarbonate	Mobay Chemical Co.
Methocel	Methyl cellulose	Dow Chemical Co.
Micarta	High-pressure laminate	Westinghouse Electric Corp.
Microthene	Polyethylene	U. S. Industrial Chemicals Co.
Mirro-Brite	Metallized acetate, butyrate, styrene, and polyester sheet	Coating Products
Moplene	Polypropylene	Novamont Corp.
Multaron	Polyester resins	Mobay Chemical Co.
Mylar	Polyester film	E. I. du Pont de Nemours Co.
Opalon	Vinyl chloride	Monsanto Chemical Co.
Orlon	Acrylic fiber	E. I. du Pont de Nemours Co.
Paraplex	Polyester resins	Rohm and Haas
Pelespan	Expandable polystyrene	Dow Chemical Co.
Penton	Chlorinated polyether	Hercules Powder Co.
Petrothene	Polyethylene	U. S. Industrial Chemical Co.

Trade Name	Plastic Family	Producer
Plaskon nylon	Nylon	Allied Chemical Corp.
Plenco	Phenolics	Plastics Engineering Co.
Pleogen	Polyester resins	Mol-rez Div., American Petrochemical Corp.
Plexiglas	Acrylic	Rohm and Haas
Plio-Tuf	Styrene (ABS)	Goodyear Tire and Rubber Co.
Pliovic	Vinyl	Goodyear Tire and Rubber Co.
Plyophen	Phenolic	Reichhold Chemicals, Inc.
Polycast	Acrylic sheets	The Polycast Corp.
Polyfilm	Polyester film	Dow Chemical Co.
Polyfoam	Urethane foam	General Tire and Rubber Co.
Polylite	Polyester resins	Reichhold Chemicals, Inc.
Poly Pro	Polypropylene	Spencer Chemical Co.
Profax	Polypropylene	Hercules Powder Co.
Saflex	Vinyl butyral	Monsanto Chemical Co.
Santofoam	Expanded flexible polystyrene	Monsanto Chemical Co.
Saran	Vinylidene chloride	Dow Chemical Co.
Scorbord	Expanded polystyrene	Dow Chemical Co.
Seilon	Vinyl, styrene, polyethylene	Seiberling Rubber Co.
Styrofoam	Expanded polystyrene	Dow Chemical Co.
Styron	Polystyrene	Dow Chemical Co.
Teflon	Fluorocarbon	E. I. du Pont de Nemours Co.
Tenite	Cellulosics and polyolefins	Eastman Chemical Products, Corp.
Texin	Urethane	Mobay Chemical Co.
Textolite	High-pressure laminate	General Electric Co.
Thermoflow	Reinforced polyester resin	Atlas Powder Co.
Tyrex	Cellulosic monofilament	E. I. du Pont de Nemours Co.
Tyril	Copolymer of styrene and acrylonitrile	Dow Chemical Co.
Ultron	Vinyl	Monsanto Chemical Co.
Uni-crest	Expandable polystyrene	United Cork Companies
Varcum	Phenolic	Reichhold Chemical Co.
Velon	Vinyl	Fireston Plastics Co.
Versamid	Polyamide resins	General Mills, Inc.
Vibrafoam	Cellular urethane sheet	U. S. Rubber Co.
Vibrin	Polyester	U. S. Rubber Co.
Videne	Polyester film	Goodyear Tire and Rubber Co.
Vuepak	Cellulose acetate	Monsanto Chemical Co.
Vygen	Polyvinyl chloride	General Tire and Rubber Co.
Zerlon	Copolymer of acrylic and styrene	Dow Chemical Co.
Zetafin	Polyolefin copolymers	Dow Chemical Co.
Zytel	Nylon	E. I. du Pont de Nemours Co.

Apply Your Knowledge

1. Make a collection of labels from various plastic articles showing the trade name and the plastic involved.
2. Every year many new plastic materials are brought on the market. Add to the list of trade names in your book.
3. Some trade names make use of the generic name of the plastic. List five trade names which obviously do this. What are some other bases for the development of trade names?
4. Some trade names have become so common that they tend to be used as generic names. For example, some people call all cameras "Kodaks" and all refrigerators "Frigidaires." Name a plastic where this has been the case.

How are plastics converted from their original raw forms into finished articles? How do the methods of processing plastics compare with those used with metal, wood, clay, or other industrial materials?

This part of the book defines five basic groups of plastics processes: molding, casting, thermoforming, reinforcing, and foaming. The individual chapters describe in some detail the variations of the five basic groups of processes and a table summarizes the outstanding characteristics of them.

PART II **processes of the plastics industry**

CHAPTER FIVE **process groupings**

Many different methods are employed to transform plastics from their raw state into finished products or into forms that will later be fabricated into finished products. Many of the processes used are adapted from other fields, notably metalworking. There is often confusion in terminology, which is partly due to the newness of the field and partly to the fact that terminology borrowed from other fields is not completely suited to plastics.

Well-designed plastics products are not made by simply cutting and fastening plastic material as if it were wood or metal. All processes of the plastics industry capitalize on the outstanding characteristic of this group of materials — their plasticity, the ease with which they can be forced into any given shape or form. All processes involve: (1) making the material soft and pliable, (2) forcing it to take the desired shape, and (3) causing it to hold that shape. The differences among the processes result from the means by which these three things are accomplished.

In grouping and understanding the many processes it is necessary to consider five elements:

(1) The temperature required to soften the plastic and to cause it to undergo a chemical change (in the case of thermosets).

(2) The force required to cause the plastic to take the desired shape and how this force is applied.

(3) The type of shaping device employed to cause the plastic to take the desired shape such as dies, molds, plugs, forms, rolls, etc.

(4) The physical state of the plastic before, during, and after the process.

(5) The plastics to which the process is suited, thermoplastics or thermosets.

Applying these considerations, there are three general groups of processes: molding, casting, and thermoforming. Reinforcing and foaming are really applications of these three, but they will be treated separately because of the differences from the more common applications of molding, casting, and thermoforming.

Molding

Molding consists of first liquifying a plastic molding compound, which is usually in powder, pellet, or putty form, with temperatures of 300° to 400° F. and forcing it into the desired shape. This shaping is done in one of three ways: between matched molds, through a die opening, or between rolls with pressures of 2000 to 15,000 pounds per square inch. It then is allowed to harden by curing (thermosets) or cooling (thermoplastics). The common individual molding methods are compression, transfer, injection, extrusion, blow, calendering, laminating, and cold molding.

Casting

Casting consists of pouring a liquid plastic over a form or into a mold with little or no heat and pressure. The plastic may be allowed to harden and cure at room temperature or some heat may be applied. The common applications of this group of processes are termed simple casting and plastisol casting.

Thermoforming

Thermoforming consists of softening a thermoplastic sheet or film with temperatures of 275 to 400° F., and stretching it over a form or into a mold by air-pressure differentials or by mechanical means. It is allowed to become rigid by cooling. The basic applications of this process are called mechanical forming, vacuum forming, and blow forming.

Reinforcing

Reinforcing involves impregnating a reinforcing agent such as fiber glass cloth or mat with a catalyzed liquid resin, forming it into a mold, and allowing the resin to harden and cure, bonding the entire object. Heat may be used to speed the curing process. The variations of reinforcing are hand lay-up, spray-up, matched molding, premix molding, pressure-bag molding, and vacuum-bag molding.

Foaming

Foaming is an application of casting or molding in which a plastic is expanded (foamed) and fused by physical or chemical means. Products can be foamed in a closed mold and removed, or they can be foamed-in-place in a cavity where they will remain.

Table 4 summarizes these five main processes by listing the variations of each. The next five chapters are the same as the five column headings.

TABLE 4
PROCESSES OF PLASTICS INDUSTRY

MOLDING	CASTING	THERMOFORMING	REINFORCING	FOAMING
Compression	Simple	Mechanical	Hand Lay-up	Foam molding
Transfer	Plastisol	Vacuum	Spray-up	Foam-in-place
Injection		Blow	Matched molding	
Extrusion			Premix molding	
Blow			Pressure-bag molding	
Calendering			Vacuum-bag molding	
Laminating				
Cold				

Study Questions

1. What single outstanding characteristic of plastics is exploited in all processes?
2. What three basic things are done to the plastic in all processes?
3. What factors must be considered in all processes?
4. What are the five basic groups of processes defined?
5. What are the main differences in temperature and pressure used in molding and those used in casting?

Apply Your Knowledge

1. Name some processes from other industries such as metals, wood, ceramics, or paper that are similar to some of the plastics ·processes. Show how they are similar.
2. In which processes would it be necessary to use thermosetting plastics? Why?
3. In which processes would it be necessary to use thermoplastics? Why?
4. What processes could make use of either thermosets or thermoplastics? Why?

CHAPTER SIX **molding processes**

In this chapter each of the various types of molding is discussed by outlining the process, illustrating the basic equipment involved, and describing some of the characteristics and applications of the process. Molding processes included here are compression molding, transfer molding, injection molding, extrusion, blow molding, calendering, laminating, and cold molding. In molding processes, both sides of the object are shaped by force from a molding surface.

Compression Molding

Compression molding is the simplest type of molding and the most common method by which *thermosetting plastics* are molded.

The Process

There are five phases to the compression molding process. First, the plastic in the form of powder, pellet, or preformed discs is *preheated* to dry it and to raise its temperature nearer the curing range. Second, the plastic "charge" is *loaded* directly into the mold cavity which is commonly held at a temperature between 300° and 400° F. depending upon the material. Third, the mold is *partially closed*; the heat and exerted pressure cause the plastic to liquify and begin to flow into the recesses of the mold. Fourth, the mold is then *fully closed*, causing the plastic to complete its flow and cure. Fifth, after the cure is completed, the mold is *opened* for ejecting the molded part.

Equipment Used

The equipment involved can be very simple. Fig. 6-1 shows a standard compression molding press. Complexity of equipment is usually the result of automatic devices to speed up production. The simple compression molding equipment consists of *a matched mold* (a plunger machined to shape one side of the object to be molded, and the mold cavity machined to conform to the other side), *a means of heating* the plastic and mold,

Fig. 6-1. **Compression Molding Press** (Dake)

and some method of *exerting force* on the mold halves to cause them to close. Fig. 6-2 shows a 200-ton compression press for molding phonograph records.

Molds are commonly made from polished, hardened steel since they must withstand great pressure and abrasive action of the plastic as it liquifies and flows. For less severe molding conditions or short-run products, softer mold materials (such as brass, mild steel, or plastics) may be used.

There are several types of mold designs employed: flash, semi-positive, and fully positive. *Flash molds* are the least complex to make and are satisfactory for thin flat shapes. Fig. 6-3 shows such a mold. It is so named because a slight overcharge of plastic "flashes" out as the mold is closed. It is this flash which blocks the plastic remaining in the cavity and causes the mold plunger to exert pressure on it. Less pressure is exerted on the plastic in this type of mold than in others; thus a less dense molding results.

In *fully positive molds,* Fig. 6-4, the cavity is recessed below the top of the mold and the mold plunger moves down into the recess during molding. This allows little or no plastic to flash out and maximum pressure is impressed on the part being molded. This produces a very dense part but requires an exact charge of plastic if the mold is to close properly and produce consistent parts. Positive molds require very careful machining because extremely close tolerances must be maintained.

Semi-positive molds combine the flash and fully positive molds. See Fig. 6-5. At the beginning of the compression stroke, some

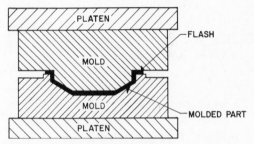

Fig. 6-3. Compression Molding — Flash Mold

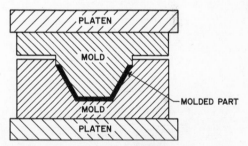

Fig. 6-4. Compression Molding — Fully Positive Mold

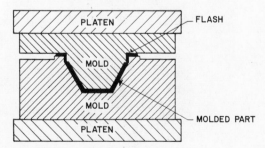

Fig. 6-5. Compression Molding — Semi-positive Mold

Fig. 6-2. **Phonograph Record Compression Press** (French Oil)

plastic is allowed to flash out, but as the mold plunger reaches the bottom of the stroke, it acts like a positive mold. This type of mold allows for some inaccuracy of charge and yet gives a fairly dense, uniform molded part.

Heat for molding may be obtained by various means but commonly the mold halves are cored, or hollowed, and steam run through the openings, or electrical heating elements inserted. Steam heat is more rapid, but electrical heat is usually more convenient. In molding thermosets where the mold is kept hot throughout the working day, electrical heat is most used. In molding thermoplastics where the mold must be cooled at the end of each molding cycle, steam is used for heating and cold water for cooling.

The means of applying force to close the mold halves could conceivably be any compression device. Commonly, some type of press is used. The press often has one stationary *platen* (flat metal platform) and another platen that is moved by a hydraulic or pneumatic cylinder. As the cylinder moves the platen, a squeezing action results. The capacity of a press is rated in terms of the total *tons of force* it will exert on the mold. Many compression presses are in the 50- to 300-ton range.

Fig. 6-6. Compression Molded Phenolic Drawer
(Union Carbide)

Characteristics and Applications

Compression molding is ordinarily used for thermosetting plastics. Alkyds, melamine, urea, and phenolics are often processed in this manner. Since thermosets harden by means of a chemical change which is aided by the addition of heat, the mold remains hot throughout the entire cycle and is immediately ready for a new charge of plastic as soon as the previously molded part is ejected. However, thermoplastics must be cooled to harden; this necessitates cooling the entire mold at the conclusion of each cycle before the part can be ejected, consequently slowing down the molding process considerably. Nevertheless, phonograph records of vinyl and styrene (thermoplastics) are compression molded because of the extreme accuracy that is needed for proper sound reproduction.

Compression molding is ideal for products of a large area and deep draw. Much electrical switch gear is made in this manner. Some plastic sheet is produced this way. Plastic dinnerware is commonly compression molded. Radio and television cabinets, furniture drawers as in Fig. 6-6, and other case-like products are common applications. Many small items such as buttons, knobs, handles, and electrical parts are molded in multiple-cavity molds.

Articles which are compression molded will usually have a parting or flash line, generally at the point of greatest dimension. For example, it may be at the rim of a knob or the edge of a plate. The flash is removed but the mold line is often evident.

Transfer Molding

In compression molding the plastic is rather stiff as it is being liquified and forced around the mold cavity. When producing parts with delicate sections or where inserts (such as metal terminals) are to be molded in place, compression molding may distort the sections, move, or break the inserts. An adaptation of compression molding called transfer molding has been developed to eliminate these shortcomings. Fig. 6-7 illustrates this type.

The Process

There are five phases to transfer molding. First, a quantity of plastic molding compound sufficient for one molding is placed in a *transfer chamber*. This chamber is usually located above and connected to a closed mold by a tube called a *sprue*. The plastic is *liquified* in the transfer chamber by the application of heat. Second, the liquified plastic is *forced from* the transfer chamber to the heated closed mold through the sprue. Third, the heat of the closed mold causes the plastic *to cure*. Fourth, after the cure is complete, the mold is *opened* and the *part ejected*. Fifth, a small amount of cured plastic remains in the bottom of the transfer chamber and the sprue. This piece *is removed* before the next cycle.

Equipment Used

The equipment for transfer molding is very similar to that used for compression molding. In fact, many compression presses are converted for transfer molding by the addition of a transfer chamber. Essentially, transfer molding equipment consists of: (1) a *heated matched mold* which has an entry hole or *gate* for the transferred plastic, (2) a *heated transfer chamber* where the plastic is softened, and (3) a *source of power* to hold the mold closed during molding as well as to provide a force to push the plastic from the transfer chamber into the mold. Fig. 6-8 shows a transfer molding press. Notice that it is similar to the previous compression molding press except it has a transfer chamber on top.

The *molds* employed in transfer molding are quite different from those used in compression molding since they are completely closed during molding. There is a connecting tube or sprue from the closed mold to the transfer chamber to allow the liquified plastic to be forced from the chamber into the mold. The terms *flash, fully positive,* and *semi-positive* have no meaning in transfer molding because the plastic is not moved into the recesses of the mold by a telescoping action of the mold halves. The mold is simply a hollow block which has been split in half with each mold cavity exactly the size and shape of

that part of the article to be molded. Fig. 6-9 shows a mold for transfer molding.

The *transfer chamber* is a cavity, usually cylindrical, containing a heating element and a ram or plunger to push the molten plastic from the transfer chamber into the mold.

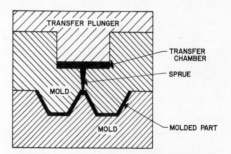

Fig. 6-7. **Transfer Molding**

Fig. 6-8. **100-ton Transfer Press** (Logan)

Fig. 6-9. **Mold for Transfer Molding** (Northwest Pl.)

Characteristics and Applications

Transfer molding is used with thermo-setting plastics, commonly the slower-curing materials. Plastics used in compression molding are also suitable for transfer molding. The choice of method depends more upon the design of the part involved than upon the plastic used.

Although transfer molding requires more complicated equipment, it offers some important advantages. The plastic is in liquid form as it enters the mold and is less likely to distort molded-in inserts than if it were in semi-liquid form as at the beginning of the stroke in compression molding. In liquid form it is also much easier to push into thin sections with fine detail. For example the distributor cap in Fig. 6-10 was transfer molded.

Since the mold is fully closed during molding there is no *flash line* to be removed, although there is a sprue that must be removed during finishing. A *parting line* shows where the mold halves have come together.

Better plastic cure is often obtained with transfer molding because the material can be more evenly heated in the transfer chamber and is further heated as it enters the mold.

The material left in the transfer chamber, the *sprue* and the *gate*, is waste material that must be removed. This waste is often about equal to the flash in compression molding.

Typical articles made by this process are terminal block insulators with many metal inserts and intricate shapes such as cups and caps for cosmetic bottles.

Injection Molding

Injection molding is the principal molding method employed with *thermoplastics*. It is a high-speed mass production process. In some ways it is similar to transfer molding of plastics or die casting with metals.

The Process

Injection molding consists of five steps. First, the thermoplastic in powder or pellet form is placed in a *hopper*. Second, the plastic is forced from the hopper into a *heating cylinder* where it is spread out against the walls with a *spreader* or *torpedo* and liquified at temperatures of 300° to 650° F. Third, the melted plastic is forced under high pressures of 5,000 to 40,000 psi through a *nozzle* into a *closed cold mold*. Fourth, the plastic *cools* and solidifies in the mold. Fifth, after cooling, the mold is opened and the part is *ejected*. See Fig. 6-11.

Equipment Used

Injection molding equipment consists of a *hopper* to store the plastic powder or pellets, a *heating cylinder* to soften the material, a *means of applying force* to inject the liquid plastic, and a closed *matched mold*.

Most injection molding presses are *horizontal* with the hopper mounted over the heating cylinder. See Fig. 6-12. The plastic drops from the hopper into the cylinder. A hydraulic *ram* or plunger forces the plastic through the heating cylinder. Electric- or steam-heating coils surround the cylinder to provide heat

Fig. 6-10. **Distributor Cap Molded in Transfer Press**
(Northwest Pl.)

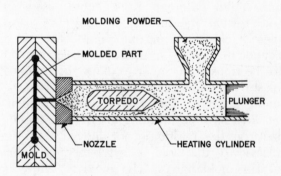

Fig. 6-11. **Injection Molding**

to liquify the plastic. The design of the spreader or *torpedo* is very important since its shape determines how evenly the plastic will be spread against the cylinder walls to provide proper liquefaction without burning. Its shape varies with the plastic involved.

Molds for injection molding are similar to those for transfer molding except that they are *cored* to hold some sort of cooling device, usually water, rather than heating devices as in transfer molding. In this process the plastic hardens by cooling and the mold must be kept below 100° to 120° F. Injection molds are usually *multiple-cavity;* the liquid plastic enters the mold cavities from the heating cylinder nozzle through a sprue, runners, and gates. The *sprue* is the connecting channel from the nozzle. *Runners* carry the plastic laterally across the mold to the *gates* which are the entries into each mold cavity.

The size of an injection molding press is usually specified in terms of the number of ounces of cellulose acetate that can be injected in one shot. Presses range in size from one-half ounce to 300 ounces. Fig. 6-13 shows a typical 16-ounce injection molding press.

Characteristics and Applications

Injection molding is ordinarily used for *thermoplastics*. Common materials processed in this fashion include acrylics, fluorocarbons, nylon, polyethylene, polystyrene, and vinyls. *Thermosets* can be injection molded, but the flow of plastic through the heating cylinder must be very carefully controlled or the material will harden and cure in the cylinder, rendering the machine useless. Since thermoplastics remain soft as long as they are held at the proper temperature there is no such problem with them.

Articles that have been injection molded will often exhibit a parting line where the two mold halves come together, usually at the point of greatest dimension. Gates where runners have entered will also be present although they are usually placed in unobtrusive spots or incorporated into the design.

Injection molding is economical where a large quantity of items is to be manufactured. Initial equipment cost is high and molds are expensive, but the process, once set up, is very rapid, with common cycles of ten seconds to two minutes. On small items such as model airplane kits several hundred individual items may be molded at one time. Fig. 6-14 shows an injection molded *"shot"* removed from the press with runners still attached. After being broken apart, the individual pieces will be assembled to make two styrene banks for small change.

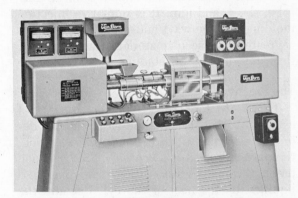

Fig. 6-12. Small Injection Molding Press
(Van Dorn)

Fig. 6-13. Sixteen-ounce Injection Molding Press
(Reed-Prentice)

Fig. 6-14. "Shot" Removed from Injection Molding Press (Monsanto)

Typical consumer products produced by this method include toys, bathroom and kitchen wall tile, refrigerator dishes, containers of all types, models, fan housings, battery cases, electrical appliance parts, radio cabinets, electric shaver housings, and medallions.

Extrusion

Extrusion is a molding process for producing *continuous lengths* of thermoplastics with consistent cross-sectional shapes such as rod, tube, sheet, and film. It is similar to injection molding in some ways and probably processes a greater volume of material in a given time than any method of molding.

The Process

There are four phases to the process of extrusion. First, the thermoplastic in powder or pellet form is placed in a *hopper*. Second, the plastic drops into a *heating cylinder* which has a *revolving screw* inside. The plastic is liquified by the heat of the cylinder and the friction created between the screw, the plastic, and cylinder walls. Heating cylinders are commonly kept at 300° to 500° F. Third, the liquified plastic is forced through a *die opening* at the end of the heating cylinder with pressures of 500 to 6000 psi. The opening in the die determines the cross-sectional shape of the piece, called the *extrudate*. Fourth, the extruded plastic is *cooled* and thus hardened as it leaves the die on a conveyor belt. It is cut into convenient lengths or rolled up. See Fig. 6-15.

Equipment Used

A plastics extruder consists of a *hopper,* a *heating cylinder* with a *feed screw* inside, a *die* with a properly shaped opening, some means of *cooling* the plastic, and a *take-off* device. Fig. 6-16 shows a typical extruder.

The *heating cylinder* must be very strong, capable of withstanding pressures as high as 10,000 psi. Heating is most commonly accomplished with electricity, but steam and oil are also used.

The *feed screw* is an extremely important part of the equipment. Different types and sizes of threads are employed for the extrusion of different materials. They are usually made from heat-treated alloy steel to withstand tensile stresses of 100,000 psi.

The *die* must be of hardened steel to resist the wear of the plastic as it is forced through the orifice. See Fig. 6-17. The opening in the die may not be the exact size and shape of the desired *extrudate* because dimensional changes occur as the material cools.

As the plastic leaves the die, it usually passes through a *water bath* for cooling. Some sort of conveyor belt or take-up reel removes the extruded plastic.

Characteristics and Applications

Extrusion is ordinarily used with *thermoplastics*. Commonly extruded materials are acrylics, cellulosics, fluorocarbons, nylon, styrenes, polyethylene, and vinyls.

The only shapes which can be extruded are those with consistent cross sections such as rods, tubes, sheets, moldings, or other archi-

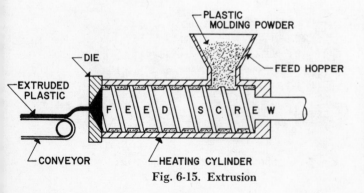

Fig. 6-15. Extrusion

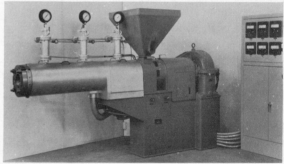

Fig. 6-16. A 3½ inch Extruder (Egan)

tectural shapes. Extruded shapes, especially sheets, can be identified by the *stress lines* on the surface.

Extrusion is a very rapid production method because it is continuous. Several times the amount of material is processed this way if contrasted with injection molding. Of course, the two processes are not used for the same purpose.

Special adaptations of extrusion are often used. Wire may be coated by passing it through the center of an extrusion die which produces a tube around it. Some film is made by extruding a tube and blowing air inside which expands and thins it to the desired size. The thin tube is then slit and flattened out for use as film. Many polyethylene bags are made by cutting thin extruded tubing and sealing the ends. Monofilament fishing line is extruded nylon. Sheet extruders may be placed in line with thermoforming equipment so that the sheet is fed directly into the forming machine before it is cooled. Fig. 6-18 shows tail light lenses extruded from acrylic plastics which are produced in a continuous strip and then cut to fit a curved aluminum frame.

Blow Molding

Blow molding is misnamed because it does not fit the general characteristics of *molding* processes (which shape softened material between two molds). In reality, it is a specialized application of *blow forming*, as there is a mold on only one side of the ma-

terial. However, because it is known in the industry by the name of *blow molding*, it will be called that here.

The Process

A thermoplastic tube, called a *parison*, is extruded between the halves of an open *split mold*. While the plastic is still soft from the extruder, the mold is closed, trapping the parison and sealing one end. Air pressure is forced through the other end, forcing the tube to stretch and follow the contours of the closed mold. The mold is kept cool and the material, being thermoplastic, becomes rigid as it comes in contact with the mold surfaces. After cooling, the mold is opened and the part ejected and trimmed. See Fig. 6-19.

Fig. 6-18. Tail Light Lenses (Du Pont)

Fig. 6-17. Closeup of Extruding Plastic

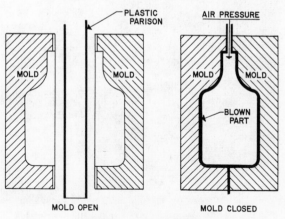

Fig. 6-19. Blow Molding

Fig. 6-20. Parison Extruded in Blow Molding Press (Mod. Plastic)

Fig. 6-21. Open Mold after Blowing (Mod. Plastic)

Fig. 6-22. Stripper Plate Breaks Blown Bottles
(Mod. Plastic)

Equipment Used

The equipment for blow molding consists of two basic units—an *extruder* to produce the parison and a *blow-molding machine* for the actual forming process. In most applications, the extruder and blow molder are one machine.

Extrusion equipment is described in a previous section. The extruder used in the blow molding operation is standard equipment with a die of appropriate size and shape to produce the proper tube for the parison.

The blow-molding portion of the equipment must provide a means of opening and closing the mold, a means of cooling the mold (usually circulating cold water), and a means of introducing air pressure into the sealed parison. Production machines have a number of mold stations so that the parison may be continuously extruded. Fig. 6-20 shows how the parison is extruded between the molds in a blow molding press. After blowing, the mold is open; notice the blown bottles in Fig. 6-21. A *stripper plate*, as shown in Fig 6-22, breaks the finished bottles from the parison.

Most equipment is at least semi-automatic. The operator often removes and trims the formed part.

Characteristics and Applications

Any *thermoplastic* can be blow molded. However, most products made in this manner are from *polyethylene*. The very common use of the *squeeze bottle* as a container for all types of fluids has made the blow molding of polyethylene an important part of the industry.

Blow molding is one of the few processes by which a hollow, one-piece article can be made. In any kind of matched molding (compression or transfer for example) this shape is impossible because the internal mold could not be removed after molding. *In blow molding, the "internal mold" is air.*

Blow molding is a high-speed process. Most machines have several mold stations so that as one article is cooling others are in various stages of manufacture and the extruder runs continuously.

Objects made by this process are relatively free from the *internal strains* set up by forcing plastic through a small sprue opening or around sharp arrises as in other types of molding. The natural flexibility of the plastic can be used to full advantage.

Tooling costs are relatively low because low pressures and temperatures are used. The plastic is soft as it is formed and thus does not have an abrasive effect on the mold.

Blow molding has limitations too. Abrupt changes in wall thickness are impractical. Since the material forms by stretching, there is a tendency to *bridge* sharp corners in the mold. For the same reason, extremely accurate control of wall thickness is difficult. The surfaces of the product are not likely to be as smooth as those produced by other types of molding. However, designs of most objects made in this manner do not call for highly polished exteriors.

Calendering

The process of calendering was adapted from the rubber industry and is used in the manufacture of paper, linoleum, and metals as well as plastics. It is the leading method for producing vinyl film and sheeting.

The Process

The thermoplastic resin, stabilizer, lubricant, colorant, and plasticizer in the case of flexible film, are mixed, blended, and liquified. This soft mixture is rolled or calendered between a series of hot horizontal rolls. The distance between the rolls controls the thickness of the film or sheet. The material, sized to thickness, passes between a series of cooling rolls which solidify the plastic. It is then wound up on take-off reels. See Fig. 6-23.

Equipment Used

The equipment for calendering consists of some means of blending and mixing the plastic compound, a series of rotating calender rolls, a series of cooling rolls, and a take-off device.

The mixing and blending equipment may be an intensive mixer or a mill; often both are used in combination. A common intensive mixer is called a Branbury mixer.

The actual calendering is done by a series of *rolls*, usually in pairs. They act much like the wringer rolls of a washing machine. The distance between them can be regulated to control sheet thickness. Rolls may be set succeedingly closer together to gradually reduce the thickness to the desired dimension. They are heated, often with circulating oil, and powered to rotate. Some may be *embossed* to produce patterned sheet. Fig. 6-24 shows a four-roll calender stack used for vinyl film.

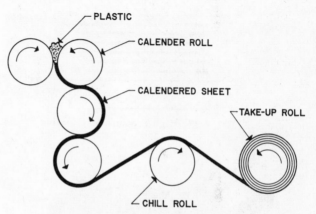

Fig. 6-23. Calendering

Fig. 6-24. **Four-roll Calender** (Adamson)

Characteristics and Applications

Calendering is similar in many ways to extrusion. It is used for such *thermoplastics* as vinyls, polyolefins, cellulosics, and styrenes. Flexible *polyvinyl-chloride* sheet and film account for the major share of the calendering done.

Calendering is a high-speed process. Films, .002 inch thick and six feet wide, are calendered at the rate of 300 feet per minute. Tolerances of less than .001 inch are possible.

Calendered sheet or film often will exhibit *stress lines* in the surface of the material al-

though improved methods have made them less obvious.

Plastics processed by this method find their way into many end products such as shower curtains, rainwear, floor coverings, clear films for packaging and for laminating over playing cards or lining food cartons, inflatable toys, swimming pool liners, and clear auto seat covers.

Laminating

In the general sense, laminating consists of *bonding two or more layers* of any material. According to this interpretation, plywood is a laminate. As related to plastics, lamination is the process of bonding layers of resin-impregnated or resin-coated materials with heat and pressure. Laminates are further classified as *high-* and *low-pressure*, depending upon the amount of pressure used for bonding. A large bulk of the so-called low-pressure laminates consists of reinforced plastics such as polyesters and epoxies rein-

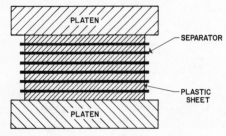

Fig. 6-25. **High-Pressure Laminating**

Fig. 6-26. **High-Pressure Laminating Press**
(French Oil)

Fig. 6-27. **Formica Laminating Press**
(Am. Cyanamid)

forced with fiber glass. This section will be concerned only with high-pressure laminates; the other group will be dealt with under the heading of reinforced plastics.

The Process

The layers of material to be laminated, often paper, cloth, or asbestos, are impregnated with a thermosetting resin. The excess resin is removed, and the remaining resin is dried but not cured. The layers of impregnated material are assembled to provide the proper thickness; heat and pressure are applied, causing the resin to flow and harden the laminate into one solid mass. See Fig. 6-25. Flat sheets are pressed between highly polished plates under pressures of 1000 to 1500 psi at temperatures of 300° to 350° F. Tubes are laminated around mandrels (the diameter of the interior), and other shapes are pressed between matched molds. The laminate can be cured in the press or mold, or it can be removed and cured in an oven.

Equipment Used

Much of the laminating done is of flat sheets. The equipment for this consists of a *platen press* which is capable of squeezing the laminate together with sufficient force, and some means of *applying heat*, usually through the platens of the press. Fig. 6-26 and 6-27 show typical high-pressure laminating presses. The first is capable of 2260 tons of force. The second is used to produce Formica from layers of paper and resin.

Although any device which could exert sufficient force on the laminate could be used, lamination in any volume is done on *hydraulic presses* capable of several hundred tons of force. Usually a multiple platen press is used so that more than one sheet can be laminated at one time. The stock to be laminated is placed between highly polished plates which in turn are placed between the press platens. Any desired pattern can be imparted from these plates.

Since the resins used are *thermosetting*, they require heat to soften the resin and to cure it. Heating is accomplished by passing steam,

hot water, or electricity through the press platens. The finished laminate may be cooled by passing cold water through the platens at the conclusion of the process.

Characteristics and Applications

High-pressure laminates are commonly made with such thermosetting resins as phenolic, melamine, silicone, epoxy, and polyester. The base material of the individual laminations is often paper, but cotton fibers, asbestos felts, mats and papers, and fibrous glass are also used.

Phenolic laminates are low cost and have good mechanical and electrical properties. *Melamines* are more costly but offer better flame resistance and have excellent electrical properties. *Silicones* are used primarily for their retention of mechanical and electrical properties even at very high temperatures. *Epoxies* are high in chemical resistance and extremely moisture resistant. *Polyesters* are low cost with average properties.

Although the average consumer is more familiar with *decorative* laminates such as those used for counter tops and wall panels, an equally important use is in *industrial* laminates, developed primarily for their mechanical, electrical, and chemical properties. Industrial laminates are used for gears, bearings, pinions, cams, and pulleys because of their high strength-to-weight ratio and resistance to corrosion. They find wide use in the electrical field as insulation, and for panels and terminal boards, as well as making excellent bases for printed circuits, Fig. 6-28.

Fig. 6-28. Laminated Phenolic Base for Printed Circuits (Union Carbide)

Cold Molding

Cold molding is a process adapted from the ceramics industry. As the name implies, it is molding done with pressure alone.

The Process

The molding compound is mixed to a doughy mass and placed in a mold similar to that used in compression molding. The mold is closed and the material pressed together with pressures of 2000 to 4000 psi. No heat is used; the compound adheres only by being pressed tightly together. The part is removed from the mold and placed in an oven. Temperatures of 450° F. for periods of seventy-two hours fuse the resin and bond the molding. See Fig. 6-29.

Equipment Used

The equipment for cold molding is very similar to that for compression molding except that no provision for heating the mold is needed. A very rapid-closing press can be used because no time is needed for the compound to liquify and flow. Multiple-cavity molds are common for small parts.

Characteristics and Applications

Two types of compounds are used in cold molding, *bituminous* and *phenolic*. The first is not a synthetic but a mixture of natural resins with asbestos fibers and other filler materials. The phenolic group is a mixture of liquid phenolic resin and asbestos fiber.

Because the resin is not cured in the mold, the process is very rapid. The only time required is to fill the mold, close the press, open the press, and remove the part. As many as 3500 pieces per hour have been produced. The number of pieces that can be cured at one time is limited only by the size of the oven.

Cold-molded articles have good electrical properties. Many of the articles produced by this method are used in electrical applications. For example, Fig. 6-30 shows some typical electrical parts. The strength of such parts is relatively low, surface finish tends to be dull, and close dimensional control is difficult.

Cold molding is specified where an inexpensive part not to be subjected to severe strain is needed. Switch bases, plugs, handles, and knobs are common applications.

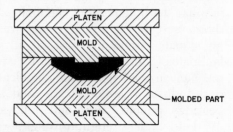

Fig. 6-29. Cold Molding

Fig. 6-30. Cold-Molded Electrical Parts
(SPI)

Study Questions

Compression Molding

1. In what form is the plastic used in compression molding?
2. What individual plastics are commonly used with this process?
3. What causes the plastic to liquify in this process?
4. What is meant by a "matched mold-plunger and cavity?"
5. What material is used for molds? Why?
6. What are three types of compression molds?
7. How are the molds commonly heated?

8. How much force is usually needed to close the mold? How is this force usually applied?
9. Name several products that are likely to be compression molded.

Transfer Molding

1. Why is transfer molding sometimes used in place of compression molding?
2. Where is the plastic liquified in transfer molding? How is this different from compression molding?
3. What is a sprue?
4. In what way is transfer molding equipment different from compression molding equipment?
5. What finishing operation is needed on a part which is transfer molded?
6. What are some products made by transfer molding? What would they have in common that would be different from compression molded articles?

Injection Molding

1. What group of plastics is used for injection molding? Why?
2. In what form is the plastic used in this process?
3. What temperature is likely to be used to liquify the plastic?
4. What pressure is used to push the plastic through the opening?
5. What kind of mold is used?
6. What is the "torpedo?" What does it do?
7. Why are molds often cooled in injection molding?
8. How is the size of an injection molding machine designated? What are common sizes?
9. What plastics are commonly processed by injection molding?
10. What is a parting line? Where will it be located on an injection-molded article?

Extrusion

1. Describe the shapes that can be made by extrusion.
2. In what form is the plastic used in extrusion?

3. What temperature is used to heat the plastic in this process?
4. What part of the machine actually controls the shape of the article made?
5. What causes the plastic to move through the machine?
6. What material is commonly used to make extruder dies?
7. How is the plastic cooled as it comes through the die?
8. Which group of materials is used in extrusion? Name several individual plastics which are often extruded.
9. Why is extrusion a more rapid process than compression molding?
10. Name several special applications of extrusion.

Blow Molding

1. What name is given to the tube used in blow molding?
2. What causes the article to take its shape in blow molding?
3. In what way is blow molding a combination operation.
4. Why must the mold be cooled?
5. What group of plastics is processed by blow molding?
6. Describe the typical blow molded shape.
7. Why are blow molded articles relatively "strain-free?"
8. What are some of the limitations to the shapes that can be produced by blowing.
9. What is a very common article you see daily that is made by blow molding?

Calendering

1. Name a non-plastic calendered material.
2. Describe the shape that is commonly made by calendering.
3. What part of the calendering machine actually produces the shape of the finished item?
4. How can patterns be impressed in the calendered sheet?
5. What other molding process is very similar to calendering? How?
6. What are some typical articles that are made by calendering?

Lamination

1. What is the general meaning of lamination?
2. What purpose does the plastic serve in lamination?
3. Which group of plastics is used in this process?
4. How much pressure is used in lamination? What temperature?
5. What kind of machine is commonly used for lamination?
6. Name several plastic resins commonly used in lamination.
7. What is a common consumer product that is made by lamination?

Cold Molding

1. What is one common difference between cold molding and all of the other molding processes?
2. What purpose does the pressing operation serve? How is this different from the purpose that pressing serves in compression molding for example?
3. What other molding process is most similar to cold molding?
4. What is the most common plastic used for cold molding?
5. Why is this process so rapid?
6. What are the limitations of articles made by this process?

Apply Your Knowledge

1. Collect a number of common plastic articles. Label each to indicate the name of the molding process that was probably used to make it.
2. Many plastic articles could be made by any of several molding processes. Take a common molded item and sketch cross-sectional views of the die or mold that would be needed to make it by each of several molding methods.
3. Articles made by each molding process have certain identifying characteristics. For example, extruded shapes have a uniform cross-section and will probably have stress marks running parallel with the direction of extrusion. List identifying characteristics for each molding process that will aid in determining which method was used with a given article.
4. List the various methods of molding and indicate whether they should be limited to use with thermosets or with thermoplastics or whether they could make use of both. Explain your reasoning in each case.
5. Visit a plastics plant where molding is being done. Get a sample of the raw material being used and a sample of the finished product if possible.
6. Estimate the relative costs of manufacturing a specified quantity of a given item by each of the appropriate molding methods. Consider equipment cost, processing time, material cost, and labor cost.
7. In which molding processes will a parting line be evident on the product? Obtain a common molded article and locate its parting line. Sketch what you think its mold would look like in terms of the parting line evident.

CHAPTER SEVEN

casting processes

In this chapter each of two basic types of casting is discussed by outlining the process, illustrating the basic equipment involved, and describing and picturing some of the characteristics and applications of the process. Casting techniques included are *simple casting* as well as three variations of *plastisol casting: dip, slush,* and *rotational.*

Simple Casting

Many products are made by casting rather than molding. In casting, the liquid is simply *poured into the mold,* rather than being forced in. Sheets, rods, tubes, and special shapes which are later processed into finished products are often made in this manner.

The Process

In casting, the plastic is prepared in liquid form. In some cases the resin is naturally a liquid and in others a granular solid is liquified by heat. Catalysts (which cause the liquid to set up) are often added. The liquid plastic is poured into a closed mold and any air bubbles are removed. The plastic is cured at room temperature or in an oven at low heat. The cured plastic is removed from the mold. See Fig. 7-1.

The Equipment

The basic equipment involved is relatively simple; however, automated devices may have more complex control systems. A hollow mold is needed with an opening through which the plastic can be poured; some means of pouring the plastic is employed.

In producing rods, tubes, or special shapes, it is common to use a two-piece metal mold having an entry hole through which the plastic can be poured. The mold is split apart to remove the finished casting.

The mold used to produce flat cast sheet consists of two pieces of highly polished plate glass separated by a gasket which controls sheet thickness. The edge is sealed and one corner left open, through which the plastic is poured. Cast acrylic sheet, Plexiglas or Lucite, is the most familiar material processed this way.

Characteristics and Applications

Both *thermosets* and *thermoplastics* may be cast. Commonly used materials for casting

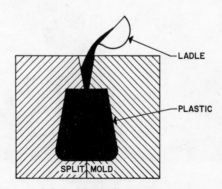

Fig. 7-1. Solid Casting with Closed Mold

include acrylics, styrenes, phenolics, polyesters, and epoxies.

Cast articles possess some properties that are superior to those of molded articles. For instance, cast acrylic sheet has superior optical properties, dimensional stability, surface hardness, tensile and impact strength. It does not have the *grain* of extruded sheet. Generally, it is more expensive because of the longer processing time involved. Acrylic sheet cast between two pieces of plate glass is shown in Fig. 7-2.

A very common application of casting employed in the electrical field is called potting or encapsulation. *Potting* is the deep impregnation of components such as transformers, capacitors, and resistors. *Encapsulation* is the enclosing of components. For many years wax or tar-like substances were used by the electrical industry for this kind of protection. They lacked certain qualities in resisting breakage and deterioration by moisture, fungus, or chemicals. Today most delicate electrical parts are protected by enclosure in phenolics, polyesters, silicones, urethanes, or epoxies. This practically eliminates failure due to attack or the presence of foreign materials. Fig. 7-3 shows some electrical components cast or *encapsulated* in epoxy resins.

A similar application is *embedment,* often with clear acrylics. Scientific and biological specimens are cast in blocks of clear plastic.

In this condition they may be studied and handled without danger of damage. Decorative medallions such as those seen on the center of automobile steering wheels are metal embedded in plastic.

A very important industrial application of casting is in the construction of tooling. Stamping and drawing dies for metals, holding fixtures, foundry molds, molds for compression and injection molding and vacuum forming are cast from epoxy compounds filled with ceramic powders or steel or aluminum dust.

Plastisol Casting

A special application of casting commonly used for the manufacture of hollow articles is plastisol casting. There are several variations: dip casting, slush casting, and rotational casting. All are based on the fact that a plastisol in liquid form is solidified as it comes in contact with a heated surface.

Dip Casting

The Process

A heated plug the size and shape of the inside of the article to be cast is dipped into a container of liquid plastisol. The mold is withdrawn at a given rate. The plastic immediately surrounding the mold adheres to it and solidifies. The slower the rate of withdrawal,

Fig. 7-2 Casting Acrylic Sheet
(Rohm and Hass)

Fig. 7-3. Electrical Components Cast in Epoxy Resins (Union Carbide)

the thicker will be the layer of plastic. The solidified plastisol and mold are cured in an oven at 350° to 400° F. After cure, the plastic is stripped from the mold. See Fig. 7-4.

The Equipment

Dip casting can be done with very simple equipment; basically it consists of a *preheating station* to heat the mold, a *dipping station*, a *curing oven*, a *cooling station*, and some *means of removal* of the finished casting from the mold.

Dip casting can be done by hand, but for accurate thickness control, timing devices are useful.

Molds should be made from a material that will hold heat well. Many different metals and ceramic materials are commonly employed.

Slush Casting

The Process

A liquid plastisol is poured into a heated hollow mold which is the shape of the outside of the object to be made. The plastisol in immediate contact with the walls of the mold solidifies. The longer the plastic remains in the mold, the thicker will be the layer of plastic that solidifies. The excess plastic, still in liquid form, is poured from the mold. The solidified plastic and mold are then cured in an oven at 350° to 400° F. The mold is opened and the part removed. See Fig. 7-5.

The Equipment

Slush casting can be done very simply with a heated hollow plaster mold. Commercially, metal molds are used with hot air or infra-red ovens for heat. Filling is often done in a vacuum or in some type of shaking device to eliminate air bubbles.

Rotational Casting

The Process

A predetermined amount of liquid plastisol is placed in a heated, closed, two-piece mold. The mold is then rotated, usually in two planes; this distributes the plastic against the walls of the mold in a thin even layer. As it comes in contact with the mold it solidifies. The mold and plastic are cured in an oven. After cure, the mold is opened and the part removed. Fig. 7-6 shows a diagram of this process.

The Equipment

The simplest equipment for rotational casting consists of a platform to which a mold is clamped and rotated in two dimensions at the same time. The equipment may be housed in

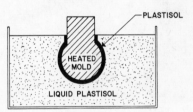

Fig. 7-4. Plastisol Dip Casting

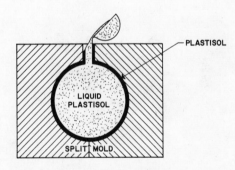

Fig. 7-5. Plastisol Slush Casting

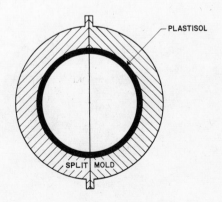

Fig. 7-6. Plastisol Rotational Casting

an oven so that gelling and curing take place at one time. Automated equipment is available which requires no handling by the operator. The machine shown in Fig. 7-7 has six rotating spindles and is capable of producing 1620 items per hour with one operator.

Fig. 7-7. Rotational Casting Machine for Plastisol (Akron)

Fig. 7-8. Doll Shoes Made by Dip Casting (Akron)

Fig. 7-9. Balls Made by Rotational Casting (Akron)

Characteristics and Applications

The various processes for converting plastisols into finished products require no pressure and thus the processing equipment is not particularly expensive. Thin walled molds or plugs are used. The molds must be capable of transmitting heat easily because fusion of the plastic is caused by heat.

Dip casting can be used to produce items with intricate shapes. The flexible plastisol is easily stripped from the plug after setting. Common articles made by this process are transparent ladies' overshoes, spark plug covers, and flexible gloves. The doll shoes in Fig. 7-8 were made by dip casting.

Slush casting is used for hollow, open articles. No parting line is produced and undercuts in the molds pose no problem. Toys and boot socks with sponge encased are made this way.

Rotational casting is used to produce completely-enclosed, hollow, seamless objects. Very even wall thicknesses are possible because the rotation causes the plastic to flow over all surfaces of the mold. Since the mold must be split, a parting line will generally be present. Many doll parts are made by rotational casting as well as novelties such as plastic fruit, and functional articles such as squeeze bulbs and toilet floats. Fig. 7-9 shows some balls made by rotational casting of plastisols.

Study Questions

Simple Casting

1. In what form is the plastic used for simple casting?
2. What type of mold is used for simple casting?
3. What kind of mold is used to make cast flat sheets?
4. What are some of the kinds of plastics that are processed by casting?
5. Why is cast sheet likely to be more expensive than extruded sheet?
6. What is the advantage of cast sheet over extruded sheet?

7. What is potting? encapsulation? embedment?
8. What use is made of cast plastics outside the plastics industry?

Plastisol Casting

1. What are three methods by which plastisols are cast?
2. In what form are plastisols?
3. What causes a plastisol to solidify?
4. How is the thickness of a plastisol casting controlled?
5. What is an important characteristic of molds for plastisol casting?
6. What type of mold is needed for dip casting? for slush casting? for rotational casting?
7. How are air bubbles often eliminated in slush casting?
8. What is the purpose of rotating the mold in rotational casting?

9. Name some articles made by each of the three methods of plastisol casting.

Apply Your Knowledge

1. Find a plastic article made by each type of casting.
2. Make a sketch of the mold that you think was used to make each item.
3. List three criteria that you could use to tell whether a sheet was cast or extruded.
4. In which of the methods of casting would no parting line be evident. Explain.
5. What characteristics of the process are likely to make casting less expensive than molding? more expensive?
6. Visit a plastics plant where casting is being done. Obtain a sample of the plastic and an article being made from it if possible.

CHAPTER EIGHT ## *thermoforming processes*

Thermoforming is one of the recently developed major processes of the plastics industry. It has become an important production process since 1950. There are many variations in equipment and method, but all are based on the fact that a thermoplastic sheet becomes as soft as a sheet of rubber when heated, can be stretched to any given shape, and will retain that shape when cooled.

There are three basic methods of thermoforming based on the means used to stretch the heated sheet: mechanical forming, vacuum forming, and blow forming. Most parts of any complexity are made by some combination or adaptation of these three. In this chapter each of the individual types is discussed by outlining the process, illustrating the basic equipment involved, and describing some of the characteristics and applications of the process.

Mechanical Forming

Mechanical forming, sometimes called *drape forming,* as the name implies, uses mechanical means to stretch the sheet to the desired shape.

The Process

A thermoplastic sheet is clamped in a frame or yoke. The clamped sheet is heated until it becomes soft, but not liquid. Most sheets soften sufficiently for forming at temperatures of 275° to 400° F. The softened sheet is forced over a plug. The formed part is held in posi-

tion until it cools and becomes rigid in the shape of the plug. The part is removed from the plug and trimmed. See Fig. 8-1.

Vacuum Forming

Vacuum forming is the method of thermoforming most commonly used. See Fig. 8-2. One of its first uses was in the manufacture of relief maps for the army.

The Process

A thermoplastic sheet is clamped in a frame or yoke or simply held against the rim of a

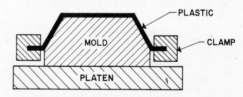

Fig. 8-1. Mechanical Thermoforming

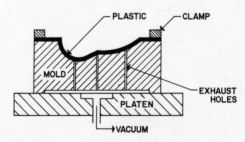

Fig. 8-2. Vacuum Thermoforming

mold, as shown in Fig. 8-3. The clamped sheet is heated until it becomes soft but not liquid. The soft sheet is sealed against the rim of a mold. A vacuum is created by removing the air from the mold cavity. Atmospheric pressure forces the heated sheet into the contours of the mold. The vacuum is held until the sheet cools and becomes rigid. The formed part is then removed and trimmed. Fig. 8-4 shows the vacuum-formed inner hull. Fig. 8-5 shows the process of trimming the excess plastic. The final step, Fig. 8-6, is to place the inner and outer hulls together to be cemented. The finished product is shown in Fig. 8-7.

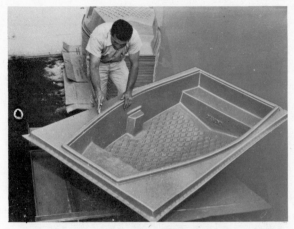

Fig. 8-5. Trimming the Excess Plastic (Marbon)

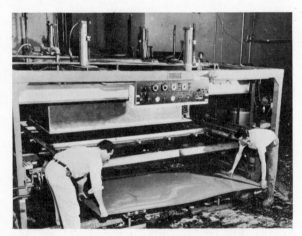

Fig. 8-3. Plastic Sheet Placed in Vacuum Forming Press (Marbon)

Fig. 8-6. Placing Hulls Together To Be Cemented (Marbon)

Fig. 8-4. The Formed Inner Hull (Marbon)

Fig. 8-7. Vacuum-Formed Boat (Marbon)

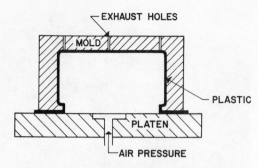

Fig. 8-8. Blow Thermoforming

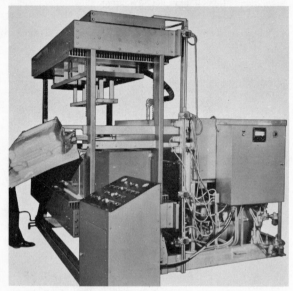

Fig. 8-9. A Combination Thermoforming Machine
(Comet)

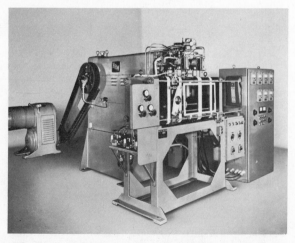

Fig. 8-10. A Blow-Forming Machine (Auto-Blow)

Blow Forming

Blow forming is the reverse of vacuum forming. Air pressure forces the sheet into the contours of the mold.

The Process

A thermoplastic sheet is clamped in a frame or yoke. The clamped sheet is heated until it becomes soft but not liquid. The softened sheet is sealed between a pressure head and the rim of a mold. Air pressure is applied, forcing the sheet against the contours of the mold. Exhaust holes in the mold allow the trapped air to escape. The pressure is maintained until the part cools and becomes rigid. Once the pressure is released, the part is removed for trimming. See Fig. 8-8.

The Equipment

Some thermoforming equipment is custom-made for a given application or even for a given product. Much of the available equipment can be used for variations of two of the types of forming—mechanical and vacuum for instance—while some of it is adaptable to all three basic types. Fig. 8-9 shows equipment for a combination thermoforming operation; the body is partially formed mechanically by the plug at the top, and then it is completed by vacuum forming. There are several elements that all equipment provides for: some type of *heating device*, some means of *holding the plastic* while it is heated, a *platen* to support the molds and plugs, a *source of vacuum or air pressure,* and a means of *lowering* the material-clamping frame or *raising* the mold. A typical blow-forming machine is shown in Fig. 8-10.

Most machines use some type of electrical radiant heating panel. In some cases two panels are used, one under the sheet and the other over it. The temperature developed by these heaters is between 650° and 1500° F. Since the forming temperature of most plastics is between 275° and 400° F, the sheet is kept under the panel for a very short time, as little as a second for thin film to one or two minutes for a thicker sheet.

Extruded sheet is commonly used for forming. This type of sheet has a tendency to shrink in one direction when heated. For that reason it must be held during the heating cycle. Most machines employ some type of double-clamping frame which grasps the plastic outside the final trim line.

A metal platen is used on most machines to support the molds. Often it contains an outlet for air pressure or vacuum.

Vacuum and air pressure are supplied by standard compressors and vacuum pumps. Vacuum pumps are usually of a high-capacity rather than high-vacuum type. Vacuums of 28 inches of mercury (approximately 14 psi) are used. A surge tank from which the air is exhausted by the vacuum pump is used to give a reservoir of vacuum. Tanks of two to 300-gallon capacity are used. Air pressures as high as 250 psi are used for heavy material to be forced into intricate shapes.

On some equipment the platen on which the mold is mounted is raised to force the mold against the heated sheet. On others, the clamp frame holding the plastic is lowered over the mold. This can be accomplished mechanically, pneumatically, or hydraulically.

Characteristics and Applications

Forming is limited to *thermoplastics*. Thermosets, once processed into fully cured sheets, cannot be resoftened for forming. Any thermoplastic sheet, theoretically, can be formed. Common materials so processed by the industry include cellulosics, vinyls, styrenes, polyolefins, and acrylics. Sheets made by casting, calendering, and laminating can be formed but the bulk of forming is done with *extruded sheet* which is less expensive and stretches more easily.

Like other industrial processes, the characteristics of thermoforming make it ideally suited to certain applications. It is often contrasted with injection molding as a means of manufacturing products. Each process has its advantages, both economic and design.

Economically speaking, forming uses low-priced equipment and inexpensive, quickly made molds. Production can be started soon after the design is completed. Design changes are easily accomplished. On the other hand, injection molding uses very expensive equipment and molds which are not easily modified. It may take months in some cases to go into production. In favor of injection molding, it uses very inexpensive granular molding powders as contrasted with relatively expensive sheet for forming. Simply, it may be said that injection molding is suited to high-volume production where thermoforming is more suited to small-volume production if both processes would be suitable means of making the product. *Forming* is often used in the design and manufacture of prototypes which will later be molded.

This is not to imply that thermoforming is not suited to mass production. There are certain design features which can be accomplished more readily with forming than with molding. Parts with very large areas like refrigerator door liners are much better produced by forming. Formed articles with thin wall sections have much greater impact strength than similar injection molded products. A molded part cannot be predecorated whereas formed masks and display signs are frequently printed in flat sheet form and later formed. Formed parts are more likely to be free from internal strains.

Thermoformed articles are seen everywhere in consumer and industrial products. Major parts of appliances are formed. Refrigerator and freezer door liners complete with formed-in compartments for eggs, butter and bottles of various types, represent one of the large volume markets for this process. Others include television masks, dishwasher housings, and washing machine covers.

Automobiles contain formed parts such as instrument panels, arm rests, ceilings, and door panels.

The lighting industry makes extensive use of thermoforming. Large patterned light diffusers made of plastic are superior to glass ones and are easy to produce.

Forming is ideally suited to advertising. The ease with which pre-printed signs and displays are formed plus their low cost has made forming an important process to fabricators of displays. Point-of-sales racks and display cases are low cost, attractive, and easy to maintain. They need not be used for extensive periods of time but may be replaced and rotated often.

Thermoformed transparent packages are competitively priced with paper containers, are more attractive, protect the merchandise against soil and loss, and often serve as containers for the item after purchase.

Many toys are thermoformed. Examples are large hobby horses, games, paint and blackboard sets, and doll furniture. See Figs. 8-11 and 8-12.

The aircraft industry was one of the early users of forming. The excellent optical and physical properties of formed acrylics have specified their use as windshields and bomber "blisters." Many interior parts such as panels, arm rests, and serving trays are also used.

Housings for typewriters, dictaphones, and duplicating machines are formed. Some luggage is formed from styrene copolymers.

Fig. 8-11. A Vacuum-Formed Toy (Union Carbide)

Fig. 8-12. Typical Blow Formed Products
(Auto Blow)

Study Questions

Mechanical Forming
1. What is another name often given to mechanical forming? Why do you suppose this name is often used?
2. In what form is the plastic used in mechanical forming?
3. At what temperature is the forming usually done?
4. What causes the article to take the desired shape in mechanical forming?

Vacuum Forming
1. In what form is the plastic used in vacuum-forming?
2. What type of device is used to control the shape of the finished article?
3. What actually forces the plastic against the shaping device?

Blow Forming
1. In what form is the plastic used in blow-forming?
2. What type of device is used to control the shape of the finished article?
3. Why must holes be used in the mold?
4. What actually causes the article to conform to the shape of the mold?

General
1. What are the basic components of any piece of thermoforming equipment?
2. By what means is the plastic commonly heated in thermoforming?
3. What is the problem encountered in using extruded sheet? Why is it so commonly used in thermoforming?
4. What is the maximum forming force that can be exerted on the plastic in vacuum-forming?
5. Which group of plastics is used with this group of processes, thermosets, or thermoplastics? Explain.
6. What are some of the economic advantages of thermoforming over injection molding?
7. How are designs often placed on thermoforming articles?
8. What are some common thermoformed articles?

Apply Your Knowledge

1. Collect a number of thermoformed articles. Label each with the type of forming used to produce it.

2. Make a sketch of the mold that you think was required to produce each article you have collected.

3. How can you tell whether an article was made by thermoforming or injection molding?

4. Locate an item made by injection molding and sketch how it would have to be modified or redesigned to be made by thermoforming.

5. Compare injection molding and thermoforming in terms of costs. Describe the general production situation to which thermoforming is suited.

6. Visit a plant doing thermoforming. Describe it to the class. Obtain a sample of the plastic they are using and a finished article if possible.

CHAPTER NINE ## reinforcing processes

There is probably no application of plastics better known to the layman than reinforced plastics. These plastics are often known simply as *fiber glass* and are thought by many not to be plastics at all.

Technically, a reinforced plastic is any plastic resin which is strengthened by the properties of a reinforcing material. High-pressure plastic laminates, discussed under the section on molding, fit this description. However, in the industry, the term *reinforced plastics* has come to mean the result of using plastic resins to bond various fibers, fabrics, mats, or rovings, usually made from glass fibers.

Manufacturers employ several methods. Some have the characteristics of molding and some the characteristics of casting. To avoid confusion, they will be treated as a group, rather than within the sections of molding and casting. The applications are called hand lay-up, spray-up, matched molding, premix molding, and vacuum- or pressure-bag casting.

In this chapter each of the individual types of reinforcing is discussed by outlining the process, illustrating the basic equipment involved, and describing and picturing some of the characteristics and applications of the process.

Hand Lay-up

The Process

A single mold or plug is coated with a release agent to prevent the resin from stick-ing to it. A coating of liquid plastic resin, usually polyester or epoxy, is brushed, rolled, or sprayed on the surface of the mold. Layers of cloth or mat, usually fiber glass, are impregnated with resin and placed over the mold. The surface is rolled to work out air bubbles and to condense the mat or cloth. The resin is allowed to harden and cure either at room temperature or in an oven. The finished casting is removed from the mold. See Fig. 9-1.

The Equipment

The equipment required for hand lay-up is the simplest of any process. It has thus become a "do-it-yourself" process. All that is needed is a mold that may be made from wood, plaster, metal, or plastic, various brushes, rollers, or squeegees for applying the

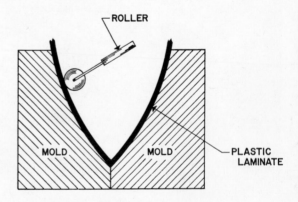

Fig. 9-1. Reinforcing — Hand Lay-up

resin, and containers in which to mix the resin, promoter, and accelerator. Fig. 9-2 shows a hand lay-up project.

Spray-up

The Process

A single mold, or plug, is coated with a release agent to prevent the resin from sticking. A two- or three-nozzle pressure gun sprays measured amounts of resin, catalyst, promoter, and chopped glass fibers or continuous roving over the surface until the desired thickness is built up. Fig. 9-3 shows a boat hull being sprayed. The material is allowed to harden and cure at room temperature or in an oven. The cured part is removed from the mold. See Fig. 9-4.

The Equipment

Molds for spray-up are similar to those used in hand lay-up. There are several types of spray guns on the market. They are somewhat different from those used for spraying paint. One type sprays resin and promoter from one nozzle, resin and a catalyst from another, and chopped glass fibers from a third. The resin sets very slowly in the presence of either the promoter or the catalyst but very rapidly when all three are mixed at the point of deposit. Another type of gun deposits a continuous glass roving in place of chopped fibers and can also be adapted to deposit some type of filler such as saw dust or mica. Fig. 9-5 shows a gun spraying resin and fibers.

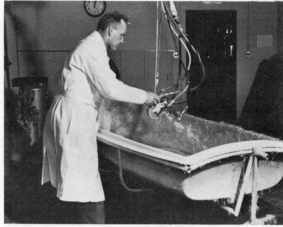

Fig. 9-3. **Spraying a Boat Hull** (Rand)

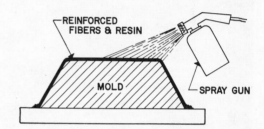

Fig. 9-4. **Reinforcing — Spray-up**

Fig. 9-5. **Gun Spraying the Resin and Fibers**
(Shell Lake)

Fig. 9-2. **Hand Lay-up**

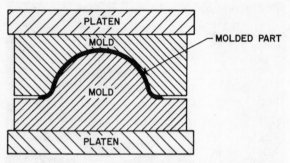

Fig. 9-6. Reinforcing — Matched Molds

Matched Molding

The Process

Fig. 9-6 shows a diagram of the process. Matched molds are coated with a release agent. The reinforcing material in mat or fiber form is preformed to the approximate shape of the finished product. The preformed material is placed on one half of the mold and the resin added to it. The two halves of the mold are pressed together and heated, causing the resin to flow, impregnate the preform, harden, and cure. After curing, the mold is opened and the part removed. Fig. 9-7 shows the matched metal molds for molding the fiber glass underbody of a sports car. Chopped glass fiber with resin binder is sprayed on a revolving vacuum

Fig. 9-7. Matched Metal Molds
(Molded Fiber Glass)

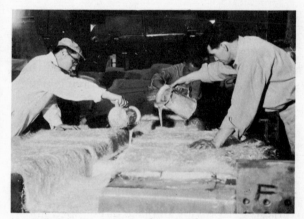

Fig. 9-9. Resin Poured over Fiberglas Preform
(Molded Fiber Glass)

Fig. 9-8. Spraying Chopped Glass Fiber with Resin Binder (Molded Fiber Glass)

Fig. 9-10. Once Cured, Molded Floor Pan Removed
(Molded Fiber Glass)

screen, Fig. 9-8, preforming the glass fibers to the desired shape. This preform is placed on the mold and a measured amount of resin poured over it. See Fig. 9-9. After curing, the molded floor pan is removed from the press, Fig. 9-10, and finished, Fig. 9-11.

The Equipment

The equipment for matched molding is very similar to that used for compression molding. Metal molds are often used. They are pressed together in hydraulic or pneumatic presses of 25- to 300-ton capacity. Heat for hardening and curing is applied through the mold by electricity or steam.

Fig. 9-11. Finished Floor Pan of the Avanti
(Molded Fiber Glass)

Premix Molding

The Process

A set of matched molds is coated with a release agent to prevent sticking of the resin. In some cases a lubricant is placed in the molding compound which eliminates release problems. Short, chopped glass fibers are mixed with resin to form a putty-like mass called a *premix* or *"gunk."* A predetermined amount of premix is placed in the mold cavity. The mold is closed under heat and pressure causing the resin and fibers to flow, harden, and cure. After cure, the part is removed from the mold. See Fig. 9-12.

The Equipment

The molds and pressing equipment for premix molding are much the same as for matched molding. Mixing equipment is needed to meter the correct amounts of fiber and resin and to mix them. Several premixes are available.

Pressure-Bag Molding

The Process

The resin and reinforcement are placed in a mold or over a partially inflated rubber bag in a fashion similar to that used in hand lay-up or spray-up. The bag is placed in the mold cavity with the resin and reinforcement between the bag and the mold. The bag is inflated with an air pressure of 20 to 50 psi. This forces the bag, the resin, and the reinforcement to follow the contours of the mold.

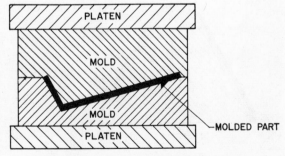

Fig. 9-12. Reinforcing — Premix Molds

The pressure is maintained until the resin hardens. The bag is then deflated and the part removed. See Fig. 9-13.

The Equipment

Most of the equipment for pressure-bag molding is custom made for a particular product. A mold is used which is often made from metal or reinforced plastics. Some means is provided to seal the rubber pressure-bag against the mold, and a compressor is used to inflate the bag.

Vacuum-Bag Molding

The Process

The resin and reinforcement are placed over a plug in a fashion similar to that used in hand lay-up or spray-up. The plug, with resin and reinforcement on it, is placed in an airtight flexible bag or envelope. The air is exhausted from the bag. Atmospheric pressure forces the bag against the mold, causing

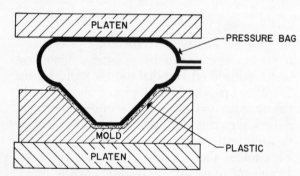

Fig. 9-13. Reinforcing — Pressure-Bag Molding

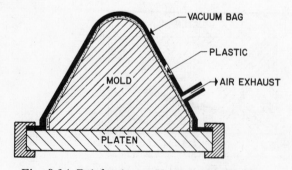

Fig. 9-14 Reinforcing — Vacuum-Bag Molding

the reinforced plastic to conform to the contours of the plug. In some cases, the bag is placed in an autoclave (or pressure tank) which places increased pressure on the surface. The vacuum is maintained until the resin hardens. The bag is opened and removed; the part is removed from the plug. Fig. 9-14 shows a diagram of this process.

The Equipment

Plugs for vacuum-bag molding may be made from metal, plastics, or wood. The vacuum bag is usually of heavy rubber and some type of vacuum pump is employed to remove the air from it. Here, as in pressure-bag molding, the equipment is custom-made for a particular product.

Characteristics

In the simplest sense, a reinforced plastic consists of a reinforcing agent bonded with a plastic resin. Several of the families of resins may be used. Epoxies, phenolics, melamines, silicones, alkyds, cellulosics, vinyls, and acrylics are used, but the bulk of the work is done with polyesters. Many of the superior properties of epoxies are increasing the use of this group.

Many *reinforcement materials* have been used where particular properties are required, but none surpasses glass, all properties taken into account. Glass reinforcement in the form of fibers ranging from .0002 inch to .001 inch in diameter is made into mat, rovings (soft rope-like bundles of continuous strands), chopped strands, and cloth. *Mat* provides medium strength and rapid build-up at a medium cost. *Rovings* are inexpensive and provide tremendous strength in one direction. *Chopped fibers* offer medium strength and easy flow in premix compounds at low cost. *Cloth* provides the highest strength in all directions but is also the most expensive.

Hand lay-up is a rather simple process used for custom-made products. Consistency from one product to the next is lacking. Because a single mold is used, only one side of the part is very smooth. The process is easy to use, however, and commonly is employed by designers and model makers in the preparation of prototypes and by the home craftsman. Common products of this process are boats, chairs, and housings.

Spray-up is a process developed for use in many of the same applications for which hand lay-up is used. It overcomes several serious production shortcomings of the latter process, however. In a reinforced plastic, strength is increased as glass content is increased, but to obtain maximum strength all fiber surfaces must be thoroughly coated with resin. Any voids reduce strength and often spoil appearance. In hand lay-up it is difficult to get complete impregnation. The resin, which must be catalyzed before application, begins to solidify and affords little time for flow. In addition, the resin is very viscous and difficult to work into the cloth or mat. Slowing down the gel time by reducing the amount of catalyst often results in the resin running to low spots on the mold producing irregular wall sections. Spray-up eliminates these problems. The resin is catalyzed and mixed thoroughly with the glass fibers at the point of application to the mold.

Manufacturers of spray-up equipment feature such fabulous applications as erection of completely self-supporting buildings over an inflated rubber mold. After spray-up is complete and the resin set, the mold could be deflated and moved to the next job. The process is useful in repair of tanks, freight cars, truck bodies, and swimming pools.

Matched molding is used to mass produce uniform commercial articles of high strength and superior surface on both sides. High initial tooling costs are recovered through increased production. Typical products are chair seats and backs, construction workers' helmets, and sports car bodies such as the early Chevrolet Corvette.

Premix molding has many characteristics similar to matched molding. Both make use of matched molds. Instead of mat or cloth for reinforcement the premix contains short chopped fibers. This produces a compound that flows readily into intricate shapes and thin wall sections. Because the fibers are short, usually one-quarter to one-half inch long, they do not interlock with one another to form the high degree of reinforcement provided by cloth or mat. In many products, additional wall thickness provides needed strength. Typical products are pump parts, transformer frames, tote trays, and housings.

Bag molding, either pressure or vacuum, provides high volume production of large parts without expensive presses or matched molds. Such articles as boats are made this way where extreme precision and close dimensional tolerances are not too important. Because only a single mold is employed, only one side of the article is smooth. Pressure-bag molding can produce more intricate shapes and better surface finish than vacuum-bag molding because of the higher pressures possible.

Applications

Reinforced plastics articles are seen in many consumer and commercial applications. In *transportation* devices they are important because of their high strength and low weight. Boat hulls are well-known applications. Cabs, interiors, and seating in trains, auto and truck bodies, wing and fuselage parts on airplanes are other applications.

Housing promises to become an important market for reinforced plastics. Corrugated fiber glass panels are already in wide use for homes and offices. The much publicized Monsanto House of the Future, on display at Disneyland, is a reinforced-plastics structure.

Simplified contoured seating is seen everywhere in contemporary interiors. Bath tubs and sinks are tough, resilient, and corrosion resistant. Baseball and football helmets of reinforced plastics are common.

Industrial parts such as tote trays, transformer components, and switch gear are reinforced plastics applications not commonly seen by the layman.

Study Questions

1. What is a common term often used in place of reinforcing?
2. Why is this term used?

Hand Lay-up

1. In what form is the plastic in hand lay-up?
2. What type of device is used to cause the article to take its shape?
3. Why is a release agent necessary?
4. What temperature is required here?
5. What materials are usable for molds for hand lay-up?
6. In what form is the reinforcing material commonly used in hand lay-up?

Spray-up

1. How is spray-up similar to hand lay-up? How is it different?
2. What reinforcing material is commonly used? In what form is it?
3. What keeps the resin from setting up and clogging the spray gun?

Matched Molding

1. What type of shaping device is used?
2. In what form is the plastic in matched molding? In what form is the reinforcement?
3. What molding process is most like this?

Premix Molding

1. In what form is the plastic here?
2. In what form is the reinforcement?
3. How is the form of the plastic and reinforcement different in this process from any of the other reinforcing methods?
4. What form of molding is like this one?

Pressure-Bag Molding

1. What type of shaping device is used in pressure-bag molding?
2. What causes the article to take its shape against the mold?
3. In what form are the plastic and reinforcement in this process?

Vacuum-Bag Molding

1. What type of shaping device is used in vacuum-bag molding?
2. What causes the article to take its shape against the mold?

3. In what form are the plastic and reinforcement in this process?

General

1. Simply speaking, what is a reinforced plastic?
2. What are some of the plastics used in this process? Which one is the most common?
3. What reinforcing material is most common? In what forms is it available?
4. What is the biggest disadvantage of hand lay-up? The biggest advantage?
5. What is an advantage other than speed of spray-up over hand lay-up?
6. Why are items made by spray-up often stronger than those made by hand lay-up? What might make the items of hand lay-up stronger?
7. What is the principal strong point of matched molding?
8. In what type of situation is premix molding best?
9. What are the advantages of pressure and vacuum-bag molding over the others?

Apply Your Knowledge

1. Locate some reinforced articles. Label each with the type of reinforcing agent used. What form is the reinforcement in each case?
2. Take an article made by one type of reinforcing and make sketches to show how it could be made by some other process.
3. Which process would be most suitable to make a very large article, a swimming pool, for example. Explain.
4. If you wanted an article of very consistent thickness and smooth on both sides, which method of reinforcing would you use? Explain.
5. In which methods would a parting line be evident on the finished article?
6. Estimate the relative costs of manufacturing a given item by each method.
7. In what form would you use the reinforcement for a pair of skiis? Explain.
8. Visit a plastics plant doing this kind of work. Which methods are they using? Learn why they chose the method.

CHAPTER TEN

foaming processes

The group of processes by which cellular plastics are converted into products is called foaming. They are adaptations of the standard processes of molding, casting, and forming. Because some of the details differ and because of the importance of this group of processes, they will be treated separately.

What causes plastics to expand or "foam?" Two principal methods are employed, physical and chemical.

In *physical foaming*, the cell-forming agent is a gas. As the plastic molding material is made, a compressed gas or a volatile liquid is included. When the material is heated, the gas expands and causes the individual particles of plastic to swell or "foam." Expandable polystyrene is one of the plastics commonly expanded in this manner.

In *chemical foaming*, the expanding agent is produced by the reaction of two chemicals. Plastics foamed in this manner are made up of at least two components. One is the plastic resin and the other is a mixture of a catalyst and a chemical which reacts with the resin or some additive to liberate a gas. When the two components are separate, no reaction takes place. When they are combined, the resulting mixture creates foam. Polyurethane foam is made in this manner.

Two principal processes of foaming are *molding expandable polystyrene* and *casting polyurethane*. Many variations are used for other plastic foams, but these two account for a large part of the foam produced and are typical of the processes used.

Molding Expandable Polystyrene

The Process
The styrene beads are pre-expanded to the desired density (usually from one to twenty pounds per cubic foot). The pre-expanded beads are loaded into a closed mold cavity. The mold is heated to about 275° F. to expand and fuse the beads. After expansion, the mold and part are cooled to prevent further expansion and resultant distortion. The mold is opened and the part ejected. See Fig. 10-1.

Equipment Used
Production equipment for molding expandable polystyrene consists of aluminum molds mounted in a press so that they can be easily opened, closed and tightly clamped

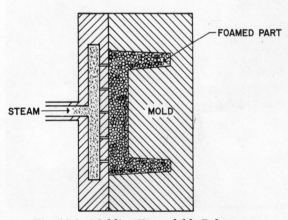

Fig. 10-1. Molding Expandable Polystyrene

95

Fig. 10-2. Machine for Molding Expandable
Polystyrene (Conapac)

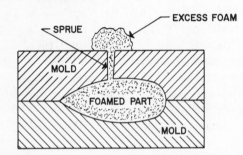

Fig. 10-3. Casting Rigid Urethane Foam

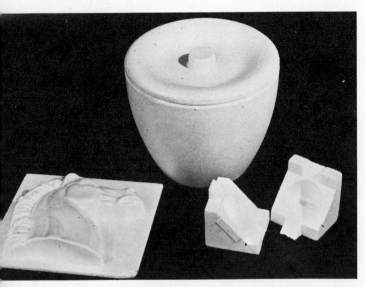

Fig. 10-4. Foamed Polystyrene Articles

together. The pre-expanded beads are blown into the mold cavities by air pressure. Heat is usually applied by steam which is forced into the molds through small holes. Cooling is accomplished by circulating cold water around the molds. Molded parts are ejected by forcing air or water through the steam holes in the mold after it has been opened. See Fig. 10-2.

Equipment for experimental or short-run production may be simply a *steam probe* which is inserted in the mold, a *steam autoclave* (pressure cooker) into which the entire mold is placed, or a *jacketed mold* around which steam is circulated.

Casting Urethane Foam

The Process

This process consists of mixing the *resin* and the *foaming agent* in proper proportions, charging them into a closed mold, allowing them to foam and fill the recesses of the mold, sometimes aiding the curing action with heat, and opening the mold to eject the finished part. See Fig. 10-3.

In some applications, the plastic is *foamed in place*. One such application is for flotation compartments in boats. The plastic is placed into a compartment in the boat and allowed to foam and fill the void. It adheres to the walls of the cavity providing support as well as buoyancy.

Equipment Used

The needed equipment is some kind of mold which can be closed and locked tightly, and some means of measuring, mixing, and pouring the foaming compound. Molds are often mounted in a press to facilitate opening and closing and to provide support for the expanding plastic. While the foam may be mixed in individual batches and poured into the mold, for production work the materials are mixed continuously as they are charged into the mold.

For *foamed-in-place* applications, the foam is mixed continuously and forced from a gun under pressure. This is economical and convenient. Only the required amount of plastic is foamed as needed.

Characteristics and Applications

Many plastics are foamed, both *thermosets* and *thermoplastics*. Two of the most common foams are styrene and urethane, but vinyls, epoxies, polyethylene, silicones, cellulosics, and phenolics are also expanded.

Any shape can be produced by either foam molding or foam casting. The material is very fluid during processing and will fill any recesses in the mold. The shape of the article is controlled largely by its future use rather than by limitations of the process.

Foam molding is well suited to high-volume mass production with automated machines. Molds need not be excessively strong or hard because the force acting on them during processing is usually not more than 50 psi and the material has no abrasive effect. Aluminum molds are commonly used.

Foamed molded products familiar to the consumer are shaped package liners for fragile articles, flotation toys and buoys, ceiling tile, and Christmas decorations. See Fig. 10-4.

Cast foam is suited to filling voids where the shell around the void serves as the "mold." Flotation chambers in boats are often filled with urethane foam by pouring the foam into the space and allowing it to expand. This adds rigidity to the walls and provides buoyancy even if the chamber is punctured. The excellent insulating properties of the foams, coupled with the ease of working with them, have made plastic foams very much used in refrigerated truck bodies as well as in home refrigerators. The ease with which a continuous thin layer of insulation can be placed in the wall of the refrigerator makes it ideally suited to mass production.

Study Questions

1. What are two methods used to cause plastics to foam?
2. How does the foaming take place in each case?
3. What plastics are commonly foamed by each method?
4. What makes these cellular plastics so light in weight?

Expandable Polystyrene

1. In what form is the plastic at the beginning of this process?
2. What type of device is used to cause the item to take its shape?
3. How much heat is needed to foam this plastic?
4. How are the molds loaded with the plastic at the beginning of the process?
5. What kind of heat is often used?
6. Why is it necessary to cool the article before removing it from the mold?

Urethane Foam

1. In what form is the plastic at the beginning of this process?
2. What is foaming-in-place? Where is it used?
3. What shaping device is used with this process?

General

1. What are some common plastics that can be expanded or foamed?
2. What limitations are there on the shapes that can be foamed?
3. What material is commonly used for molds? Why is this a good material?
4. What two purposes are served by a foamed flotation chamber in a boat?

Apply Your Knowledge

1. Find some foamed articles. Cut them apart and observe the cell structure. Is it open- or closed-cell in structure? What would be the importance of this for buoyancy?
2. Examine a molded styrene article. Do you see any marks on its surface? What produced them?
3. Compare the costs of manufacturing with molded foam as opposed to chemical foam.
4. Devise an experiment to determine the density of a block of foam. What is the density of a given foamed-plastic item?
5. Visit a plant that manufactures items from foamed plastics. Obtain a sample of the plastic and a finished article if possible.

CHAPTER ELEVEN **summary of processes**

This chapter brings together, in Table 5, the five basic groups of plastics processes and their many variations. It enables a comparison of the methods in terms of temperature requirements, typical forces required, the devices which actually shape the plastics, the physical states assumed by the plastics at various stages, and the class of plastics used.

TABLE 5
SUMMARY OF PROCESS FACTS

Process	Temperature Requirements (degrees F.)	Typical Force Required (psi)	Type of Shaping Device	Physical State of Plastic			Type of Plastic Used
				(Entering Process)	(During Process)	(Conclusion of Process)	
COMPRESSION MOLDING	Mold— 280 to 380	2,000 to 15,000	Matched molds	Solid, powder, or pellet	Liquid, or soft solid	Solid	Thermosets usually, or thermoplastic
TRANSFER MOLDING	Transfer chamber and mold— 280 to 380	6,000 to 12,000	Closed mold, sprue to transfer chamber	Solid, powder, or pellet	Liquid	Solid	Thermosets
INJECTION MOLDING	Cylinder— 300 to 650, mold— 100 to 140	5,000 to 40,000	Closed mold, connection to injection nozzle	Solid	Liquid	Solid	Thermoplastics
EXTRUSION	Cylinder 300 to 500	500 to 6,000	Die opening shaped to cross section of extrudate	Solid	Liquid	Solid	Thermoplastics
BLOW MOLDING	Mold— cold to 200 parison— 300 to 500	40 to 100	Hollow split mold	Soft solid	Soft solid	Solid	Thermoplastics
CALENDERING	Rolls— 300 to 400	Force depends on viscosity, roll length, and diameter	Pairs of smooth or patterned rolls	Liquid	Liquid	Solid	Thermoplastics

98

Process	Temperature Requirements (degrees F.)	Typical Force Required (psi)	Type of Shaping Device	Physical State of Plastic			Type of Plastic Used	
				(Entering Process)	(During Process)	(Conclusion of Process)		
LAMINATING	300 to 400	1000 to 1500	Usually flat or patterned platens	Solid or liquid	Liquid	Solid	Thermosets	
COLD MOLDING	Room temp. for pressing, 450 to cure	2000 to 4000	Matched molds	Solid	Solid	Solid	Thermosets	
CASTING	Room temp., often cured at 200 to 300	None	Open mold or closed mold with sprue hole	Liquid	Liquid	Solid	Thermosets or thermoplastics	
PLASTISOL CASTING	250 to 350	Rotational force in one type; others, none	Solid pattern, or split hollow mold	Liquid	Liquid	Solid (often flexible)	Thermoplastics	
THERMO-FORMING	275 to 400	5 or 10 up to several hundred	Solid pattern or open mold	Solid	Solid (soft)	Solid	Thermoplastics	
REINFORCING	Room temp., some cure at 200 to 300	None in some, several hundred for others	Solid pattern, open mold, matched molds	Liquid or putty	Liquid	Solid	Thermosets	
FOAM MOLDING	250 to 275	Approx. 50 to hold mold together	Closed mold	Gas-filled beads	Softened beads	Solid (closed cell)	Thermoplastics	
FOAM CASTING	Room temperature	Approx. 50 to hold mold together	Closed mold	Two liquids	Liquid	Solid	Thermosets or thermoplastics	

Apply Your Knowledge

1. Obtain a sample of a product made by each process and label by process.
2. Select a product made from plastics and visualize how it could be made by each of the processes listed. Sketch the type of shaping device that would be required. Are there any processes that could not be used to make it? What design modifications would be necessary or desirable to make it by various processes?
3. Find a process from other fields that is similar to the various plastics processes.

What processes were taken rather directly from other fields? What processes have no counterpart in other fields?
4. Notice that in only three of the processes listed does the plastic remain in a solid physical state during the process. What other characteristics of these processes are similar?
5. Notice which processes require the greatest forces. Explain why.
6. What would you predict to be the relationship between the force required and the cost of the mold or die?

7. Compare various processes by pairs, pointing out similarities, for example: injection molding and transfer molding, injection molding and extrusion, blow molding and blow forming, etc.

8. Many products could be made by any of several processes. Illustrate with a product why the particular process chosen was used and why it was a good (or poor) method.

This part is devoted to operations auxiliary to most of the basic processing methods. It deals with cutting and finishing, joining and fabricating, and preparation of tools from plaster, plastics, wood, and metals. Detailed, step-by-step procedures are not usually given. Some of the operations are adaptations from other fields such as metalworking and woodworking; technicians and students will probably be generally familiar with them. Cases where the standard practice does not apply will be noted. It is felt that with an understanding of the process the worker should have no problem with the details.

The operations outlined are those that would commonly be used with custom work rather than production. The procedures are adaptable to laboratory, experimental, and school shop developmental work rather than to mass production. The basic principles and procedures are, of course, the same.

PART III *cutting, finishing, fabricating, and tool making*

101

CHAPTER TWELVE

cutting and finishing

Most products made from plastics by any of the production techniques require some additional work in the form of trimming, smoothing, polishing, drilling, tapping, or assembling. Few articles are made in their entirety by fabrication, but many molded or formed parts are fabricated into finished articles.

This section deals with the common operations of cutting, drilling, tapping and threading, and smoothing and polishing. In many cases the operations are similar to those performed on wood or metals. Detailed discussions of the operations will be given only where the procedure for plastics differs considerably from standard procedures for wood or metals.

Cutting Plastics

Plastics can be cut by methods commonly employed for wood, metals, and paper. The choice of method and tool is largely dependent upon the shape to be cut, the thickness of the material, and the brittleness or toughness of the stock. Modifications in cutting tools are often necessary to improve cutting action and to reduce cracking or tearing.

Shearing

Scissors or snips: Plastic film and sheeting up to .015 or .020 inch thick can often be cut with scissors or snips. Brittle materials like cast acrylic or general purpose styrene are exceptions and tend to craze along the cut.

Shears: Straight cuts on tough plastics can be made successfully with a hand- or foot-operated shear like that used for sheet metal. This is the preferred method for most thermoplastics except for such brittle materials as cast acrylic, general purpose styrene, and cellulose butyrate. Even these materials can be sheared if heated to 150°-180° F.; however this is usually not practical except in production operations. Fig. 12-1 shows a squaring shear used to make straight cuts on plastic sheet.

Shearing is preferred over sawing because it is faster, safer, gives a smoother cut, and does not generate frictional heat to damage the plastic. Shearing will often produce a

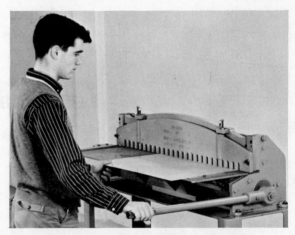

Fig. 12-1. A Squaring Shear (Di-Arco)

"white" edge at the line of cut. It is important to use a shear with a firm hold-down near the blade to eliminate tearing.

Sawing

Some plastics are brittle and will chip or crack in shearing; these should be sawed. Most materials over ³⁄₁₆ inch or ¼ inch in thickness will have to be sawed. Although blades for wood or metal may produce satisfactory results, specially designed blades are often superior for given applications.

Many plastics, especially those reinforced with glass fibers or asbestos, have a severe abrasive effect and will dull saw teeth rapidly. Specially hardened teeth are desirable in cases of this kind. The result of overheating the plastic in sawing is "gummed up" blades. Saws should be cleaned frequently and provided with sufficient clearance to reduce side friction.

Hand Saws: Many hand saws can be used to cut plastics. Hand crosscut saws with 10 or 12 points per inch can be used for sheet stock. Hack saws work well for cutting rod and tube as well as being used for fine cutting. The hack saw in Fig. 12-2 is being used to trim a formed part. Coping saws and jeweler's saws are fine for intricate curves and enclosed holes. A veneer knife is useful to trim the flange or rib from thermoformed parts. See Fig. 12-3. The use of hand saws is ordinarily limited to craft-type work or custom cutting.

Circular Saws: The table saw commonly used in woodworking will cut plastic sheet up to one inch thick satisfactorily. Speeds for wood, 10,000 to 12,000 surface feet per minute, are satisfactory for many plastics. Carbide-tipped blades will hold up longer with less maintenance, but hollow-ground cross-cutting blades with zero rake and 12-15 teeth per inch will do many jobs well. All blades must be kept clean and sharp. In Fig. 12-4 an overarm saw is used to saw plastic sheet.

If the plastic sheet is masked on one or both sides, the masking paper should be left on during sawing to reduce chipping and scratching. Standard table sawing procedures should be followed. The guard should be kept in

Fig. 12-3. A Veneer Knife (Di-Acro)

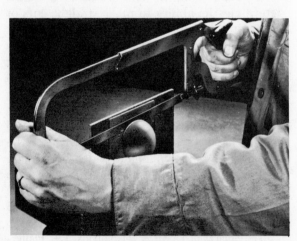

Fig. 12-2. A Hack Saw (Di-Acro)

Fig. 12-4. Sawing Sheet on Overarm Saw (Cadillac)

place and the operator should wear goggles to protect his eyes from dust and particles. Since stock less than one-eighth inch thick may tend to buckle, some type of hold-down should be used.

Band Saws: Band saws provide an advantage over circular saws in cutting plastics because the blade is longer and each tooth has more chance to cool and clear away the chips during cutting. However, band saws are generally not as accurate for straight cutting and do not produce as smooth a cut. Note Fig. 12-5 where a band saw is used to trim the flange on a formed part. A number of factors should be considered in selecting the proper band saw blade.

(1) *Blade Material.* Blades for small-quantity variety work are made from standard carbon-alloy steel. The area around the teeth is hardened while the remainder of the blade is flexible. The standard carbon-alloy steel provides the least expensive general-purpose blade, although for production cutting of specific materials other blade materials may be advantageous.

(2) *Tooth Shape.* Two tooth shapes, *precision* and *buttress*,[1] will perform most plastics cutting jobs satisfactorily. The precision tooth is the most common. It has a deep gullet with a smooth radius at the bottom. The rake angle is zero and the back clearance is thirty degrees. This tooth produces a smooth and accurate cut.

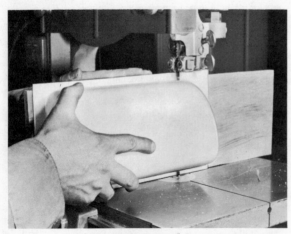

Fig. 12-5. A Band Saw

TABLE 6
MINIMUM RADIUS WHICH CAN BE CUT BY BAND SAW BLADES OF VARIOUS WIDTHS

Minimum Radius	Blade Width
7¼″	1″
5⁷⁄₁₆″	¾″
3¾″	⅝″
2½″	½″
1⁷⁄₁₆″	⅜″
⅝″	¼″
⁵⁄₁₆″	³⁄₁₆″
⅛″	⅛″
¹⁄₁₆″	³⁄₃₂″
Square corner	¹⁄₁₆″

The buttress tooth is similar to the precision tooth except that the teeth are more widely spaced to produce a *skip-tooth* effect. Because of the shallow, wide gullet, this tooth enables a coarser pitch to be put on a narrower band, thereby increasing tensile strength of the blade. The large gullet capacity is ideal for sawing thick materials because there is ample space for the chips to be carried from the kerf or cut without binding. This tooth is used for deep cuts in softer materials.

(3) *Pitch.* The coarseness of a blade is expressed in the number of teeth per inch or pitch. Desirable blade pitch is determined by the thickness of the material to be cut; thin materials require greater pitches.

(4) *Blade Width.* The width of a blade, determines its ability to make straight cuts or to manipulate curves. A narrow blade is best used to cut a curve with a small radius, while a wide blade gives a more accurate straight cut. Table 6 gives the approximate minimum radius which can be cut with a blade of given width.

(5) *Blade Thickness or Gauge.* Manufacturers have somewhat standardized the relationship between blade width and blade thickness. For example, blades ½ inch wide are often .025 inch thick, blades ¾ inch wide are .032 inch thick, and 1 inch blades are .035 inch thick.

[1]Trademarks of DoAll Saw Company, Des Plaines, Illinois

TABLE 7
SELECTION GUIDE FOR BAND SAW BLADES

Kind of Plastic	Thickness of Material	Tooth Shape	Speed (Ft./min.)	Pitch	Feed
Acrylic	0–¼ ″	Precision	4000	14	Light
	¼–½	Precision	3500	10	Light
	½–1	Precision	3000	6	Light
	1–3	Buttress	2500	3	Medium
	3–6	Buttress	1800	3	Medium
Styrene	0–¼ ″	Precision	2500	10	Light
	¼–½	Precision	2000	6	Light
	½–1	Precision	1500	4	Light
	1–3	Buttress	1500	3	Medium
	3–6	Buttress	1000	3	Medium
Cellulosics (except cellulose nitrate)	0–¼ ″	Precision	4500	10	Light
	¼–½	Precision	3500	6	Light
	½–1	Precision	2500	4	Light
	1–3	Buttress	1800	3	Light
	3–6	Buttress	1500	3	Medium
Phenolics (unfilled) Melamines Ureas	0–¼ ″	Precision	6000	14	Light
	¼–½	Precision	5000	10	Light
	½–1	Precision	4000	6	Medium
	1–3	Buttress	3500	3	Medium
	3–6	Buttress	3000	3	Medium
Expanded Styrene	0–¼ ″	Precision	10000	10	Light
	¼–½	Precision	10000	10	Light
	½–1	Precision	8000	6	Light
	1–3	Buttress	8000	3	Light
	3–6	Buttress	8000	3	Light

Adapted from **Tool Selection Charts,** DoAll Company, Des Plaines, Illinois

(6) *Side Clearance or Set.* The kerf made by the saw must be greater than the thickness of the blade or it would be impossible to cut contours; even on straight cuts there would be excessive friction. Two methods of providing this clearance are often used with blades for plastics, *raker-set and wave-set.*

Raker-set is the most common and consists of bending one tooth to the right, the next to the left, and leaving the third straight. The straight tooth serves to *rake* the chips from the kerf. Saws with this type of set cut smoothly and accurately.

In *wave-set* one group of teeth is set varying amounts to form a curve to the right, and the next group varying amounts to the left to produce a wavy effect. Blades of this type are used for cutting materials of differing cross sections such as tubing, angles, and channels.

The proper sawing speed, expressed in *feet per minute*, must be considered when using band saws. Only general rules can be outlined for proper speeds for various materials. Generally, soft, thin materials can be sawed at higher speeds. Table 7 gives approximate relationships between common plastics.

Standard band-sawing procedures should be followed. The operator should wear goggles. A common problem is that band-saw tires are likely to become coated with plastic dust and chips. A stiff brush or file card can be used to remove this deposit.

Jig Saws: Cutting with the jig saw is ordinarily limited to intricate curves or pierced work on plastic sheet up to ¼ inch in thickness. *Skip-tooth* blades are available to provide more chip clearance than that provided by standard wood-cutting blades. A common problem encountered in jig sawing, especially of thick stock, is that too little clearance is provided so that chips weld in behind the cut.

Slitting Saws: A small diameter (1½ to 2 inch) slitting saw, mounted in a drill press or on a shaper table, is ideal for certain trimming operations. In removing the flange from thermoformed articles this saw has the advantage of following the contour of the formed shape and producing a fine cut which minimizes further smoothing. A guide and guard must be used with the saw, and the operator should wear goggles. Fig. 12-6 shows a typical setup. The plastics should always be fed *against* the rotation of the blade for safety.

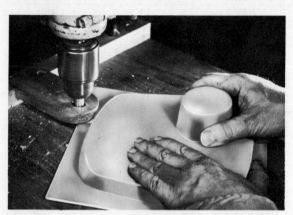

Fig. 12-6. Slitting Saw Mounted in Drill Press

Drilling Plastics

Standard hand and power drilling equipment can be used for working plastics. For most custom drilling of holes up to one-half inch in diameter, drills sharpened for metals can be used. Where production drilling is to be done or where large or deep holes must be produced, special adaptations may be desirable. Two factors should be considered, drill shape and drilling speed.

Drill Shape

Fig. 12-7 shows the nomenclature of a drill. Drills ground for general-purpose drilling in metals usually have a point angle of 118° and a lip relief angle of 8 to 12°. For plastics, point angles may be somewhat smaller (as little as 60°) and lip relief angles somewhat larger (as large as 20°). In general, hard, brittle plastics will require larger (blunter) point angles and smaller relief angles; tougher plastics will require smaller point angles and larger relief angles.

Drills especially designed for particular plastics operations are available. They have wide highly polished flutes to facilitate chip removal and narrow lands to reduce friction.

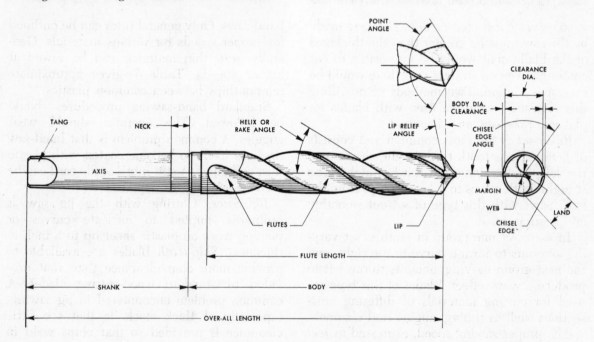

Fig. 12-7. Drill Nomenclature

TABLE 8
GUIDE TO SPEEDS
FOR DRILLING PLASTICS

Drill Size	Speed for Thermoplastics (rpm)	Speed for Thermosets (rpm)
No. 33 and smaller....	5000	5000
No. 17 through 32.....	3000	2500
No. 1 through 16......	2500	1700
1/16″.................	5000	5000
1/8″..................	3000	3000
3/16″.................	2500	2500
1/4″..................	1700	1700
5/16″.................	1700	1300
3/8″..................	1300	1000
7/16″.................	1000	600
1/2″..................	1000	600

TABLE 9
SIZES FOR TAP DRILLS

Unified National Coarse Series (UNC, USS)

Size	Threads per inch	Outside Diameter of Screw	Tap Drill Size
1	64	.073	52
2	56	.086	48
3	48	.099	44
4	40	.112	41
5	40	.125	35
6	32	.138	31
8	32	.164	28
10	24	.190	22
12	24	.216	13
1/4	20	.250	5
5/16	18	.3125	G
3/8	16	.375	O
7/16	14	.4375	3/8
1/2	13	.500	7/16
9/16	12	.5625	31/64
5/8	11	.625	17/32
3/4	10	.750	21/32
7/8	9	.875	49/64
1	8	1.000	7/8
1 1/8	7	1.125	1.000
1 1/4	7	1.250	1.125

American National Pipe Threads (NPT)

Nominal Size	Threads per inch	Outside Pipe Diameter	Tap Drill Size
1/8	27	.405	R
1/4	18	.540	7/16
3/8	18	.675	37/64
1/2	14	.840	23/32
3/4	14	1.050	59/64
1	11 1/2	1.315	1 5/32

Drilling Speed

It is difficult to give specific speeds for the various drilling problems. Factors affecting the speed are the type of plastic being drilled, and the diameter and depth of the hole to be produced. In general, hard materials will be drilled with slower speeds than will soft materials. A general guide for drilling speed for thermosets and thermoplastics is given in Table 8.

Tapping and Threading

Most plastics can be tapped and threaded with equipment used for metals. Two characteristics of the materials must be kept in mind, however. Thin sections of plastics are generally weaker than metals, and many plastics tend to gum and clog the tap or die.

As coarse a thread as possible should be used. *Unified National Coarse* Series (UNC, NCS, or USS) are preferred to National Fine Series (UNF, NFS, or SAE). The coarse thread is less likely to be stripped either during the tapping or threading operation or in use. In some cases a *National Pipe Series* thread is specified; for example, many electrical fittings use NPT fittings.

When tapping or threading, the tap or die should be backed out frequently to remove the chips. Grinding the flutes on a tap to widen or deepen them also aids in chip removal. If chips are allowed to clog the tap or die the thread is likely to be damaged. If a lubricant is needed, wax is better than oil because it does not need to be cleaned from the plastic.

The drills specified for metals can be used with plastics, but it is generally better to use a drill which allows a maximum thread depth of 75 percent to reduce the possibility of spoiling the thread during tapping. Table 9 shows recommended tap drill sizes for UNC and NPT series.

Smoothing and Polishing

Plastics can be smoothed and polished by techniques similar to those used for wood and metals. The major difference is that most

Fig. 12-8. Filing Saw Edge of Formed Part

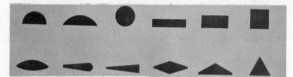

Fig. 12-9. Common Cross-sectional Shapes of Files
(Nicholson)

Fig. 12-10. Comparison of Blunt and Tapered Files
(Nicholson)

Fig. 12-11. Determining Length of File (Nicholson)

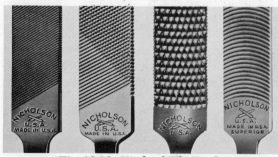

Fig. 12-12. Kinds of File Teeth
From left to right: single-cut, double-cut, rasp-cut,
and curved tooth. (Nicholson)

plastics tend to soften with heat; the frictional heat of continued sanding or polishing will cause the surface to melt. The use of coolants will reduce this problem.

The amount of smoothing needed is greatly reduced by a proper job of molding, casting, or forming. With high quality tooling, smoothing and polishing is usually restricted to *flash lines* and *edges*.

Common smoothing and polishing operations are filing, scraping, sanding, ashing and buffing, and tumbling.

Filing

In places where a large amount of plastic is to be removed, filing is often used. Typical examples are the removal of large amounts of flash on molded articles and the smoothing of the sprue on an injection-molded article flush with the molded surface. See Fig. 12-8.

The selection of the proper file for the job is done on much the same basis as for metals. Files have three characteristics to consider: kind, size, and cut.

The *kind* of file refers to its shape both in cross section and in profile. Cross-sectional shapes fall into four geometrical classes: *quadrangular, triangular, circular,* and miscellaneous (*special shapes* for special purposes). Note Fig. 12-9.

The profile shape is either tapered or blunt. *Tapered* files become narrower and/or thinner from tang to point, while *blunt* files retain their cross-sectional size throughout their length, Fig. 12-10.

The *size* of a file is usually specified by its *length*, exclusive of the tang. Generally, length and thickness are proportional, with long files being wider and thicker. Fig. 12-11 shows how a file is measured.

The *cut* of files refers to the type of the teeth and their coarseness. There are three types of teeth suitable for plastics: single-cut, double-cut, and rasp-cut. Fig. 12-12 shows the various types of teeth.

(1) *Single-cut teeth* are a series of diagonal edges. They produce a smooth cut but remove material slowly.

(2) *Double-cut teeth* are a series of diagonal grooves intersecting to produce points instead of long edges. They cut more rapidly but tend to leave a scored surface.

(3) *Rasp-cut teeth* are a series of individual sharp teeth. Files of this type remove material very rapidly with a minimum of clogging but leave a very rough cut. They are not suitable for very hard materials because the teeth tend to wear rapidly.

Coarseness of cut varies with spacing between teeth and is designated by four terms: *coarse, bastard, second,* and *smooth cut.*

The selection of a file for plastics should be made on the same basis as for metal or wood. For example, if a smooth surface is required on a concave curve, the file selected may be an eight- to ten-inch, half-round file with single-cut teeth of either second- or smooth-coarseness. If a large amount of material is to be removed from the convex surface of a fiber-glass laminate, a ten- or twelve-inch mill file with double-cut bastard- or coarse-teeth can be used.

Special mention should be made of files for hard plastics and those for very smooth cuts on soft plastics. The Nicholson File Company supplies many of its standard files with a specially designed tooth. If one specifies that the file is to be used *for hard plastics,* it will be provided with high sharp teeth that offer greater resistance to the abrasive effect of most thermosets.

Soft plastics, including most thermoplastics, tend to clog standard files excessively. A special *shear-tooth* file is recommended for this use. It is a single-cut file with a longer angle than the ordinary mill file (45° as compared to about 60°). It also has wider gullets to provide greater chip clearance.

Scraping

Cut edges or flash lines can be scraped with a hand scraper blade. The blade can be sharpened by simply filing and whetting the edge at ninety degrees or beveling the edge to 45° and burnishing it in a manner similar to that for scraping wood.

Fig. 12-13 shows a scraper being used to remove saw marks on a cut edge. The work must be held firmly to avoid chattering, and the blade inclined in the direction the scraper is moved.

In many cases a careful job of scraping may be all the smoothing that is needed. For instance, on the cut edge of a thermoformed part of modified styrene, scraping will produce a matte finish similar to that on the surface of the sheet.

Sanding

Most plastics scratch easily; therefore sanding is not often used to produce a polished surface. It is used more often for semi-finishing operations or to remove a fairly large amount of material to shape or true a surface.

Hand sanding: Cut edges or flash lines may be sanded with 100 to 150 grit paper. Generally, the surfaces of plastic sheet or molded and formed parts should not be sanded. If they become scratched sufficiently to warrant sanding, they should be wet-sanded, first with

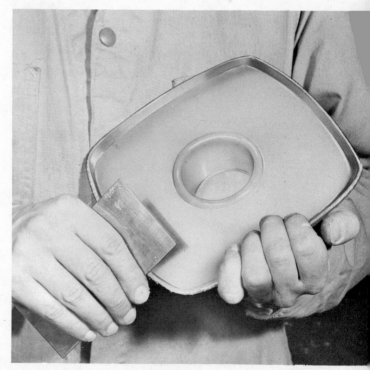

Fig. 12-13. Scraping Cut Edges (Di-Acro)

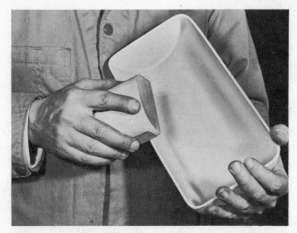

Fig. 12-14. Hand-Sanding a Formed Part (Di-Acro)

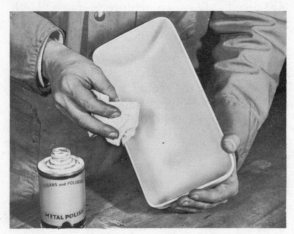

Fig. 12-15. Hand Buffing (Di-Acro)

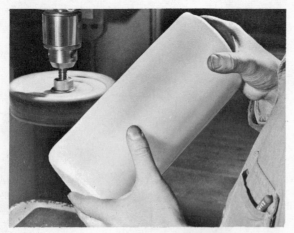

Fig. 12-16. Buffing on a Drill Press
(Di-Acro)

320-A *Wet-or-dry* paper on a rubber or felt block and then with 400-A paper. See Fig. 12-14.

Machine sanding: Machine sanding by various means is often done to remove flanges or to shape edges. To reduce loading of the abrasive and overheating the material, 60 to 100 grit, opencoat abrasives are used. This leaves a uniformly scratched surface which is satisfactory for some purposes but which requires further smoothing for others.

A disc sander can be used to true up straight edges or to shape convex curves. An open-end stationary belt sander can be used for concave curves and edges. An oscillating spindle sander is best for concave curves and pierced designs. Portable belt and disc sanders can be used to shape large surfaces such as those on laminated-plastic tooling.

Buffing and Ashing

Buffing is a polishing operation using a cloth or felt that contains fine abrasive. The coarseness of the abrasive used depends upon the original roughness of the part and the degree of luster desired. Buffing will not true a surface, but rather reaches into depressions and polishes them, giving the plastic a lustrous appearance. Care must be taken to avoid overheating the plastic with excessive speeds and pressures in machine buffing. Parts should

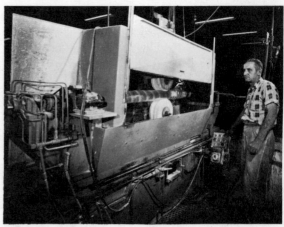

Fig. 12-17. Polishing Acrylic Rods on an Asher
(Cadillac)

be washed between successive buffings to remove abrasive deposits.

Hand Buffing: Small parts can be buffed by hand. Buffing compounds consisting of a fine abrasive suspended in a liquid can be used with wool pads or cloths as in Fig. 12-15.

Machine Buffing: The first machine buffing operation is called ashing. It consists of buffing with a stitched cotton wheel and a slurry of pumice and water. Ashing wheels may be operated at speeds up to 5000 surface-feet per minute because the wet abrasive cools the plastics.

After ashing, the plastic may be buffed with a dry cotton wheel and fine abrasives. Common abrasives used are tripoli, jeweler's rouge, and various *Learock* compounds. A separate wheel should be used for each abrasive grit to avoid contamination. Wheel speeds of 1800 to 2000 surface-feet per minute should be used. Buffing on a drill press is illustrated in Fig. 12-16.

When the scratches produced by buffing are sufficiently fine, the plastic should be buffed on a wheel to which only tallow has been applied. The tallow fills in tiny scratches, hiding them. The *tallow wheel* should be of open unbleached cotton. Wheel speeds of 1800 to 2000 surface-feet per minute are satisfactory.

Final cleaning is done by buffing with a clean loose wheel of flannel or chamois at speeds of 2000 to 2500 surface-feet per minute. The acrylic rods in Fig. 12-17 are being polished on an asher with a slurry of pumice and water.

Tumbling

Individual sanding and polishing is very time-consuming. An economical method for removing flash and polishing a large number of parts is tumbling. The process consists of placing the plastic parts in a rotating tumbling barrel with suitable abrasives and lubricants. As the barrel rotates, the parts are rubbed against the abrasive and each other with a smoothing effect.

The coarseness of the abrasive, the speed of tumbling, and the length of the tumbling cycle determine how much material is removed.

Figs. 12-18 and 12-19 show a commercial tumbler; the interior of the tumbler is shown in the latter. The abrasive grit is sprayed over the parts as they are tumbled on an endless rubber belt.

Table 10 summarizes the typical applications of these five smoothing and polishing processes.

Fig. 12-18. A Commercial Tumbler
(Wheelabrator)

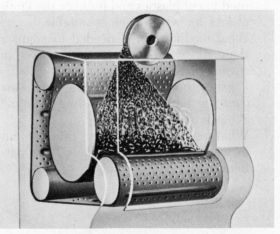

Fig. 12-19. Interior of Commercial Tumbler
(Wheelabrator)

TABLE 10
SMOOTHING AND POLISHING SUMMARY

Process	Typical Applications
Filing	To remove flash, shape parts, remove large amounts of plastics
Scraping	To remove flash, semi-finish edges, remove saw marks, smooth edges of tough plastics such as high impact styrene, ABS
Sanding	To remove flash, semi-finish edges, produce matte finish on sheet surface, remove deep scratches, shape large areas as on reinforced-plastic tooling
Buffing	To produce high luster, "reach" into scratches and depressions
Tumbling	To remove flash from large numbers of parts, polish large numbers of parts

Study Questions

1. What determines whether a plastic should be cut with a saw or a shear?
2. Why is shearing generally the preferred method of cutting if it is usable?
3. What are two major causes of blades becoming dull in sawing plastics?
4. Name the various hand saws that may be used to cut plastics and indicate the kinds of jobs for which each is suitable.
5. What modification is needed to adapt a standard woodworking table saw to cutting plastics?
6. What is the advantage of the band saw over the table saw for cutting plastics? What is the disadvantage?
7. What factors must be taken into account in selecting a band saw blade for a particular cutting problem?
8. What is the maximum width blade that should be used to cut a circle 5 inches in diameter?
9. What type of band saw blade and what cutting speed would you use to cut cellulose acetate ⅛ inch thick?
10. What is a "skip-tooth" blade for the jig saw?
11. What is a slitting saw and how is it used?
12. On drills used for plastics are point angles larger or smaller than those used for metals?
13. What is the general rule for the relationship between hardness of material, drill point, and relief angles?
14. What is a general rule for drilling speed?
15. What are two characteristics of plastics that present problems in tapping and threading that are different from those presented by metals? How are the differences taken into account?
16. How is the tap drill size determined for plastics?
17. What size tap drill would you select for a ½ inch, no. 13 screw?
18. For what general purpose is filing used with plastics?
19. What factors must be considered when selecting a file suitable for plastics?
20. How is a special file for soft plastics different from standard metal-cutting files?
21. For what purpose is scraping commonly used with plastics?
22. In what places are molded parts usually sanded?
23. For what purposes are the various types of machine sanders used in plastics work?
24. What is buffing? ashing?
25. What abrasives are used with buffing and ashing?
26. What is tumbling? Why is it so named?
27. What actually does the smoothing in the tumbling operation?

CHAPTER THIRTEEN

joining and fastening

Although very few *properly designed* plastics products are completely fabricated from sheets, rods, and tubes it is often necessary to join plastic parts to other plastics or to other materials. Some of the methods employed are similar to those used for wood and metals. Methods used for joining plastics may be grouped according to the principle on which the bond is made: *cohesion, adhesion,* or *mechanical linkage.*

Basic Joining Methods

Cohesion involves an actual intermingling of the molecules of the materials being joined. There is no foreign substance in the joint; some means is employed to cause the two materials to flow together and fuse. Two techniques in this category are *solvent cementing* and *thermal welding.* The principle is similar to that involved in welding metals where no filler rod is used.

Adhesion makes use of a film which adheres to each of the materials to be joined. In this case an adhesive, a substance different from either of the materials, remains in the joint. Gluing of wood is a common example of joining by adhesion.

Mechanical linkage involves the production of a link between the two materials which simply holds the two together physically with neither flow of either material nor "sticking." Wood screws serve as mechanical fasteners in joining wood, and seams in sheet metal operate as mechanical links.

While many plastics can be joined by more than one method, unique properties of the materials and specific requirements of the joint usually will specify the use of one method over others.

In order to join materials by *cohesion* it is necessary that the material become fluid to allow intermingling of molecules. Generally, thermosets are resistant to liquefaction by any means and are not suited to solvent cementing or welding. With thermoplastics, some materials exhibit an *amorphous* structure (non-crystalline) and others a crystalline structure. Those with the latter makeup resist the attack of solvents, but amorphous substances are dissolvable. Thus such amorphous plastics as *acrylics, styrenes,* and *cellulosics* are commonly solvent cemented. Any thermoplastic will melt with the proper heat and can be welded. Welding requires more equipment and is commonly used with materials that cannot be readily solvent cemented. Polyethylene, vinyls, and nylon are often welded. Joint strength can be comparable in both applications.

Usually, cohesive bonding involves a joining of *similar pieces.* Different materials may be joined by cohesion only when the flow properties of the two are similar.

Adhesive bonding is suitable for joining any materials, similar or dissimilar. It is necessary to find an adhesive that will stick to the materials involved. Although adhesive-bonding can be used with any plastic, it is generally not used where solvent cementing is satisfactory. This means that the most common application of adhesive bonding is with *thermosets* or where dissimilar materials are to be joined.

Mechanical fasteners can be used with any materials. The decision to use mechanical fasteners and the further choice of the particular fastener to use are based upon the strength of the plastic, the firmness required in the joint, and the appearance.

Table 11 summarizes these joining methods and their applications.

Cohesive Bonding

Solvent Cementing

This process consists essentially of applying a solvent to soften the areas to be joined, pressing the softened areas together in the proper position, and maintaining pressure until the solvent evaporates.

In some applications only a pure solvent is used while in others a small amount of the

TABLE 11
APPLICATIONS OF JOINING METHODS

Principle	Method	Application
Cohesion	Solvent Cementing	Used primarily with amorphous (noncrystalline) plastics which are readily attacked by solvents. Not commonly used with insoluble plastics such as crystalline thermoplastics or with thermosets. Common plastics joined this way are acrylics, styrenes, and cellulosics.
Cohesion	Thermal Welding	Can be used with all thermoplastics, particularly suited to those with a crystalline structure. Not used for thermosets. Common plastics joined this way are polyethylene, vinyl, and nylon.
Adhesion	Adhesive Bonding	Can be used with all plastics. Problem is one of finding an adhesive that will join with the material involved. Generally not used if solvent cementing can be used. Used to join dissimilar materials, either different types of plastics or plastics to wood, metals, ceramics, etc.
Mechanical Linkage	Mechanical Fasteners	Can be used with any plastic. Can be used to join dissimilar materials. Problem generally is to design the plastic part with proper shape and strength to hold the fastener.

TABLE 12
SOLVENT CEMENTS FOR ACRYLICS

Composition[1]	Application[1]
CAST ACRYLICS	
Methylene chloride (60%) Methyl methacrylate, monomer (40%), Hydroquinone (.006% by wt.)	Maximum joint strength, good weathering resistance
Methylene chloride (90%), Diacetone alcohol (10%)	Medium joint strength, quick setting
1-1-2 Trichloroethane (Vinyl trichloride)	Low tensile strength, easy to use
Ethylene dichloride	Medium joint strength, quick setting, easy to use
Methylene chloride	Medium joint strength, extremely rapid setting, joints apt to be cloudy
MOLDED ACRYLICS	
Methylene chloride (50%), Denatured alcohol SD-30 (50%), Acrylic molding powder (15% by wt.)	Both indoor and outdoor
Methylene chloride (60%) Methyl methacrylate monomer (40%) Benzoyl peroxide catalyst (2.4 gm at 50% peroxide strength per lb. cement)	Both indoor and outdoor
Methylene chloride (50%) Glacial acetic acid (50%) Acrylic molding powder (50% by wt.)	Both indoor and outdoor
Methylene chloride (70%) Methyl methacrylate monomer (20%) Glacial acetic acid (10%)	Indoor use only
Methylene chloride or Ethylene dichloride	Indoor use only

[1]Compositions by volume unless otherwise specified
Source: Rohm and Haas

plastic to be cemented is dissolved in the solvent. The latter is referred to as a *glue cement* or a *dope cement*. It has a higher viscosity than pure solvent and leaves a deposit of the plastic in the joint after the solvent evaporates. The higher viscosity is an advantage where the cement must be brushed onto the joint while the plastic deposit aids in filling some irregularities in the joint.

When selecting a solvent for a given application it is necessary, of course, to choose one that will attack the plastic to be cemented. See

Table 12, for example. In addition, the boiling point of the solvent must be taken into account. Those with low boiling points evaporate rapidly. If the rate of evaporation is too rapid, the solvent will disappear before it has had time to soften the plastic sufficiently to produce a good bond. The fumes resulting from rapid evaporation may also attack the surface of the plastic causing *"blushing"* (*clouding*) or, in extreme cases, *crazing*. Such harmful effects may not become apparent until hours or even days after cementing.

On the other hand, very slow evaporation may require too much time to produce a bond, which would be a disadvantage in cases where parts are to be assembled by hand without the use of a clamping fixture.

The ideal solvent is one with as rapid an evaporation rate as is consistent with the absence of harmful effects. Tables 13 and 14 list the boiling points as a guide to setting speeds. Many commercial solvents are combinations of individual chemicals. Tables 12, 13, and 14 list solvents suitable for cementing three thermoplastics commonly joined by this technique: acrylics, cellulosics, and styrenes. Many of the solvents can be obtained at local drug stores.

TABLE 13
SOLVENT CEMENTS FOR CELLULOSE ACETATE AND BUTYRATE

Solvent	Boiling Pt.
Methylene Dichloride	106° F.
Acetone	135
Methyl Acetate	140
Chloroform*	142
Ethyl Acetate	171
Methyl Ethyl Ketone	176
Ethylene Dichloride*	183
Isopropyl Acetate*	194
Nitro Methane	216
Dioxane	216
Nitro Ethane	239
Methyl Cellosolve*	257
Butyl Acetate*	259
Cellosolve*	275
Methyl Cellosolve Acetate	293
Ethyl Lactate	311
Cylohexanone	313
Diacetone Alcohol	331
Butyl Lactate*	385

Mixtures for Cementing Acetate to Acetate

Acetone (70%) Ethyl Acetate (30%)
Ethyl Acetate (30%) Acetone (40%) Ethyl Lactate (30%)
Acetone (70%) Methyl Cellosolve Acetate (30%)

Mixtures for Cementing Butyrate to Butyrate

Acetone (70%) Methyl Cellosolve Acetate (30%)
Butyl Acetate (80%) Butyl Lactate (20%)
Acetone (30%) Butyl Acetate (50%) Methyl Cellosolve Acetate (20%)

*For Butyrate only
Compositions by volume
Source: Tennessee Eastman Company

TABLE 14
SOLVENT CEMENTS FOR STYRENES

Solvents	Boiling Pt.
Fast Drying:	
Methylene Chloride	104° F.
Carbon Tetrachloride	170
Ethyl Acetate	171
Benzene	176
Methyl Ethyl Ketone	176
Ethylene Dichloride	183
Medium Drying:	
Toluene	232
Perchloroethylene	250
Ethyl Benzene	276
Xylenes	280–291
Diethyl Benzene	365
Slow Drying:	
Mono-Amyl Benzene	396
Ethyl Napthalene	495

Source: **Plastics Engineering Handbook,** Society of the Plastics Industry, Reinhold Publishing Corp., 1954.

UNIT 1
HOW TO SOLVENT-CEMENT THERMOPLASTICS

Solvent-cementing requires great care to produce a good joint[1]. Careful attention must be paid to the preparation of the joint, the application of the cement, and the holding of the material until the solvent evaporates.

Procedure

1. *Prepare the joint.* All surfaces to be joined must be clean. The joint must fit as well as any joint in wood; the cushioning effect of the solvent will not compensate for a poor joint. It may be necessary to mask parts where no cement is desired.

2. *Apply the cement to all surfaces to be joined.*
    a. Cement may be *brushed* on the surfaces to be joined. This is usually satisfactory for small areas, but on large surfaces the cement is not likely to be applied evenly.
    b. A preferred method of application is called *soak cementing.* Solvent is poured into a flat pan to a depth of about $\frac{1}{16}$ inch. The plastic surfaces to be joined are placed in the solvent and kept there until a cushion is produced. Small brads or wires in the bottom of the pan prevent the plastic from adhering to the bottom. To prevent excessive solvent from creeping up the sides of the plastic, place a piece of felt in the pan to serve as a wick to dispense the solvent. See Fig. 13-1.

3. *Place the joint together and hold or clamp until solvent evaporates.* Great pressure is not needed, but it is important that the joint be properly positioned and held there until it is set. If the pieces are moved before setting, the bond may be broken or cement moved to areas not covered by the joint. See Fig. 13-2 for sample fixtures.

[1]This is the first of a series of how-to units located throughout the book. These units form the basic operations needed for activities. To make it easy to refer to these procedural steps during activities, the unit topics are listed at the front of the book.

Thermal Welding

The process of welding plastics is similar to that used with metals. Heat is applied to liquify the surfaces; they are held together to permit a flow of material; and the joint is cooled, allowing fusion. The different techniques vary in the means of heat application to the joint. There are five methods commonly used: (1) by a heated tool, (2) by friction, (3) by hot gases, (4) by induction, and (5) by high-frequency electricity.

(1) The most common application of *heated-tool* plastics welding is employed in the heat sealing of film. Many foods are packaged in plastic bags that have been heat-sealed. The device used in this operation has

Fig. 13-1. Soak Cementing

Fig. 13-2. Fixture for Holding Cemented Parts

electrical resistance elements to heat rollers, jaws, or metal bands. The tool develops sufficient heat to melt and fuse the thin plastic. See Figs. 13-3 and 13-4.

Plastics commonly assembled by this process are polyethylene, styrenes, vinyls, and cellulose acetate. Temperatures of 250°-400° F. are used. Cellulose nitrate cannot be heat-sealed because it burns rapidly. Fluoro-carbons, cellophane, and polyester (Mylar) films cannot be heat-sealed but are sometimes coated with a plastic that allows sealing.

(2) *Friction welding* involves rubbing two pieces of plastic together with sufficient speed and pressure to melt and fuse the materials. Joints of good appearance and strength are obtainable because the plastics remain in constant contact, thus excluding air to cause oxidation. It is a process easily adaptable to common equipment such as drill presses and lathes, Fig. 13-5.

In practice, the frictional heat is produced by rotating one piece of plastic against the other. This means that the rotating part usually must be circular in shape. The joint should be designed to allow maximum surface contact and to provide some place for flash to be contained. Practically any thermoplastic can be joined in this fashion.

(3) *Hot-gas welding* is most similar in appearance to gas welding of metals. Since most thermoplastics burn in an open flame, a gas torch like that used with metals is impractical. Plastic-welding torches play a jet of air or nitrogen at temperatures of 400°-600° F.

under three to four pounds per square inch. The air is heated electrically or with gas.

Butt joints are beveled to 60° and a filler rod of the parent material is used. All surfaces must be completely clean and free from oil, grease, or mold release. Fig. 13-6 shows a typical hot-gas welding operation.

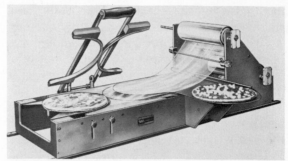

Fig. 13-4. Large Heat Sealer for Pizza Packages
(Weldotron)

Fig. 13-5. Friction-Welding Thermoplastics
(Du Pont)

Fig. 13-3. Heat-Sealer for Small Packages
(Weldotron)

Fig. 13-6. Hot-Gas Welding (Seelye)

(4) In *induction welding*, heat is induced by a high-frequency electrodynamic field in a metallic insert placed between the plastics to be joined. The thin insert remains a part of the joint.

One of the most important advantages of this method is its speed. The fusion is instantaneous and the time required to make the joint is largely the time it takes to position the materials in the heater. Practically any thermoplastic can be welded in this manner.

(5) In *high-frequency heat-sealing*, the plastics to be joined are held together between electrodes. High-frequency (RF) energy is passed through the electrodes and the plastic. The electrical resistivity of the plastic causes heat to be developed within the plastic with the result that it melts and fuses.

This electronic heat sealing is rapid and produces watertight joints at least as strong as the material. Materials that can be heat-sealed with resistance elements can be sealed with high-frequency electricity also. Fig. 13-7 shows a commercial machine for this type of work.

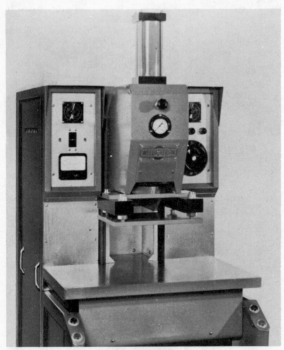

Fig. 13-7. High-Frequency Heat-Sealing Machine
(Weldotron)

Adhesive Bonding

The process of adhesive bonding consists of applying a suitable adhesive to the surfaces to be joined, pressing the coated surfaces together, and holding them in place until the adhesive sets either at room temperature or with the addition of heat.

The selection of an adhesive involves consideration of at least several factors: the *specific adhesion* of the adhesive to the materials to be joined, the *service requirements* of the bond, and the limitations imposed by *curing*.

Adhesives used for wood and paper are usually not suitable for most plastics applications. Hundreds of specially compounded adhesives are available for specific applications and adhesive manufacturers should be contacted for recommendations. There is probably no completely general-purpose adhesive for plastics such as is found for wood or paper. Perhaps this explains why few adhesives for plastics are sold in retail stores.

Two somewhat general-purpose adhesives that have made their appearance in retail outlets are epoxy-resin-based, and contact-bond-cements.

Epoxy-resin-based adhesives with 100 percent solids contain no solvent and thus will not attack the surface of any plastic. On the consumer market they are generally sold in two separate tubes, one containing the resin and the other a catalyst. While separated, both remain inert. When the two are mixed in the joint, the adhesive sets. Most will cure at room temperature, but the addition of heat speeds the cure and often results in greater strength.

Contact-bond cements have become well known in recent years because of their extensive use in the application of high-pressure plastic laminates for counter tops. This cement is applied to both surfaces and allowed to dry tack-free. The dry cement will stick only to itself. As the two surfaces are brought together they make immediate *contact* and cannot be moved. In some cases additional heat adds to the joint strength.

Mechanical Linkage

Mechanical joining of plastics can be done in two general ways: (1) by means of various types of separate mechanical fasteners, and (2) by swaging, or press or shrink fitting.

Mechanical Fasteners

Many of the mechanical fasteners used are standard assembly devices used with wood and metals.

(1) Standard *machine screws* are available in metal or plastic. Plastic screws are not as strong as metal and care must be exercised in screwing them into the tapped hole. Parts may be made with molded threads or they may be drilled and tapped to receive the machine screw.

(2) *Self-tapping and drive screws* make their own threads as they are inserted. A hole of proper size must be drilled to avoid cracking the part and some extra depth should be provided to give clearance for the chips formed.

(3) *Standard bolts and nuts* are used much as with wood and metal.

(4) *Rivets* of many types are available in metal and plastic. Eyelets are often used to provide a bushing around the rivet where movement is required between the parts.

(5) *Spring clips* provide inexpensive methods for rapid assemblies.

(6) Manufacturers provide a variety of miscellaneous devices such as hinges, catches, clips, dowels, etc.

Swaging and Press Fitting

Upsetting a projection on one part to hold it to another is a practical method of mechanically joining plastics. Generally, the part to be upset or *swaged* should be heated with a soldering copper. This is the equivalent of spreading a rivet head except that heat is used rather than mechanical force.

Press or shrink fitting is employed to join plastics to dissimilar materials. Press fitting may be used with plastics that have high tensile strength. A hole somewhat smaller than the part to be inserted is made in one part and the part to be joined is pressed into it. Shrink fitting takes advantage of the fact that plastics expand as they are heated. An undersized hole is made in one part; the part is heated; the two parts are pressed together; the assembly is cooled, shrinking the hole around the insert.

Study Questions

1. What are three basic means by which plastics are joined?

2. Explain each method.

3. Give an example of the use of each method in a situation where it would be impossible or undesirable to use any of the others.

4. What actually holds the two pieces together in an assembly that has been solvent cemented?

5. What is "glue cementing?" Why is it used?

6. What are two factors to consider in selecting the proper solvent for cementing? Describe the ideal solvent in terms of these two factors.

7. How is a joint prepared for proper cementing?

8. How is cement generally applied to the joint?

9. Which cement, of those listed, will provide the best strength with cast acrylic plastic?

10. What is the relationship between boiling point of a solvent and drying speed?

11. What are five ways in which plastics are melted for welding?

12. How is film commonly heat-sealed?

13. How are friction welds made? Can both thermosets and thermoplastics be welded readily in this manner?

14. How is gas welding of plastics different from gas welding of metals?

15. What must be present in the joint for induction welding?

16. How is the plastic melted in high-frequency heat-sealing?

17. How does adhesive bonding differ from solvent cementing?

18. What are two adhesives commonly used with plastics that can be obtained readily in retail stores?

19. What are two ways in which mechanical fastening can take place?

20. List some standard fasteners that are useful for plastics as well as for other materials?

21. What is shrink fitting? Give an illustration of an article on which a shrink fit is used.

CHAPTER FOURTEEN   ## *tools for plastics work*

In many of the operations of the plastics industry, the quality of the finished article is largely determined by the care with which the mold, plug, or die has been made. Much of the work in plastics is in the use of these tools, but the really creative, skilled work in the field is in making the tools and setting them up. This chapter is concerned with the latter part of the field.

The special devices which cause plastics to take various shapes during processing are called *tools* or *tooling*. They are further classified as molds, plugs, and dies.

A *female mold*, often called simply a mold, is a tool containing a *cavity* with contour and texture corresponding to that desired on the convex side of the article to be manufactured.

A *male mold* is a generally *convex* tool with texture and shape corresponding to that desired on the concave side of the article to be manufactured.

A *matched mold* consists of a male and female mold shaped to control *both sides* of the desired article with space between them to produce the required thickness in the article.

A *plug* is a male mold used in thermoforming.

A *die* is a tool with a specially shaped opening through which soft plastic is pushed to produce a continuous length of uniform cross-section.

The tool-making procedures described here are limited to those adaptable to laboratory, experimental, and design work. Much of the high-volume work of the industry is done with expensive metal tooling made by highly skilled tool and die makers. The expense of these tools and the difficulty of modifying them for design changes often make them impractical for experimental work.

Procedures for making tools from plaster, plastics, wood, and metals are discussed and explained.

Tools from Gypsum Plasters

Design and experimental work are greatly facilitated by patterns and molds which can be built and modified quickly. Great strength and durability are usually not too important in this type of work because the tool is used for only one or a few products.

A line of high-strength gypsum plasters has been especially developed for this purpose. The various plasters within the line are low in cost, easily worked, very strong, and adaptable to experimental work or short-run production in the making of thermoforming molds and plugs, laminating tools, casting molds, and patterns for making cast tools from plastics or metals. Very little equipment is required to work with them.

Casting Plasters

Most people are familiar with plasters used in casts for holding broken bones or for casting dentures. These plasters are often termed, plaster of paris or dental plaster. In the industry they are known as *soft plasters*. For the purpose of tooling they have limited value and have been replaced by a number of *high-strength plasters*.

All plasters are manufactured from a natural mineral called *gypsum*. Chemically, gypsum is calcium sulfate with water of crystallization ($CaSO_4 \cdot 2H_2O$).

In the manufacture of soft plasters, gypsum rock is mined or quarried, then crushed and pulverized. The flour-like gypsum is then heated in kettles to remove three-fourths of the water of crystallization, dumped into pits, and cooled. It may then be formulated as desired and packaged. Ordinary plaster made in this manner will require at least 60 pounds of water per 100 pounds of plaster to obtain a mix that can be poured.

High-strength plasters are made by placing carefully selected gypsum rock ranging from ½ inch to 1½ inch in size into pressure vessels, where the removal of water, calcination, takes place. After the necessary amount of water of crystallization has been driven off, the gypsum is cooled. It is then pulverized, screened, and packaged. Plaster made in this manner will require only 30 to 40 pounds of water per 100 pounds of plaster to obtain a mix that can be poured. Such plasters are four to five times as strong as soft plasters and possess other desirable characteristics such as low expansion and a wide range of densities.

Plaster obtains its strength in setting by the development of numerous needle-like crystals which become tightly interlaced. As more water is added to the mixture, the crystals are driven farther apart, producing a less dense and weaker casting. For example, if 90 pounds of water is added to 100 pounds of dry plaster, the casting will have a compressive strength of 1500 pounds per square inch; if only 30 pounds of water is added to 100 pounds of dry plaster, the casting will exhibit strengths of 12,000 pounds per square inch. To obtain maximum strength, then, it is important to use no more water than is necessary to produce a pourable mixture.

All plasters expand as they set. The amount of expansion that takes place during the setting process can be controlled by the manufacturing process. Some plasters exhibit expansion rates as low as .0024 inch per foot. Special formulations made especially for the pattern making trade expand as much as 5⁄16 inch per foot. In tooling for plastics, a low expansion rate is generally desired.

The setting process of plasters is an exothermic reaction with a considerable amount of heat being given off. As soon as the wet plaster begins to heat, the setting process begins and little further working time in a plastic state remains. Even after it has set, the plaster still contains a large amount of moisture and will remain somewhat soft until completely dry.

Plasters for Tooling

The United States Gypsum Company has developed a number of gypsum plasters suited to various purposes. They are classified according to four types: *low-expansion* plasters for tooling, *super-hard* cements, *general-purpose* cements, and *high-expansion* plasters for shrinkage compensation.

The various plasters are described and summarized in Table 15.

Low - Expansion Plasters

Ultracal 30. This type is recommended where extreme accuracy and additional surface hardness are required, as in duplicator models. It is harder and stronger than Hydrocal A-11 and B-11 and has the lowest expansion of any gypsum cement available, yet its gradual set and ample plasticity make it ideal for splash casting. It is colored green for identification.

Ultracal 60: This plaster is similar in all respects to Ultracal 30 except that it is provided with a setting time of about one hour. It is designed for very large models and molds where additional working time and the highest degree of accuracy are called for.

Hydrocal A-11: This material is a high-strength gypsum cement with a low-setting expansion. It is adaptable to the production of strong, tough, patterns and duplicator models. It has a fairly short period of plasticity and will set in approximately 25 minutes.

Hydrocal B-11: This material has a low-setting expansion, a high degree of plasticity, and a gradual setting action. Therefore it is especially suited for loft template type work where a large amount of trowelling and smoothing are necessary. It sets in about 25 minutes.

Hydrocal B-11 (slow set): This plaster is similar to regular Hydrocal B-11 except that it has a setting time of about one hour. It should be used for very large work where additional working time is needed.

Super - Hard Cements

Hydro-Stone: This is the hardest and strongest of the gypsum cements. When mixed properly, it has a heavy syrupy consistency and should be used to pour solid models or patterns. It is recommended for dies where extreme surface hardness is required. Its expansion rate is greater than most plasters.

General - Purpose Cements

Industrial White Hydrocal: This is a general-use gypsum cement with a setting time of about 25 minutes. It has some tendency to "tear" in screeding operations. Though its expansion rate is higher than the Hydrocals, it has somewhat higher wet and dry strength.

Pattern Shop Hydrocal: This plaster has a moderate expansion rate and is particularly suited to pattern and model making by plastic-stage forming techniques. Its long period of plasticity makes it ideal for template work. It can be screeded, carved, or otherwise worked in a semi-set state. It has a lower strength and less hardness than the Hydrocals or Ultracals but considerably more than the soft plasters.

High - Expansion Cements

Medium-High Expansion: This is a plaster formulated to expand $\frac{1}{16}$ to $\frac{3}{16}$ inch per foot as it sets. The expansion is uniform in all direc-

TABLE 15
PROPERTIES OF GYPSUM PLASTERS

Name of Plaster[1]	Normal Consistency[2]	Setting Time (Minutes)	Typical Setting Expansion (Inches per inch)	Average Compressive Strength (psi)	Reaction
Ultracal 30	35–38[2]	25–35	.0003	7300	Alkaline
Ultracal 60	36–39	75–90	.0002	7300	Alkaline
Hydrocal A-11	40–42	20–25	.0005	4500	Alkaline
Hydrocal B-11	46–49	20–25	.0005	3800	Alkaline
Hydrocal B-11 (slow set)	46–49	45–55	.0004	3800	Alkaline
Hydro-stone	28–32	20–25	.002	11,000	Alkaline
Industrial White Hydrocal	40–43	20–30	.003	5500	Neutral
Pattern Shop Hydrocal	54–56	20–25	.0015	3200	Neutral
Medium-High Expansion Hydrocal	48–50	25–35	.010[3]	2100	Both Slightly Acid
	44–45	25–35	.015[4]	2100	
High-Expansion Hydrocal	40–42	25–35	.020[5]	1700	
	35–37	25–35	.026[6]	1700	

[1]Trade names of products of United States Gypsum Company
[2]Parts water to 100 parts plaster by weight
[3]Often expressed as $\frac{1}{8}$″ per foot
[4]Often expressed as $\frac{3}{16}$″ per foot
[5]Often expressed as $\frac{1}{4}$″ per foot
[6]Often expressed as $\frac{5}{16}$″ per foot

tions. It is used to make patterns for metal castings of aluminum or zinc alloys. It is colored yellow for identification.

High-Expansion Hydrocal: This plaster has the highest expansion of any plaster. It will "grow" uniformly in all directions as much as ⅛ to 5⁄16 inch per foot.

Working with Gypsum Plasters

The basic methods of working with gypsum plasters are listed here. The methods described are limited to those primarily concerned with applications to plastics work.

UNIT 2
HOW TO MEASURE AND MIX GYPSUM PLASTERS

To insure maximum strength and good working properties it is essential that gypsum plasters be properly mixed. Clean mixing equipment and accurate measuring devices are necessary. Always follow manufacturer's directions.

Procedure

1. *Weigh out proper amounts of water and plaster.* One pound of dry plaster with the proper amount of water added will produce about twenty-two cubic inches of wet plaster. Follow the manufacturer's directions for the amount of water to use. See Table No. 15. Tap temperature water is satisfactory; cold water will slow down the setting process and hot water will speed it up.
2. *Pour the water into a mixing bowl.* Either a smooth-surface stainless-steel bowl or a rubber bowl is satisfactory.
3. *Add the weighed dry plaster to the water.* Plaster is always added to water to avoid dry pockets in the mix. The plaster should be strewn into the water to avoid its piling up. The plaster should remain in the water for two to five minutes before mixing.
4. *Mix the plaster to proper consistency.*
   a. Small amounts (2-15 pounds) can be mixed by hand with a spatula. The mixture *should not be whipped* because this mixes air into it. It should be

stirred until it creams somewhat; this reduces the tendency for the particles to settle out.
   b. Large amounts should be power mixed. A one-quarter-inch electric drill or a drill press can be used. A mixing paddle can be made with a four- to five-inch round rubber disc mounted on a shaft. As the rubber disc rotates it waves and agitates the plaster. The mixture should be thoroughly creamed.
5. *Pour plaster immediately.* Note in the manufacturer's instructions, the working time of the mixed plaster.

UNIT 3
HOW TO MAKE A ONE-PIECE OPEN-CAVITY CAST-PLASTER MOLD

The casting technique for plaster mold making is similar to that used in casting other materials. It consists of mounting a *pattern* in a *flask,* pouring the plaster around it, and allowing it to set. This technique provides an easy means for making molds for thermoforming, laminating and casting.

Procedure

1. *Prepare pattern.* Patterns may be made from many materials such as wood, metal, plastics, or plaster. Since the plaster will accurately reproduce the pattern surface, it is essential that the surface be exactly as desired on the mold. Patterns made of materials that are affected by moisture should be carefully sealed. Note that the pattern must have *draft* (be tapered with no undercuts) so that it, and later the molded article, can be withdrawn from the mold.
2. *Assemble pattern, flask and mounting board.* The pattern should be mounted on a flat, smooth, mounting board. This board can be made of glass, sheet plastic, metal, hardboard, or waterproof plywood. Mounting of the pattern can be done by screwing from underneath or by using double-coated tape. Position the flask around the pattern and fasten it to the mounting board. It may be assembled

with screws, double-coated tape or with a fillet of modeling clay on the outside. See Fig. 14-1.

3. *Apply mold release.* Carefully cover all parts of the pattern, mounting board, and flask, which will contact the plaster. In some cases the flask becomes part of the finished mold and should not be coated with a release.

4. *Mix plaster according to directions.* See Unit 2.

5. *Pour plaster.* Pour plaster into the lowest corner of the flask as shown in Fig. 14-2, and allow it to flow around and over the pattern. Pouring directly on the pattern results in air pockets which leave voids in the mold.

6. *Vibrate or shake the mold to remove air bubbles.* Vibration by hand or tapping will jar the air bubbles away from the pattern.

7. *Strike off mold.* Using a steel straightedge remove any excess plaster that projects above the top edge of the flask.

8. *Allow to set.* Plaster gives off heat as it starts to set. Setting time varies with the type of plaster used, temperature, and humidity of the environment.

9. *Remove pattern.* As soon as the plaster has set, the pattern should be pulled. Care should be exercised to see that it pulls evenly to avoid chipping. On large patterns, it may be well to cast ejection bolts into the mold.

10. *Dry the mold.* Even after the plaster is set up firmly, it contains much water. For some uses, such as in tools for reinforced plastics, it is not necessary to completely dry the mold. Usually, plaster left in a reasonably dry room will lose its excess moisture in a few days to a week. Forced drying is not recommended because it is likely to cause cracking.

11. *Finish the mold.* If a careful job has been done in preparing the pattern and in making the casting, there will be no finishing operations needed. It may be necessary to soften the arrises with sandpaper, however. Fig. 14-3 shows a finished mold and its pattern.

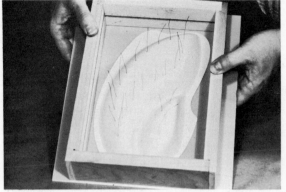

Fig. 14-1. Unit 3, Step 2 — Pattern Mounted on Mold Board with Flask

Note wires in pattern to form holes in mold for vacuum forming.

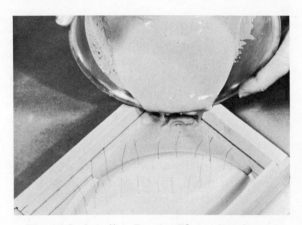

Fig. 14-2. Step 5 — Pouring Plaster into Corner

Fig. 14-3. Step 11 — Finished Mold and Pattern

UNIT 4
HOW TO MAKE A
TWO-PIECE CAST-PLASTER MOLD

Many applications require a completely closed mold. Such a mold is required for casting objects on which all sides are contoured or in foaming plastics where the foam must be contained as it expands. In such applications the mold is made in two or more pieces so that it can be disassembled to open the cavity.

There are several procedures for making a two-piece mold. If a split pattern is prepared, each mold half can be made by the same process as used for a one-piece open-cavity mold. Care must be taken in mounting the pattern halves to assure proper alignment, of course.

In some cases it may be easier to use a solid pattern or to use an actual product as the pattern. The following procedure applies to this use. The general procedure is to pour the plaster up to the desired parting line, allow this plaster to set, and then to pour the other mold half directly against the first half.

Make First Mold Half

1. *Prepare pattern.* Determine parting line so that there will be no undercuts in the mold half. On symmetrical objects this will be the center of the article. Apply mold release to the pattern.
2. *Prepare flask.* Select or make a flask large enough to allow approximately one inch of plaster all around the pattern. Apply mold release to the flask.
3. *Mount pattern in flask.* The means of mounting will depend upon the shape of the pattern. The pattern must be suspended in the center of the flask. If the pattern is light in weight, all that need be provided is a stop to limit the height to which it can rise as the plaster is poured under it. If the pattern is heavy, some support under it to keep it from sinking below center will be needed.
4. *Measure and mix plaster for one mold half.* See Unit 2 on mixing.
5. *Pour plaster for one mold half.* Pour plaster into the lowest corner of the mold and allow it to flow under the pattern and up to the desired parting line.
6. *Vibrate mold to remove air bubbles.* Carefully tapping the sides of the flask will force the air bubbles away from the surface of the pattern. Make sure the pattern does not shift in this operation.
7. *Allow mold half to set.*

Make Second Mold Half

8. *Remove pattern from first mold half.* The pattern should be thoroughly cleaned to remove any plaster that may have spilled on it. At times the plaster tends to creep up the surface of the pattern and form a

Fig. 14-4. Unit 4, Step 10 — Assembling Flask around First Mold Half, Pattern in Place

Fig. 14-5. Step 12 — Pouring Second Half of Mold

ridge at the edge of the cavity. The mold should be sanded to produce a flat, sharp parting line.

9. *Apply mold release to pattern, mold half, and flask.* Make sure that a good coat of release agent is on all parts so that it will be possible to separate the two halves.
10. *Replace pattern in cavity.* Make sure that it registers properly. See Fig. 14-4.
11. *Measure and mix plaster* for second half.
12. *Pour second half.* Pour into the lowest corner of the flask and allow the plaster to cover the pattern, as illustrated in Fig. 14-5.
13. *Vibrate mold to remove air bubbles.*
14. *Strike off excess plaster on top edge of flask.*
15. *Allow to set.*
16. *Separate mold halves.* Remove flask, carefully separate mold halves, and pull pattern. In Fig. 14-6 is a two-piece mold with its pattern.

UNIT 5
HOW TO USE LOFT-TEMPLATE TECHNIQUE FOR PLASTER TOOL

The loft-template technique consists basically of mounting a series of thin ribs to define the shape of the mold and then striking plaster in between to make the total form. This method is especially suited to the develop-ment of irregular non-symmetrical shapes. It is commonly employed to make forms for laminated plastics or vacuum forming molds.

Procedure
1. *Make needed templates.* Lofted templates can be made from hardboard, aluminum, steel, or marine plywood. Spacing and location of templates will depend upon the shape of the object. Generally, templates will be placed closer together where there are abrupt changes in shape. Template contours should be sanded until they are smooth and true. On large templates, ventilation holes should be drilled to allow the plaster to dry.
2. *Mount templates on a base.* The mold base should be very stiff and warpfree. Steel, aluminum, hardboard, or marine plywood may be used. The templates should be fastened securely to the base, with spacing in proper position to define the final shape. On large molds, the templates should be fastened together with tie rods. Hardware cloth or burlap should be draped between the templates to support the plaster.
3. *Apply base coat of plaster.* Fiber bats, soaked in plaster, should be laid in the spaces between the templates and worked out to fill the spaces. See Fig. 14-7. The

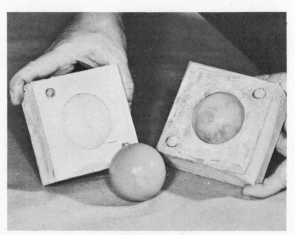

Fig. 14-6. Step 16 —
Two-piece Mold and Pattern

Fig. 14-7. Unit 5, Step 3 — Applying Fiber Bats
Soaked in Plaster (U.S. Gypsum)

Fig. 14-8. Step 4 — Applying Second Coat of Plaster (U.S. Gypsum)

Fig. 14-9. Step 5 — Screeding the Surface Coat (U.S. Gypsum)

Fig. 14-10. Step 7 — The Finished Tool (U.S. Gypsum)

edges of the templates should be left exposed because they are needed to guide the final contour.

4. *Apply second coat.* After the base coat has set, another mix of plaster should be screeded on with a toothed spreader to within one-quarter inch of the top edges of the templates, Fig. 14-8. The toothed spreader will produce a striated surface to provide a good bond with the final coat.

5. *Apply surface coat.* The final surface coat in Fig. 14-9 is screeded with a smooth scraper striking off the excess on the template edges.

6. *Smooth surface.* After the mold has set and has at least partially dried, it should be sanded to smooth out the scraper marks and to give the final contour.

7. *Finish surface.* Several coats of lacquer or shellac will seal the pores and produce a smooth dense surface. Note the finished tool and the pattern in Figs. 14-10 and 14-11.

UNIT 6
HOW TO USE CIRCULAR SCREEDING TECHNIQUE FOR PLASTER TOOL

Many forms, molds, and patterns used in plastics work are circular in top view with various cross-sectional shapes. Many such tools are made by turning wood or metal on

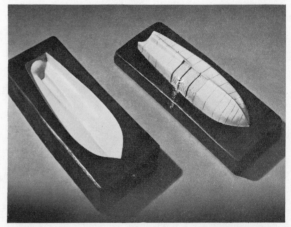

Fig. 14-11. Step 7 — Pattern of Mold Boat Hull
Mold is cast from lofted pattern. (Hendrich-Blessing)

a lathe. However this type of tool can often be made more easily and at less expense by the circular *screeding technique* using plaster.

The process consists of pivoting a *screed* with the desired cross-sectional profile cut into it through a mass of wet plaster, causing the molding medium to assume the shape of the screed.

This method can be applied to the making of either convex or concave tools such as thermoforming molds and plugs, forms for reinforced plastics, or patterns for tools to be cast from metals.

Two basic variations of the technique are used: (1) the plaster remains stationary and the screed is moved through it, or (2) the screed is firmly mounted and the plaster is rotated through it on a rotating turntable. The procedure described below is for the first method.

Procedure

1. *Make screed.* Use a stiff, water-resistant material such as metal or hardboard. The stiffness required will depend upon the size of the screed. For lengths up to 12 inches, sixteen gauge galvanized iron is satisfactory. The desired cross-sectional profile is *cut in reverse* in the screed. For example, if a convex plaster part is desired, the shape cut from the screed should be concave. All contours must be smooth and accurate. A pivot bearing must be attached to the screed.

2. *Prepare base.* The base on which the screeding is done should be smooth, flat, and carefully sealed. A pivot to receive the bearing on the screed should be mounted on the center of the board. A brass pin ¼ to ½ inch in diameter is satisfactory. See Fig. 14-12.

3. *Mix first application of plaster to a thicker-than-normal consistency.* Either Pattern-Shop Hydrocal or Ultracal 30 is a satisfactory plaster. On very large tools a slower set might be required.

4. *Place plaster on base.* Place the required amount of wet plaster on the center of the base in approximately the desired shape, as shown in Fig. 14-13.

5. *Rough screed.* Place screed on pivot and rotate it through the wet plaster, striking it off to the proper shape. See Fig. 14-14. Fill major voids and continue rotating the screed until the proper shape is produced

Fig. 14-12. Unit 6, Step 2 — Core and Screed Mounted on Base

Fig. 14-13. Step 4 — Placing Plaster over Core

Fig. 14-14. Step 5 — Rough Screeding to Approximate Shape

and the plaster begins to set. Clean off the screed thoroughly.

6. *Mix second application of plaster to normal consistency.*

7. *Finish screed.* Apply a thin coat of the second plaster mix and move the screed through it for the desired smooth finish.

8. *Finish part.* Allow plaster to dry thoroughly, remove from base, and apply several coats of lacquer. Fig. 14-15 pictures a finished pattern.

Tools from Plastics

Much of the tooling used by the plastics industry is itself made from plastics by casting or lamination. While either a cast or laminated tool will often serve the purpose well, certain applications will call for only one or the other.

Laminated tools are generally stronger and can be readily made in large sections with fairly thin cross section. *Cast tools* can often be made more rapidly but are not very suited to large areas. They have less strength than laminated tools and therefore must often be made thicker and heavier. In tooling for small objects, cast tools are very fine .

Each manufacturer of tooling compounds supplies specific and detailed instructions concerning the use of the material. These should be followed accurately and, only general directions will be outlined here.

Fig. 14-15. Step 8 — Finished Pattern to Make Cast Aluminum Mold

Cast-Plastic Tools

Cast tools are commonly made from epoxy compounds containing various additives such as aluminum or steel dust.

UNIT 7
HOW TO MAKE SINGLE-PIECE CAST-PLASTIC TOOLS

This type of tooling is often used in thermoforming, casting, or in hand lay-up laminations.

Procedure

1. *Make or select pattern.* The tool will be only as good as the pattern. Extreme care should be taken to make the pattern true and smooth. Any of a number of materials can be used for patterns including wood, metals, plaster, or plastics.

2. *Prepare pattern.*

   a. Make sure the pattern is dry. Heat is generated as the casting resin cures. Any moisture in the pattern will cause dimensional changes or irregularities in the tool surface. Wood and plaster patterns should be oven dried before plastic tooling is made from them.

   b. Fill all pores in the pattern. Any lack of smoothness in the surface will result not only in a poor tool surface but may make it difficult to separate the cast tool from the pattern.

   c. Mount the pattern on a base. Smooth metals, wood, or glass make good bases. The pattern should be securely fastened to the base to prevent its shifting around and also to aid in pulling the pattern when the tool has cured. If the base of the pattern is irregular, it may be filleted with modelling clay to prevent the casting resin from seeping between the pattern and the base.

   d. Coat the pattern and base with a release agent. Casting plastics adhere to all pattern materials. Most manufacturers recommend a particular release for their casting resins. Care must be taken to make sure that all parts of the pattern and base are completely covered with release.

e. Fasten the pattern and base to a flask as shown in Fig. 14-16. The proper flask size should provide adequate wall thickness in the finished tool and yet not waste casting resin. If the flask becomes part of the finished tool, no release agent is needed on it. However, the flask must be coated with the release agent if it is to be removed.

3. *Prepare the casting compound.*

a. Weigh or measure proper amounts of resin and hardener. Most compounds can be purchased in properly measured units. If the unit available is not the amount needed, however, weigh the ingredients according to the manufacturer's directions.

b. Add the hardener to the resin.

c. Mix the resin and hardener. Since casting resins are very heavy, a mechanical mixer is desirable. With small quantities, hand mixing is satisfactory. Avoid *beating;* it produces air bubbles in the casting.

4. *Pour the compound in the flask.*

a. Pour the compound slowly into the lowest corner of the flask, allowing it to gradually cover the pattern and fill the flask. Note Fig. 14-17. This method reduces the likelihood of getting air bubbles in the casting. This must be done while the compound is still fluid.

b. Tap the sides of the flask to remove air bubbles. Most compounds have a working life of twenty to forty minutes.

5. *Cure the casting.*

a. Many resins cure at room temperature. The reaction during curing is exothermic, generating a good deal of heat.

b. Some resins must be heated to 300°-350° F. for curing. Excessive heat should be avoided; it often causes bubbling on the surface of the tool.

6. *Pull the pattern.*

a. Remove fastening devices that hold the flask and base together.

b. If the pattern and base are securely fastened, carefully pry uniformly around the edges to avoid chipping the edges of the finished tool. The finished tool is shown in Fig. 14-18.

Fig. 14-16. Unit 7, Step 2e — Plaster Pattern Mounted in Flask

Fig. 14-17. Step 4a — Pouring the Casting Compound

Fig. 14-18. Step 6b — The Flask, Pattern, and Finished Cast Mold

UNIT 8
HOW TO MAKE TWO-PIECE MATCHED CAST-PLASTIC TOOLS

This type of tooling is used in any application where material must be compressed or forced together or where both sides of the object being made must be controlled. Typical uses are in compression molds, injection molds, shell molds for metal casting, or mechanical thermoforming with matched molds.

Fig. 14-19. Unit 8, Step 3c — Pattern Mounted in Completed First Mold Half.
Notice that it is placed in the flask ready for second half to be poured.

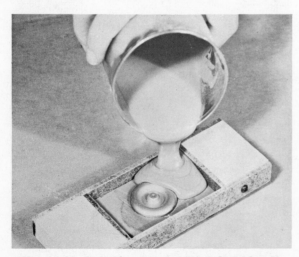

Fig. 14-20. Step 3f — Pouring Second Mold Half

Procedure

1. *Prepare the pattern and flask.*
   a. A split pattern, divided at the parting line, will facilitate mold making.
   b. The flask should be as deep as the combined thickness of the two mold halves.
2. *Make the first tool half by the same method as used to make a single-piece tool.*
   a. Mount one half of the split pattern on a mold board.
   b. Position the flask around the pattern and fasten it to the mold board.
3. *Make the second tool half.*
   a. Remove the first tool half from the mold board and flask, leaving the pattern half in place.
   b. Position the second pattern half over the first.
   c. Replace the tool half in the flask, allowing the proper amount of depth for the second mold half, as seen in Fig. 14-19.
   d. Coat all exposed surfaces of the pattern, tool, and flask with mold release.
   e. Prepare the casting compound.
   f. Pour the casting compound into the lowest corner of the flask, allowing it to cover the pattern and fill the flask to the proper height, Fig. 14-20.
   g. Cure the casting.
   h. Remove the casting from the flask.
   i. Separate the halves of the tool.
   j. Remove the pattern halves.

Laminated-Plastic Tools

Laminated tooling is usually made from an epoxy or polyester resin reinforced with fiberglass cloth, mat, or fibers.

UNIT 9
HOW TO MAKE LAMINATED-PLASTIC TOOLS

While simple cast-plastic tools are easy to make and very serviceable it may be necessary to provide greater strength than is practical with such tooling. Cast plastics gain their strength from increases in thickness; a large tool may be very heavy. In such cases, laminated tooling may be more practical, since it gains its strength from reinforcement, often fiber glass cloth or mat, and can be made thinner and lighter. In addition, laminated plastics can be made somewhat flexible, which is often an advantage in separating the product from the tool.

Procedure

The procedure for making laminated-plastic tooling is essentially the same as that for making products by reinforcing. Refer to the Units 26 and 27 in Chapter 20, *Reinforcing*.

Tools from Wood

Wood is always a valuable material for developmental work. It is easy to shape to the original form, and it is readily modified for design changes. Its lack of resistance to abrasion, its relatively low compressive strength, and the adverse effect of changes in moisture content, limit its use to tools for thermoforming and reinforcing. It is often used to make patterns for tools to be made from other materials.

Standard hand- and machine-processing techniques are used to shape the tools. Routers are especially valuable for producing fillets, grooves for ribs, and rounding over arrises and corners.

Tools for thermoforming must be made with glues that will not soften with heat. Most animal glues, urea resin adhesives, and resorcinal resin adhesives are satisfactory. Because polyvinyl acetate (white glues) are thermoplastics, they are likely to soften under heat.

In selecting a wood to be used several characteristics should be kept in mind.

(1) The wood should be *stable*. It should resist changes in dimension and tendencies to warp. Kiln-dried lumber is preferable in all cases. Radial-sawed lumber is recommended over tangential patterns because of reduced warping tendencies.

(2) The wood should be a type in which there is minimum tendency for the grain to *raise*. Woods with a lack of prominent grain pattern are best. It is good to raise the grain with light sponging and then to sand it smooth.

(3) The wood should be *pitch-free*. Many softwoods, pine for example, may contain pitch that is drawn out of the tool as it is heated during thermoforming. This is not important in tools for reinforced plastics where little or no heat is present.

(4) The wood should be *firm*. Generally, diffuse-porous woods will hold up better in thin sections than will ring-porous woods.

(5) The wood should be *easy to work*. Extreme hardness is not needed in wooden tools but the wood should shape easily.

Ideal woods for tooling are *mahogany*, *cherry*, and *basswood*. In many applications almost any wood that can be readily shaped and smoothed will produce good results.

A finish is put on a wooden tool for two reasons. It fills up the pores and makes the surface smooth, reducing the tendency for markoff in thermoforming and for adhesion of the plastic in reinforcing. It also protects the tool by making it tougher and more resistant to changes in moisture content.

If a tool is to be used only a few times, it is merely waxed with paste wax. Lacquer makes a good finish for more permanent tools. Figs. 14-21 and 14-22 show two wooden tools and the parts made from them.

Fig. 14-21. Wooden Tool and the Part Made from It

Tools from Low-Melting Metals

A tooling media especially suitable for laboratory and experimental work is found in a group of low-melting metal alloys. They are safe, easy to work, and produce high quality tools for various applications in plastics processing.

The Alloys

One group of suitable low-melting alloys is produced by the Cerro Corporation under the general name, Cerro Alloys. Their chief component is bismuth — a heavy, coarse, crystalline metal which has the unique property of expanding as it changes from liquid to solid. In the Cerro Alloys, bismuth is combined in various percentages with other metals such as lead, tin, cadmium, and indium. Alloys containing approximately fifty percent bismuth exhibit little volume change as they solidify. Those with greater percentages of bismuth expand as they cool while those with less shrink as they cool.

Most metals shrink as they cool, pulling away from the surface against which they are cast. The tendency of bismuth to expand results in very fine and dense surface detail in the casting.

The Cerro Alloys melt at temperatures ranging from 117° to 338° F. Some of the alloys are eutectics and others are non-eutectics. A *eutectic* is an alloy having the lowest melting point possible for the particular combination of metals. It exhibits a sharp

TABLE 16
MELTING POINTS FOR CERRO ALLOYS

Metal	Temperature
Cerrobend	158° F.
Cerrobase	255
Cerrotru	281
Cerrocast	281–338

melting point, i.e., the temperature at which it solidifies is the same temperature at which it liquifies. Non-eutectics are combinations of metals in such percentages as to give a higher melting point than for a eutectic containing the same metals. They soften over a *range of temperature*. Table 16 lists the melting temperatures of the common Cerro Alloys suitable for mold making. The range of melting temperatures is listed for Cerrocast, a non-eutectic.

Cerrotru and Cerrocast most commonly are used because their higher melting temperatures (though still not much above that of boiling water) allow warmer molding conditions. They also exhibit greater hardness and better dimensional accuracy.

Tool Making

Tools of high luster can be produced with low-melting alloys. No machining is needed on tool surfaces; they can be used as cast, but to achieve optimum results, two factors must be taken into account: (1) The pattern surface, against which the tool is to be made, must be smooth and polished. (2) The metal at the pattern surface must cool as rapidly as possible. Slow cooling results in a porous surface which is undesirable for plastics work.

Metal patterns can provide both of these factors. Such materials as aluminum, brass, and steel can be highly polished and because they are excellent conductors of heat can chill the alloy quickly as it comes in contact with the pattern.

In experimental work often it is not convenient to make the pattern from metal. More commonly used materials are wood, plaster, soap, or plastics. These materials can present

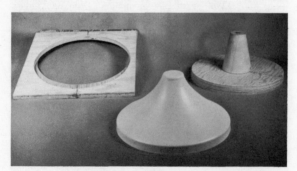

Fig. 14-22. Finished Part with
Wooden Plug and Yokes

a good finish against which to cast the alloy, but they are poor conductors of heat and will not cause rapid cooling of the cast alloy. When a poor conductor is used as a pattern material, rather than pour the alloy around the pattern, it is better to spray it on, thus depositing it in a relatively cool state. The pressure from the spray gun will flatten the metal against the pattern surface, instantly cooling it, and will reproduce with extreme accuracy any detail on the surface. For example, a finger print can be reproduced with the metal spray. The gun is moved over the surface of the pattern so that only a very thin layer of metal is deposited at one time; no large mass of metal is present to hold the heat. The specially designed spray gun heats the metal to the melting point and keeps it hot to prevent clogging the nozzle.

UNIT 10
HOW TO MAKE TOOLS
FROM LOW-MELTING ALLOYS

Low-melting alloys can be used to make tools for any plastics process that is accomplished at temperatures below the melting point of the alloy, 281° to 338° F. Tools made by this process can be used for thermoforming, casting, and injection molding. To obtain extremely accurate surface detail spraying of the metal is preferred to pouring. Several spray guns are available which include a melting pot to liquify the metal and a source of air pressure for spraying at 35-40 psi. Fig. 14-23 shows a commercial spray gun for spraying low-melting alloys.

Procedure

1. *Prepare pattern.* The pattern may be made from any convenient material such as wood, metal, plaster, soap, or plastics. The surface should be exactly as desired on the finished tool. If a porous material such as wood is used, it is well to fill and seal its surface. If a metal pattern is used it should be heated to about 200° F. For most materials no release agent is needed because there is little tendency for the sprayed metal to adhere to the pattern surface.

2. *Mount pattern on mold board and position flask, or chase.* A flask is used where it is desired to fix the outside dimensions and shape of the mold, as shown in Fig. 14-24. A chase is often used with thermoforming or injection molding tools to add support to the mold and provide a means of mounting it in the press.

Fig. 14-23. Commercial Spray Gun

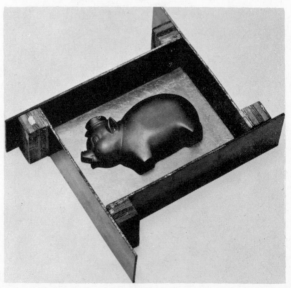

Fig. 14-24. Unit 10, Step 2 — Pattern Mounted on Mold Board with Flask in Place

3. *Prepare spray gun.* Heat the pot to liquify the metal. Adjust the air pressure and spray pattern to produce a fine spray. Ordinarily, 35 to 40 pounds of air pressure is satisfactory.

4. *Spray surface of pattern, mold board, and flask or chase.* Spraying should be done in a manner similar to that used for spray-ing paint. It is best to aim the nozzle so that the line of spray strikes the pattern at approximately 90 degrees. A fine even coat should be deposited on all surfaces to be covered. Note Fig. 14-25. This process should be continued until a layer of $\frac{1}{16}$ inch to $\frac{1}{8}$ inch has been built. Too rapid a build up in any spot may develop ex-cessive heat, resulting in warping of the surface.

5. *Build up the tool thickness.*
   a. *With metal.* After a layer has covered the entire surface of the tool, addi-tional thickness can be developed with a coarse spray. Rapid filling can be done by pouring the metal with a ladle. If cooling coils are needed in the finished tool, they may be em-bedded at this time.
   b. *With plaster.* In tools where high strength is not needed, the layer can be backed with casting plaster. Since most plasters have an alkaline reac-tion, the metal should be coated with lacquer before the plaster is poured.

6. *Remove pattern.* Care should be taken in pulling the pattern to avoid damaging the finished tool. No further treatment is needed. See Fig. 14-26 for the finished tool.

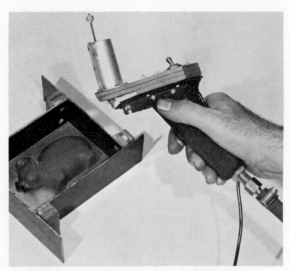

Fig. 14-25. Step 4 — Spraying the Metal

Fig. 14-26. Step 6 — Finished Mold with Pattern Removed

Tools for Production Work

Tools used for long-run production work with automatic or semi-automatic machines are commonly cast and/or machined from metals. Steel is probably the most common material used for this purpose, especially with molds for compression and transfer molding. Beryl-lium copper is often substituted for injection molds, and aluminum is very prominent in processes such as blow molding and thermo-forming where the mold is not subjected to great abrasion.

The processes employed in the manufacture of tools from metals include milling, turning, drilling and boring, grinding, hobbing, cast-ing, electroforming, electrical discharge ma-chining, plating, welding, and heat treating.

TABLE 17
TOOLING MATERIALS RECOMMENDED FOR
VARIOUS PLASTICS PROCESSES

Process	Tooling Material						
	Plaster	Reinforced Plastics		Wood	Low-Melting Metals	Cast Aluminum	Steel
		Cast	Laminated				
Thermoforming	X	X	X	X	X	X	
Injection Molding		X			X	X	X
Compression Molding		X					X
Foam Molding						X	
Foam Casting	X	X	X	X	X	X	
Plastisol Casting	X	X	X			X	
Reinforcing	X	X	X	X	X	X	

Since the contents of this book are devoted largely to *design and experimental work,* or short-run production in plastics, the tool-making techniques of the metals industries are not discussed here. Such tools are usually made by skilled tool and die makers.

Application Summary

Table 17 summarizes the tooling materials covered in this chapter as recommended for the various plastics processes.

Study Questions

Plaster Tools

1. Why are gypsum plasters especially suited to experimental work with plastics?
2. What is the common name applied to *soft plasters?*
3. What is the basic material from which plasters are made?
4. How is the composition of soft plaster different from that of high-strength plaster?
5. What is the structure of plaster that causes it to develop strength?
6. How does the amount of water added to dry plaster affect its strength?
7. What happens to the size of a block of plaster as it sets?
8. What are the four types of plaster developed primarily for making tools?
9. What is the outstanding property of each type?
10. Look at the chart on properties of casting plasters. Make a generalization concerning the relationship between amount of water needed and compressive strength of the dried plaster.
11. What is the effect of water temperature on speed of setting of mixed plaster?
12. Why is the dry plaster added to the water rather than water being added to the dry plaster?
13. How can you tell when the plaster has been mixed sufficiently?
14. What are the various techniques by which plaster tools are made for use in processing plastics?
15. What preparation is needed to get a pattern ready for casting in plaster?
16. What is a flask as used in plaster casting?
17. How should plaster be poured? Why is it necessary to do it properly?
18. When should the pattern be removed from the cast tool?
19. What finishing operations are ordinarily necessary on a cast-plaster tool?

20. How is the parting line determined for a two-piece mold?
21. What preparation is needed after the first half of a two-piece mold is set before the second half can be cast?
22. What kinds of shapes are usually made by the loft-template technique?
23. What controls the shape of the object made by the loft-template technique?
24. How is the plaster mixture different for loft-template work from that for simple casting?
25. What shapes are generally made by the circular screeding technique?
26. How is the shape of the object controlled in circular screeding?

Plastic Tools

27. Generally, how would you decide whether to use a cast- or laminated-plastic tool?
28. What are the various techniques by which tools are made for processing plastics?
29. What use is often made of single-piece cast-plastic tools?
30. What materials can be used for patterns from which cast-plastic tools are made?
31. What preparation of the pattern is needed before casting?
32. What are common components of the plastics used in tooling?
33. How should the plastic be poured over the pattern? Why?
34. How are cast-plastic tools cured?
35. What use is commonly made of two-piece cast-plastic tools?
36. Where in this book can you look for instructions on how to make laminated-plastic tools?

Wooden Tools

37. What are the principal advantages of wood as a tool making material? What are its principal disadvantages?
38. What glues should be used for building up wood that is to be used for tools?
39. What characteristics should be taken into account in selecting a wood from which to make a tool for plastics work?
40. Why do wood tools often require a finish?

Low-Melting Metal Tools

41. What is the advantage of low-melting metals for plastics tools?
42. What is the principal ingredient in low-melting alloys? What unusual property does it possess?
43. What is a eutectic? A non-eutectic?
44. What is the range of melting temperatures of the low-melting Cerro alloys?
45. What two factors must be taken into account if a high luster is to be obtained on a tool made from low-melting alloys?
46. What materials can be used for patterns for making tools from low-melting alloys?
47. What critical factor determines whether a tool made from low-melting metal will be satisfactory for a given application in plastics?
48. What preparation of the pattern is needed before it can be sprayed with metal?
49. How should the spray gun be pointed during the spraying operation?
50. How soon can the pattern be pulled from a sprayed-metal tool?

Machined and Cast-Metal Tools

51. What materials are commonly used to make tools for production work?
52. What processes are commonly employed to make production tools?

This part of the book is devoted to explanations of six of the basic processes of the plastics industry. For each, there is a discussion of product design factors controlled by the process, the design and construction of tools needed, the plastics which are commonly processed in this manner, the equipment needed, and descriptions of procedures. As in the previous section, the operational procedures are aimed toward custom work rather than mass production. The steps in the procedures are somewhat general because the details will be determined by the peculiarities of the individual piece of equipment used.

Processes included in this section are thermoforming plastic sheet, injection-molding thermoplastics, compression-molding thermosets, molding and casting cellular plastics, plastisol casting, and reinforcing.

PART IV

working with plastics processes

CHAPTER FIFTEEN

thermoforming plastics sheet

One of the more recent methods developed for processing plastics is thermoforming. It is very adaptable to laboratory or experimental work because it uses simple tooling and equipment. Design modifications are easy to make. Custom work is practical in terms of time, material, and tooling costs, and the process is also suited to high-volume mass production.

Product Design

There are many product design factors that apply generally to all of the variations of thermoforming. Others apply specifically to a given technique. The general design factors will be discussed first followed by those related specifically to the individual processes.

General Factors

The basic shape of a thermoformed object is an open, hollow, thin-walled object. Pictured in Fig. 15-1 are some typical shapes. Solid shapes cannot be produced by this process. Since a heated sheet is stretched over a form, the plastic will be *thinner* after the process. The greater the depth of the object, the greater the thinning will be. In stretching, it is necessary for one side of the sheet plastic to stretch more than the other side. This means that very heavy sheets cannot be used because the difference will be too great in the amount of shrinkage from one side to the other. Except for special applications, maximum sheet thickness is usually one-quarter inch.

In stretching, the plastic sheet tends to bridge across fine detail in the form. The thickness of the sheet determines the amount of detail produced. With thin sheets (.002 to .020 inch) very fine surface detail is possible.

Designs usually should not call for sharp corners or arrises. (An *arris* is the sharp line where two surfaces meet as between a top and an edge; usually three arrises meet at a corner.) The plastic tends to thin excessively or to tear in such places. Deep depressions of small diameter are difficult to produce. Large radii and smooth curved shapes are easiest to produce.

Designs should not call for large flat areas. The formed part is likely to lack flexural strength. It is preferable, where a large area is needed, to form ribs or corrugations for

Fig. 15-1. Typical Thermoformed Shapes

support. Such reinforcing features enable the design to be produced with thinner material with no loss in strength.

Mechanical Forming with Plug and Yokes

Shapes adaptable to production by this process possess straight lines or convex (outward) curves; only very slight concave (inward) curves can be formed. The height of the object should not exceed the minimum dimension of the base of the object. Markoff will occur on the inside of the formed article.

Mechanical Forming with Matched Plug and Mold

This is the only process that will allow the production of detail on both sides of the article. Controlled wall thickness is possible more with this technique than with any of the others. It is generally suitable to rather shallow draws only.

Vacuum Forming with Mold

Shapes adaptable to this process are rather shallow with large amounts of draft. A deep, vertical-walled object will thin excessively at the sides. Where a series of small depressions must be placed very close together, this is a suitable procedure.

Vacuum Forming with Plug

Of all techniques, this allows for greatest depth of draw with most uniform distribution of material. With proper design, the height of the object can be as much as twice the minimum dimension of the base of the object. Markoff will occur on the inside of the object. This is not a desirable technique where a series of projections are to be placed close together because the plastic tends to loosely bridge one projection to the next.

Blow Forming with Mold

Possible shapes using this technique are similar to those made by vacuum forming with a mold except that greater depth of objects is possible. Where undercuts and fine detail with heavy sheets are required, this is the most adaptable technique. Markoff occurs on the convex side of the article.

Free Blowing

In any forming operation where the plastic comes into contact with a plug or mold, markoff will occur to some degree. Where extreme optical clarity is desired, the free blowing technique is the best. Since nothing but air contacts the plastic, there is no markoff. Shapes produced by free blowing will always tend toward a hemisphere. With the proper material very even thinning of the plastic will occur.

Tool Design

Once a part has been designed it is often possible to thermoform it with a plug, a mold, or with matched plug and mold. The choice of tooling is dependent upon several factors.

(1) On which side is markoff least objectionable?
(2) With which type of tooling will the maximum force be applied?
(3) Which will be easiest to make?
(4) Which type of tooling is most adaptable to the shape to be produced?

Even carefully smoothed tooling is likely to cause some change in the appearance of the surface of the plastic that comes in contact with it. If the concave side of the formed part should be the smooth, a mold should be used; if the convex side should be smooth, a plug should be used. This generalization would be reversed if it is desired to press a design into the surface of the sheet. In cases where intricate designs are desired on both sides of the formed part, matched plugs and molds are required.

In blow or vacuum forming, the force causing the sheet to form will be directly proportional to the surface area of the section to be formed. For example, with a perfect vacuum, approximately 14 pounds of atmospheric pressure will act on each square inch of surface area. If the area of a portion of the object to be pushed into a groove in the tool is one square inch, the total pushing force will be only fourteen pounds. If the area to be pushed down is ten square inches, the total force applied will be 140 pounds. In addition, the larger area of plastic will be more flexible than the smaller area and thus is easier to form.

The tool designer should design in such manner that the portion of the sheet to be formed to the deepest draw is of the largest area. Figure 15-2 shows this principle used with an instrument tray. Notice that the area of the depressions in the finished article is less than the area between the depressions. In this case it is better to use a plug than a mold. Where all areas are sizable, or where very thin plastic is used, this factor is less important.

Generally it is easier to shape convex forms than concave. Therefore, the *plug* is usually easier to make than the *mold*. In cases where other factors make a mold more desirable for thermoforming, it may be better to make a plug first, form a part from it, and use that part as a pattern to make a cast or sprayed mold. Slight modifications in design are usually easier to make with plugs than with molds. Tooling for designs requiring a number of depressions or projections is more easily made as a plug. The individual parts of the plug can be made separately and then fastened to a plate, while in a mold a series of depressions must be machined into the mold.

Articles with zero degrees to two degrees of draft (taper) on the sides are more easily removed from molds than from plugs. The plastic tends to shrink as it cools. This pulls it away from the mold, making it easier to remove while shrinkage tends to lock the part on a plug.

The tooling for thermoforming is not subjected to much surface abrasion, so it is not necessary to use an extremely hard and durable material. In vacuum or blow forming where the tool has a large area, it may be subjected to a great deal of force; therefore the tooling should be very stiff to resist flexure and breakage. In production work it is desirable to use a material that is a good heat conductor because the formed part must cool before it can be removed. With short-run or experimental work this is not as important.

Experimental work is usually done with wood or plaster tools while production work makes use of metal or plastic tooling.

Specific design and construction features are outlined below for the individual thermoforming applications.

Mechanical Forming with Plug and Yokes

Plugs should be constructed with as much draft as possible. While formed parts can be removed from plugs with no draft, two degrees to ten degrees greatly facilitates part removal. All arrises and corners on the plug should be rounded to prevent cutting and thinning. Since the *top yoke* sizes the opening in the part, it must be made very accurately. The opening in the top yoke should be the size of the base of the plug plus two times the thickness of the plastic to be formed, plus an allowance of $\frac{1}{16}$ inch to $\frac{1}{8}$ inch for clearance. See Fig. 15-3. The *bottom yoke* serves mainly to hold the plastic during heating and forming. Accuracy of opening is not as important as in the top yoke but the two openings should be concentric. The arrises on the yoke should be rounded to provide easy slippage of material without scratching. The height of the plug should be enough to allow for the thickness of the bottom yoke and the clamping frame.

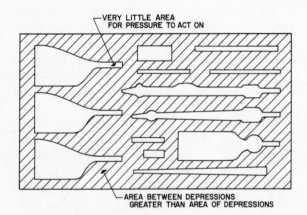

Fig. 15-2. A Thermoformed Instrument Case

A plug rather than a mold should be used with vacuum forming.

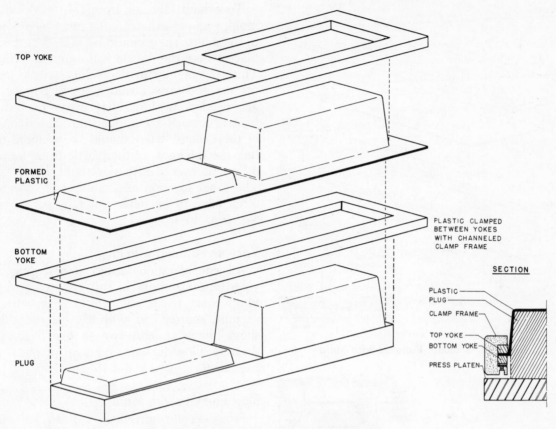

Fig. 15-3. Mechanical Forming with Plug and Yokes

Mechanical Forming
with Matched Plug and Mold

The plug and mold should have as much draft as possible. The plug should be as much smaller than the mold as the desired thickness of the finished part. Both plug and mold must be as smooth as possible to reduce markoff. See Fig. 15-4.

Vacuum Forming with Mold

The sides of the mold should have as much draft as possible. While no difficulty is encountered in removing the part from a straight-sided mold, it causes excessive thinning of the part. All molds must be completely airtight. A good seal must be provided between the source of vacuum and the mold and between the plastic and the mold. A vacuum chamber should be provided under the mold so that all vacuum holes will be connected to the vacuum source.

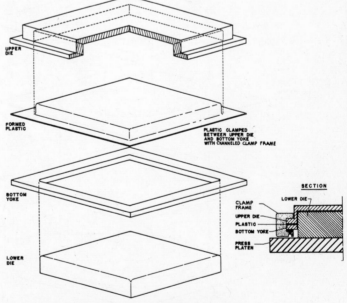

Fig. 15-4. Mechanical Forming with
Matched Plug and Mold

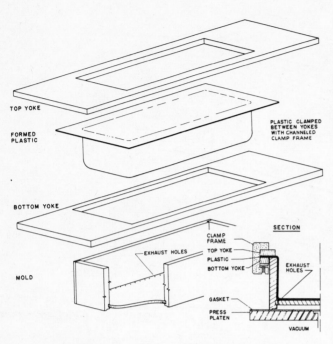

Fig. 15-5. Vacuum Forming with Mold

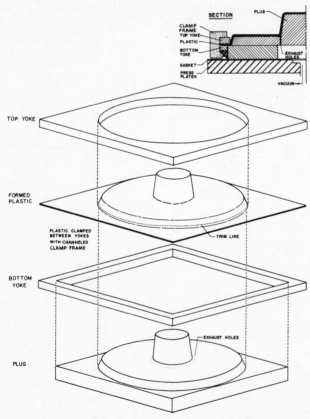

Fig. 15-6. Vacuum Forming with Plug

To exhaust the air from the inside of the mold, vacuum exhaust holes must be provided in the mold. They should be placed in the last place where the plastic will move in forming. This is generally in deep depressions, inside corners and arrises, and grooves. Some holes are needed in large flat areas to prevent blisters formed by trapped air. The diameter of the exhaust holes should be no more than half the thickness of the plastic to be formed; otherwise excessive markoff is likely to occur. The exact location and number of holes will often have to be determined by experiment. See Fig. 15-5.

Vacuum Forming with Plug

All considerations listed under plug and yoke forming apply in this type of forming. Plugs must make an airtight seal with the vacuum source and with the plastic. Plugs should have at least two to five degrees of draft to allow for easy removal of parts. See Fig. 15-6.

Blow Forming with Mold

Provision for airtightness must be made between the plastic to be formed and the pressure source. The mold of course must not be airtight to allow trapped air to escape. Inside arrises and corners should be filleted if possible. In individual forming operations it may be possible to regulate the air pressure so that it does not push the plastic sharply into the corners, but in production work an excess of pressure is used and the inside of the mold must be exactly the shape desired on the part.

If reverse curves or undercuts are desired, the mold must be made in such a manner that it can be disassembled after the part is formed.

Air-escape holes must be drilled in the form to allow the contained air to escape as the plastic is formed. Holes should be in the last place that the plastic would generally move in forming; corners, inside arrises, and grooves are common locations. The diameter of the holes should be no more than one-half the thickness of the plastic to be formed.

Molds must be very strong because the total force applied to them by the air pressure is usually very great. See Fig. 15-7.

Free Blowing

Because the shape of the opening in the free-blown part is controlled entirely by the opening in the yoke, it must be made very accurately. The edge of the hole should be rounded to provide some slippage and to avoid scratching.

The incoming air used in the blowing operation should be baffled in some manner to avoid a single blast of air in one spot. Baffling may be accomplished by placing an auxiliary platen over the pressure head with a series of small holes spread over the entire forming area. See Fig. 15-8.

Materials Used

By the nature of the process only *thermoplastics in sheet form* can be used for thermoforming. Any thermoplastic sheet can be formed but certain ones are used more commonly because of various properties they possess.

The means by which the plastic sheet is manufactured affects its forming characteristics. Most forming is done with *extruded or calendered sheet* because of its lower cost. Such sheet has a tendency to shrink in one direction when it is heated and must be held firmly in a frame or yoke during heating and forming. *Cast sheet* has little or no tendency to change shape during heating and will produce articles of high optical clarity and fewer internal stresses. However, because it is expensive, it generally is used only where these properties are important.

Of all plastics used in thermoforming, *high-impact polystyrene* is the "work horse." It is a low-cost sheet with exceptional forming properties. Though not available in transparent form, a complete range of colors from translucent to opaque can be obtained.

Cellulosics are widely used in packaging and display work because of their high optical clarity, toughness, and resistance to weathering.

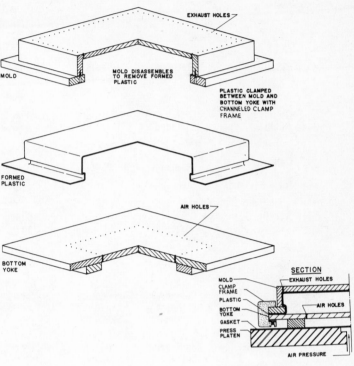

Fig. 15-7. Blow Forming with Mold

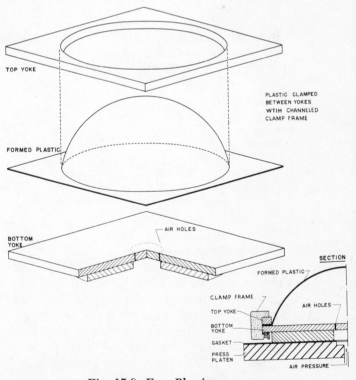

Fig. 15-8. Free Blowing

TABLE 18
GUIDE TO THERMOPLASTIC SHEET

Plastic	Methods of Forming	Sheet Cost	Clarity	Color	Finish	Special Forming Characteristics
Cellulose Acetate	Cast, Extruded	Medium	Transparent to Opaque	Unlimited	Glossy, Matte	Very easy to form.
Cellulose Acetate Butyrate	Extruded	Medium high	Transparent to Opaque	Unlimited	Glossy, Matte	Good deep-drawing qualities.
Acrylic	Cast, Extruded	Cast-high Ext.-med.	Transparent to Opaque	Unlimited	Glossy	More force to form. Very even stretch. Good for free blow.
Vinyls Rigid	Calendered, Extruded, Laminated	Medium high	Transparent to Opaque	Unlimited	Matte, Press-polished is glossy	Very consistent stretch. Good for preprinting.
Flexible	Calendered, Cast	Medium to Low	Translucent to Opaque	Unlimited	Satin	
Styrenes Copolymer	Extruded	Low	Opaque	Unlimited	Matte, Glossy	Maximum, allowance on heat control. Easy to form.
Hi-Impact	Extruded	Low	Translucent to Opaque	Unlimited	Matte, Glossy	
Blends	Calendered, Laminated	Medium	Opaque	Unlimited	Matte, Grained	Stiffer to form than other styrenes.
Polyethylene Low Density	Extruded	Low	Translucent to Opaque	Natural milky colors made.	Matte, Glossy	Very close heat control needed.
High Density	Extruded	Med. High	Translucent to Opaque	Natural milky colors made.	Glossy	

Acrylics, especially *cast* acrylics, are the primary materials used in windshields and outdoor advertising displays where their exceptional clarity, resistance to weather, and brilliant colors are used to good advantage. Their cost prohibits their use in applications where these properties are not needed.

Rigid vinyls have very fine stretching qualities and *plastic memory*. They are used for prototype work in the making of distorted patterns for preprinted thermoforms.

The *ABS plastics* are probably the toughest of all materials used in thermoforming. They are commonly used for making carrying cases and dash boards for automobiles and boats.

Table 18 lists the properties and applications of the most used materials for thermoforming.

Equipment

The equipment needed for thermoforming depends upon the particular application to be used. All methods require two items of equipment, a source of heat and some means of holding the sheet for heating and forming.

In some experimental work, an ordinary *baking oven*, with temperatures of 240-550° F. controlled thermostatically, can be used. This is very satisfactory for heating cast acrylic plastic but for most other materials there is a very rapid heat loss when the material is removed from the oven, with resultant difficulty in maintaining proper heat control. Fig. 15-9 shows oven-heating of a clamped sheet.

Much more satisfactory is some type of *heating panel* mounted directly above the forming equipment. Infrared or radiant panels producing temperatures from 660°-1200° F. are commonly used. The proper temperature is attained by controlling the time the plastic is held under the panel and the distance between the panel and the plastic. Some means is necessary of swinging or sliding the heat source away from the plastic when it reaches the proper temperature. One type of heater panel is shown in Fig. 15-10.

It is essential to clamp the sheet in some type of *frame* during heating and forming. As mentioned previously, extruded and calendered plastics tend to shrink in one direction when heated; the frame prevents this. For experimental work, two one-half inch plywood yokes are satisfactory. On the laboratory press in Fig. 15-11 the sheet is mounted between plywood yokes with two aluminum channels. The sheet can be held in place between the yokes with clamps or screws. On some of the models of laboratory equipment, adjustable, clamping frames are provided. Fig. 15-12 shows an adjustable frame which requires no yokes.

The means by which the forming force is applied depends, of course, upon the particular forming application to be used. In *mechanical forming*, it is often possible to simply push the heated plastic over the plug by hand and clamp it in place until it cools. Also various presses can be fabricated or

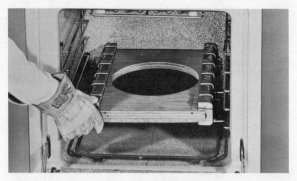
Fig. 15-9. Heating a Plastic Sheet in Oven

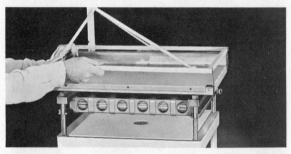
Fig. 15-10. Heating Panel Mounted over Forming Press (Di-Acro)

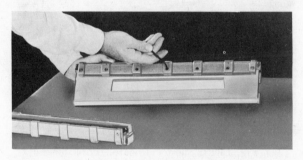
Fig. 15-11. Sheet Mounted between Plywood Yokes (Di-Acro)

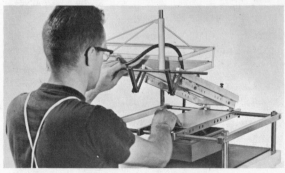
Fig. 15-12. Adjustable Hinged Clamp Frame (Di-Acro)

adapted. The shop-fabricated machine in Fig. 15-13 uses a hydraulic jack and a platen.

In *blow forming*, it is necessary to clamp the heated sheet over a pressure head. Pressure can be supplied from an air line or from any type of standard air compressor. Forming pressures of thirty pounds per square inch are usually sufficient for most laboratory work. Fig. 15-14 shows a piece of shop-made equipment for free blowing. It can be connected either to an air line or directly to a compressor.

In *vacuum forming*, it is necessary to clamp the mold or plug and heated sheet over a source of vacuum. Vacuum can be supplied

from any ordinary vane- or piston-type vacuum pump or even from a tank-type vacuum cleaner. The source of vacuum should be high volume rather than high vacuum.

At least one laboratory-type thermoforming press is available that will perform all of the applications — mechanical, blow, and vacuum. It is complete with heater panel, clamping arrangement, and vacuum and pressure pump. See Fig. 15-15. Other laboratory models are available that will perform individual operations.

Procedures

The basic operations for thermoforming plastics sheet are outlined in this section. With the exception of the first operation, "How to Make Bends," the equipment used in the illustrations and for procedures is the Di-Acro plastics press. On shop-fabricated equipment, modifications in procedures must be made.

Fig. 15-13. Shop Fabricated Press for Mechanical Forming

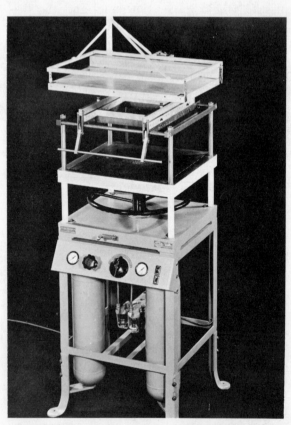

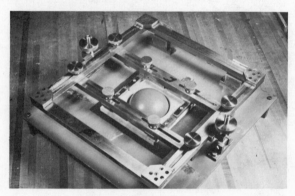

Fig. 15-14. Shop-Fabricated Press for Blow Forming

Fig. 15-15. Laboratory Press for Mechanical, Vacuum, and Blow Forming (Di-Acro)

UNIT 11
HOW TO MAKE BENDS

There are many cases where a simple bend is needed in a thermoplastic sheet. Often it is desired to make the bend without distorting the remainder of the sheet. To accomplish this, heat only the portion of the sheet where the bend will be.

1. *Heat strip heater.* Most strip heaters operate electrically. The heater also may be simply a steam pipe.
2. *Position plastic on strip heater.* Place the plastic with the bending line directly over the heating element. Do not allow the plastic to actually touch the source of heat because it is likely to melt and stick. See Fig. 15-16.
3. *Properly heat plastic.* The plastic will gradually soften and sag as it nears the proper temperature. With plastics over $\frac{1}{16}$ inch thick it may be necessary to turn them to warm the other side.
4. *Bend plastic.* Remove plastic from heater and bend by hand as shown in Fig. 15-17. It should bend only along the heated line.
5. *Place on cooling fixture if needed.* With thick plastic, cooling may take several minutes, and the part can be held in the proper position more easily on a fixture than by hand. If duplicate parts are to be made, more accurate control is possible on a fixture. Note Fig. 15-18.

UNIT 12
HOW TO THERMOFORM MECHANICALLY WITH MATCHED PLUG AND MOLD

In cases where very close dimensional control or sharp changes in shape are required, this method of forming is advantageous.

1. *Cut the plastic.* An allowance of approximately one-half inch around the final trim line is needed. Since the plastic is not clamped in a set of yokes for heating in this process, a greater allowance may be needed for very large pieces.

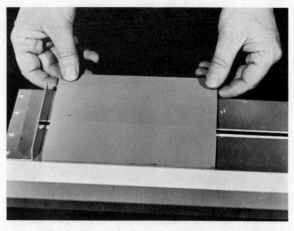

Fig. 15-16. Unit 11, Step 2 — Positioning Plastic on Strip Heater

Fig. 15-17. Step 4 — Bending Plastic to Desired Angle

Fig. 15-18. Step 5 — Placing Bent Part on Cooling Fixture

Fig. 15-19. Unit 12, Step 3 — Mold and Plug
Positioned on Press

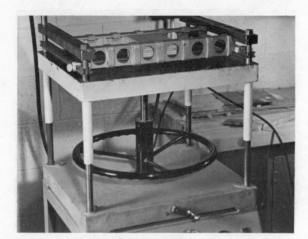

Fig. 15-20. Step 8 — Forcing Mold and
Plug Together

Fig. 15-21. Step 10 — The Formed Part

2. *Mount plug in upper frame of press and set stops to position it.*
3. *Position mold on platen in matched position under plug.* Make sure that the two mate exactly as they should go together for forming. See Fig. 15-19.
4. *Place plastic on mold and raise platen to uppermost position.*
5. *Slide plug out of position.* This allows the heat from the heater panel to reach the plastic. The stops will allow the plug to be returned to the proper position just prior to forming.
6. *Heat plastic.* Swing heater panel into position and heat plastic to the proper forming temperature.
7. *Move plug back into position against stops.*
8. *Form plastic by raising platen to force matched plug and mold together,* Fig. 15-20.
9. *Allow plastic to cool.*
10. *Remove formed part.* Lower the platen and separate the plug and mold. The finished formed part is shown in Fig. 15-21.

UNIT 13
HOW TO THERMOFORM MECHANICALLY WITH PLUG AND YOKES

1. *Cut the plastic.* An allowance of approximately one-half inch around the final trim line is usually sufficient. See Fig. 15-22.

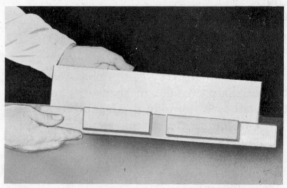

Fig. 15-22. Unit 13, Step 1 — Plug with Plastic
Cut to Fit (Di-Acro)

2. *Mount the plastic between two yokes,* Fig. 15-23.

3. *Position the plug on the press with the mounted plastic directly over it.* Make sure that the opening in the yokes is perfectly aligned with the plug, as shown in Fig. 15-24.

4. *Heat the mounted plastic,* Fig. 15-25.

5. *Form the plastic.* Raise the platen to force the plug through the opening in the yokes, stretching the plastic to conform to the shape of the plug.

6. *Allow the plastic to cool.*

7. *Remove the formed part.* Disassemble the yokes and remove the part. The formed part is pictured in Fig. 15-26. NOTE: For small shallow draws this operation can be done by hand. See Fig. 15-27. Notice the formed object still mounted in the yokes, Fig. 15-28, with the wood plug and line-up pins.

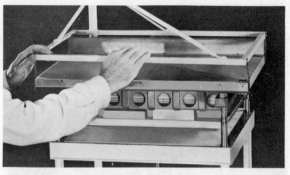

Fig. 15-25. Step 4 — Heating the Plastic (Di-Acro)

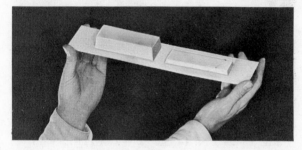

Fig. 15-26. Step 7 — The Formed Part (Di-Acro)

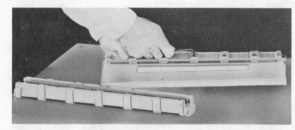

Fig. 15-23. Step 2 — Mounting the Plastic in the Yokes (Di Acro)

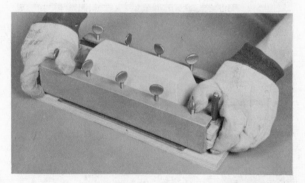

Fig. 15-27. Hand Forming a Small Part

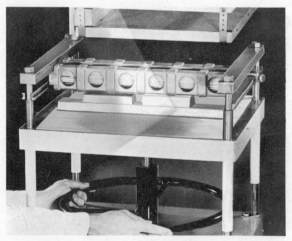

Fig. 15-24. Step 3 — Mounted Plastic Positioned over Plug (Di-Acro)

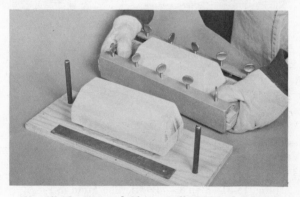

Fig. 15-28. Formed Object Still Mounted in Yokes

UNIT 14
HOW TO VACUUM-FORM
WITH MOLD

1. *Cut the plastic.* An allowance of approximately ½ inch around the final trim line is sufficient. See Fig. 15-29.

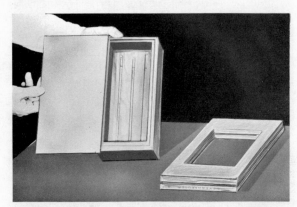

Fig. 15-29. Unit 14, Step 1 — Cut Plastic with Mold and Yokes (Di-Acro)

Fig. 15-30. Step 2 — Mounting Plastic between Yokes (Di-Acro)

Fig. 15-31. Step 3 — Positioning Mold in Press (Di-Acro)

2. *Mount the plastic between two yokes,* Fig. 15-30.
3. *Position the mold over the vacuum exhaust,* as shown in Fig. 15-31. Provide some means of sealing the mold to the vacuum exhaust. A rubber gasket or masking tape provides a good seal.
4. *Position the mounted plastic over the mold.* Make sure that the opening in the yoke is lined up with the mold. Note Fig. 15-32.
5. *Heat the plastic,* Fig. 15-33.
6. *Force the mold against the heated plastic as in Fig. 15-34 to form a seal between the plastic and the mold.*

Fig. 15-32. Step 4 — Positioning Mounted Plastic over Mold (Di-Acro)

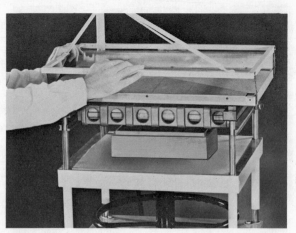

Fig. 15-33. Step 5 — Heating the Plastic (Di-Acro)

7. *Form plastic by exhausting the air from the mold*, as shown in Fig. 15-35.
8. *Allow to cool.*
9. *Remove the part from the mold,* Fig. 15-36.

UNIT 15
HOW TO VACUUM-FORM WITH PLUG

1. *Cut the plastic.* An allowance of approximately ½ inch around the final trim line is usually sufficient.
2. *Mount the plastic between the yokes in a clamping frame.*
3. *Center the plug over the vacuum exhaust.*
4. *Position the mounted plastic over the plug.* Make sure that the opening in the yokes is perfectly aligned with the plug shape.
5. *Heat the mounted plastic.*
6. *Force the plug against the heated plastic creating a seal between the plug and the plastic and partially forming it.* See Fig. 15-37.
7. *Form plastic.* Apply the vacuum, drawing the air from inside the partially formed plastic. Atmospheric pressure will press the plastic against the contours of the plug. Note Fig. 15-38 where the vacuum drawn under the plug has forced the plastic against it.
8. *Allow to cool.*
9. *Remove the formed part.*

Fig. 15-35. Step 7 — Forming (Di-Acro)

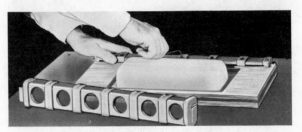

Fig. 15-36. Step 9 — Removing Formed Part from Yoke (Di-Acro)

Fig. 15-37. Unit 15, Step 6 — Partially Forming by Mechanical Means

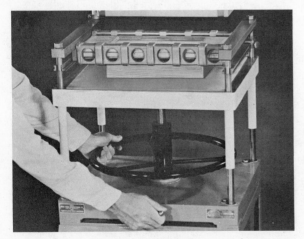

Fig. 15-34. Step 6 — Making the Vacuum Seal (Di-Acro)

Fig. 15-38. Step 7 — Vacuum Applied

Fig. 15-39. Unit 16, Step 2 — Mounting the Plastic in Forms (Di-Acro)

Fig. 15-40. Step 3 — Mounted Plastic Positioned over Pressure Head (Di-Acro)

Fig. 15-41. Step 5 — Regulating the Air Pressure (Di-Acro)

UNIT 16
HOW TO FREE-BLOW

1. *Cut plastic.* An allowance of ½ inch outside the final trim line is usually sufficient.
2. *Mount the plastic under the hole in the yoke.* See Fig. 15-39. It is often better to mount the plastic between the top yoke (with the proper hole in it) and a baffle plate which diffuses the air as it forms the plastic.
3. *Position the mounted plastic over the source of pressure,* Fig. 15-40.
4. *Heat the plastic.* Very even heat is needed in free blowing to assure a symmetrical shape.
5. *Blow to shape.* Regulate amount of air pressure to blow the part to the desired height as shown in Fig. 15-41.
6. *Cool the plastic.* Continue holding pressure until the part will hold its shape. Note Fig. 15-42.
7. *Remove the formed part,* Fig. 15-43.

Fig. 15-42. Step 6 — Cooling the Part with Pressure Maintained (Di-Acro)

Fig. 15-43 Step 7 — Removing Formed Part from the Yoke (Di-Acro)

UNIT 17
HOW TO BLOW-FORM INTO MOLD

1. *Cut the plastic.* An allowance of approximately ½ inch outside the final trim line is usually sufficient. Since the plastic is not mounted in a frame, more than this amount may be needed on large pieces.

2. *Mount mold in upper frame of press and set stops.* See Fig. 15-44.

3. *Place plastic directly on platen under mold.* See Fig. 15-45.

4. *Heat plastic.* Slide mold out of position and heat plastic with heater panel.

5. *Move mold back into position against stops and raise platen to seal plastic and mold,* Fig. 15-46.

6. *Blow to shape by blowing compressed air against plastic.*

7. *Allow to cool.*

8. *Remove formed part.* Remove mold from press and pull formed part from it. See Fig. 15-47.

Fig. 15-45. Step 2 — Positioning Mounted Mold over Pressure Head

Fig. 15-46. Step 5 — Mold Sealed against Heated Plastic

Fig. 15-44. Unit 17, Step 2 — Mounting Mold in Channel Clamps

Fig. 15-47. Step 8 — The Formed Part

Study Questions

1. Describe the basic shapes that can be produced by thermoforming. What limitations are there to forms to be produced by this process?
2. What determines the thickness of the sheet to be formed?
3. How is sheet thickness related to fineness of detail desired on its surface?
4. How are large flat areas strengthened in thermoformed objects?
5. What are six variations of thermoforming? What outstanding shape characteristic can be obtained by each?
6. What factors must be considered in choosing the type of tooling to use?
7. How do you decide whether to use a mold, a plug, or a matched plug and mold?
8. How can you calculate the total force that will be exerted on the plastic and the mold when thermoforming by blowing or with a vacuum.
9. For what reason is the plug often made instead of the mold?
10. How is the mold or plug designed to make it easier to remove formed parts?
11. What materials are often used for tool making for experimental work?
12. What parts of the tooling are most important in determining the shape and quality of a part made by mechanical forming with plug and yoke?
13. How is the size of the plug determined in matched-plug-and-mold forming?
14. What is the major reason for putting as much draft as possible on the vertical walls of a mold for forming with vacuum?
15. Where is the vacuum created in vacuum-forming plastic with a mold?
16. Generally, where are vacuum holes placed in a vacuum-forming mold? How large should they be to cause a minimum of markoff?
17. Where is the vacuum created in vacuum-forming plastic with a plug?
18. How can reverse curves and undercuts be obtained in blow-forming plastic with a mold?
19. Why are holes needed in blow-forming plastic with a mold?
20. How is free-blowing different from the other methods of thermoforming? How is the resulting shape different? Why is a baffling of the air often desirable?
21. Which group of plastics is used for thermoforming? Why?
22. Which individual plastics are used with this process? Which one is most common?
23. What are the elements of thermoforming equipment?
24. What are some means of clamping a sheet of plastic for heating?
25. What heating devices are common for thermoforming?

CHAPTER SIXTEEN

injection-molding thermoplastics

Of the large number of thermoplastics products on the market today probably more are made by injection molding than by any other process. In industry, it is a high-speed, high-volume production process; laboratory and developmental work can readily be done with small laboratory equipment.

Product Design

One of the first problems faced by the designer of injection molded products is the location of the *parting line*. Injection molds are generally made in two parts; this means that during molding a small amount of plastic can "flash" between the halves. If the mold halves fit very tightly no more than a line will be visible. This is called the parting line.

On articles with a flat back where only one half of the mold contains the cavity, the parting line will be along the arris formed by the flat back and the sides of the article. This produces a sharp arris which might have to be softened after molding. On objects with contours on both sides, the parting line will be at the plane of greatest dimension. See Fig. 16-1 for a comparison of the parting lines.

The design of the article should be such that the parting line is easily polished or is unobtrusive. Proper placement of the parting line can enhance the design. Fig. 16-2 shows how a design for a knob can be modified to take advantage of the parting line.

Injection molded parts must be devoid of undercuts. Reverse tapers lock the part to the mold. At least one-half degree of draft should be provided on all wall sections, and where possible, more draft is desirable.

Objects of variable wall thickness and with different contours on the two sides are readily

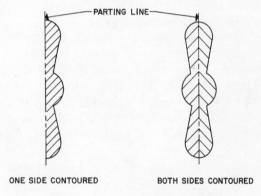

Fig. 16-1. Comparison of Parting Lines on Single- and Double-Contoured Parts

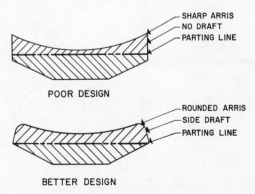

Fig. 16-2. Design of Parting Line for Injection Molding

produced by this process. Any changes in wall thickness should be gradual. Even long thin projections are practical if the plastic used in molding is sufficiently tough.

Large, flat, thin sections are generally undesirable. If it is necessary to injection-mold such a shape, ribs or reinforcing curves should be molded in. All radii and fillets should be as large as possible.

One of the important design advantages of injection molding is that extremely fine detail can be readily molded into the surface of the part since the plastic is in liquid form and under great pressure in this process. For example, fine facial features in toy figurines are easy to obtain by this process.

Tool Design

A mold used in injection molding contains a number of components, each of which serves a particular function. Each component is described and illustrated in this section. Fig. 16-3 shows the various components.

Sprue

The term *sprue* has two meanings. It refers to the inlet through which the plastic is injected to the mold cavity and it is also used to designate the piece of hardened plastic that

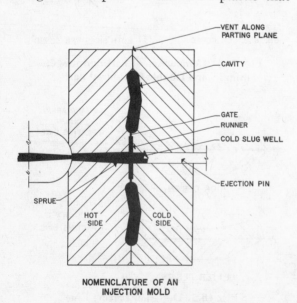

NOMENCLATURE OF AN
INJECTION MOLD

Fig. 16-3. Parts of an Injection Mold

remains in this inlet at the conclusion of the molding cycle. In tool design, the craftsman is concerned with the sprue as an inlet to the cavity.

Most injection molding machines have a nozzle screwed to the end of the injection cylinder. A *sprue bushing* is connected to this nozzle and some part of the mold. The sprue, or hole in the bushing, is tapered two to six degrees with the smaller end nearer the nozzle. The small end of the sprue is usually $\frac{5}{32}$ inch to $\frac{9}{16}$ inch in diameter, depending upon the amount of plastic to be injected.

Cold-Slug Well

The first part of the plastic to be forced into the mold is cool and does not flow well. A *cold-slug well* opposite the sprue traps this cold plastic which is called a cold slug. It serves to anchor the part to the mold as it is opened at the end of the cycle.

The cold-slug well should be at least as large in diameter as the large end of the sprue. It is generally undercut with a slight taper to serve as an anchor.

Runners

It is generally not desirable to inject the plastic directly into the mold cavity. The flow of plastic from the machine is first to the cold slug well and then through grooves called *runners* toward the mold cavities. The *plastic* that solidifies in these grooves is also called a runner. The cross-sectional shape of the runners may be round, half-round, or trapezoidal. The size of the runners depends upon the amount of plastic to be injected.

Gates

The runners are reduced in size where they enter the mold cavities. This entrance is called a *gate;* the small piece of plastic that solidifies at this point is also called a gate. A gate should be located at the thickest part of the molded piece because it is easier to fill a thin section from a thick one. The diameter of the gate should be as small as possible because it is at this point that the excess plastic in the form of runners and cold slugs is separated from the plastic part. Small gates are easier to break off and polish after cooling.

Vents

As the plastic enters the mold cavities some provision must be made for the escape of trapped air and gases. Small grooves, called *vents*, are placed along the parting line. They should be only about .005 inch deep and .125 inch wide. Larger vents are likely to allow the plastic to creep out of the cavity in the form of flash and will increase the problem of polishing the finished part.

Ejection Devices

Some means of forcing the molded part from the mold at the end of the cycle is needed. Very flat smooth parts may be easy to eject, while deep drawn, rough surfaced parts may be difficult. Commonly, some type of *ejection pin* is built into the mold. As the mold opens, the pin moves forward, pushing the part from the cavity. The surface of the pin should be as large as possible, and the pin should fit well in the mold to avoid flash. Several pins may be needed in complex molds.

Since the cold-slug well is slightly undercut, some force, usually a pin placed at its bottom, is required to remove the cold slug. Pins may be placed at the bottom of other deep depressions or places where the part is likely to resist removal. Ejection pins will usually leave some mark on the part and should be placed where this markoff is not objectionable.

Mold Cavities

An injection mold is usually in two parts, the hot side and the cold side. The hot side is nearer the injection nozzle and is so called because it becomes warm with heat transferred from the injection cylinder. The cold side, being away from the nozzle and thus remaining cooler during operation, solidifies the plastic. It is often cored out for circulating cold water.

The cavities which shape the molded article are cut into one or both of the mold halves. If a flat-backed article is to be made, the cavity is cut only into the cold side. If an article with contours on both sides is to be made, it is necessary to cut cavities into both halves.

Mold Materials

Molds for injection molding are commonly made from hardened steel. For prototype and experimental work, molds made from low-melting metal alloys and cast epoxy plastics are also used. Procedures for making molds from the latter two materials are outlined in this section.

Materials Used

In theory, any thermoplastic can be injection molded. Common materials processed in this manner are acrylics, cellulosics, nylon, vinyl, polypropylene, fluorocarbons, acetals, polystyrene, and polyethylene.

In most discussions of the use of various plastics for injection molding, general instructions are given that apply to all materials except nylon. The problems that arise in molding *nylon* stem largely from its melting properties. This plastic has a very sharp softening point and becomes extremely fluid when it does melt. Most other materials soften more gradually and have higher viscosities in their melted form. In molding nylon, molds must be very tight to prevent excessive flashing of the plastic and some provision must be made to shut off the nozzle when the mold is opened. Close control of the temperature of the heating cylinder is necessary and the material must be very carefully dried before melting.

Polystyrene is one of the easier materials to injection mold. Since it has some tendency to "hang up" in the mold, at least two degrees of draft must be provided on all mold walls to facilitate its release.

Vinyls decompose with prolonged exposure to high temperatures and the decomposed plastic may have a corrosive effect on the heating cylinder. Vinyls have a great affinity for water and must be carefully dried before molding.

Cellulosics mold well and easily. However, they have a very high water absorption ratio, and must be dried just prior to being molded.

Acrylics present few special problems in injection molding.

ABS plastics are somewhat more sensitive to heat than are either acrylics or styrenes.

Polyethylene is one of the most commonly used materials in injection molding. It has a tendency to stick to the walls of the heating cylinder, but higher nozzle temperatures help to correct this.

Equipment

With many processes in plastics, experimental work can be done with laboratory constructed equipment or with some kind of standard press modified for use. This is generally not practical with injection molding.

There are many different brands of injection molding equipment on the market. Though they have different individual features, all of them have two basic units: a mechanism which supports, opens, and closes the mold, and some means of melting the plastic and injecting it into the mold.

On most presses the components are oriented horizontally, but on some they are vertical.

Versatility is more important in a laboratory machine than in a production machine. In selecting a model for experimental purposes, it is best to get one on which it is easy to change molds and nozzles for different jobs with different materials. With some presses, only mold inserts are changed; with others a number of components must be disassembled to replace a mold.

The following specifications should be considered with any injection molding machine: capacity in ounces of plastic that can be injected with one plunger stroke, the locking force in tons supplied by the mold-clamping device, the maximum opening possible in the mold area, the maximum mold area available, the length of the clamping stroke, the length of the plunger stroke, the maximum plunger pressure, and the provision for varying the temperature of the heating cylinder.

For laboratory work, a manual or semi-automatic machine is satisfactory. With a manually operated machine the operator must move hand levers to close the mold, inject the plastic, and open the mold. With a semi-automatic machine the operator starts the cycle by closing the mold. Mechanisms in the machine then inject the plastic, open the mold, and return to position for the next cycle.

Procedures

This section will deal with the modifications of standard tooling procedures to adapt them to injection molding of thermoplastics and with the actual injection-molding operation with laboratory type equipment.

The general procedures for mold making are outlined in the section, "Tooling Techniques and Procedures." Two tooling materials are particularly suited to experimental work in injection molding, cast epoxy plastics and low-melting metals. Because the basic steps for making such molds are described in the tooling section, discussion here will be limited to the adaptations of these processes for injection molding.

The particular piece of injection molding equipment to be used will control the specifics of the mold to be made. Two factors about the equipment must be considered: (1) the

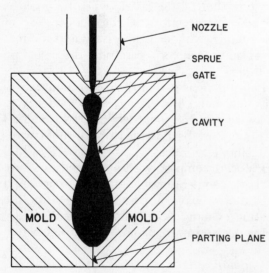

Fig. 16-4. **Injection along Parting Line of Mold**

NOZZLE

SPRUE

GATE

CAVITY

MOLD

MOLD

PARTING PLANE

point at which the plastic is injected into the mold, and (2) the means by which the mold is held in the press and clamped during injection.

(1) *Point of injection.* On many machines the sprue is placed in the hot side of the mold, and the plastic is injected at right angles to the parting plane as shown in the previous Fig. 16-3. On the laboratory press illustrated here the sprue is placed in the parting plane so that the material is injected along it as shown in Fig. 16-4.

(2) *Holding and clamping the mold.* On many machines, the molds are held in chases which are mounted on guide rods or ways. The hot side of the mold is usually stationary and fastened to the nozzle. The cold side moves along the guide rods and is forced against the hot side by some type of clamping device which holds it in place during injection. By reversing the action of the clamping device, the mold is opened and the part ejected.

On the laboratory press illustrated here, the two mold halves are simply held in a vise at the base of the machine and under the nozzle. This type of mechanism is not convenient for production work but is much easier to set up and modify for experimentation.

After the mold has been cast or sprayed, it is necessary to add the sprue, cold-slug well, vents, and runner and gating system. These depressions can be milled or filed with rotary or needle files. In experimental work, it is usually better to begin by making runners, vents, and gates smaller than will probably be needed eventually. Trials with injection will indicate how they should be modified. The previous section on tool design gives general rules for size and location of these parts.

In cases where the mold is mounted in a chase, a modification of the mold-making procedure may be needed. Figs. 16-5 through 16-8 show the construction of a sprayed metal mold for making a spring clothes pin. The metal is contained in a chase and tubes are cast in place to allow circulating a coolant through the mold during operation.

Fig. 16-5. Patterns Mounted on Mold Backing
They are now ready for spraying of low-melting metal. (Cerro)

Fig. 16-6. Spraying the Metal
Note the chase surrounding the pattern. (Cerro)

Fig. 16-7. Pouring the Backing of Metal
Note the tubes poured in place. (Cerro)

Fig. 16-8. The Finished Mold (Cerro)

In the case where the mold is held in a vise, it is important that the outsides of the mold are true and parallel so that the vise can exert even pressure with no danger of cracking the mold or allowing it to open during injection. If the cast or sprayed mold is not true, it should be machined or hand filed.

UNIT 18
HOW TO INJECTION-MOLD THERMOPLASTICS

Injection molding presses vary in how the mold is clamped and how the plastic is injected. The procedure given here is generally for the simple laboratory press illustrated in Fig. 16-9. It is a one-quarter ounce machine with controlled electric heating and a pneumatic injection cylinder. The mold is simply two rectangular blocks clamped in a cam lock vise. The plastic is injected along the parting plane of the mold. The nozzle is not connected to the mold and a valve prevents the plastic from flowing until the forward movement of the plunger engages the nozzle to the mold.

1. *Set up the press.* Spray mold release in the mold cavity. Mount the molds in the proper position so that the nozzle is lined up with the sprue as shown in Fig. 16-10.
2. *Load the hopper with plastic.*
3. *Transfer the plastic to the heating cylinder.* A metering device allows the operator to fill the heating cylinder with plastic. The plastic should not overflow the cylinder because it tends to come up around the plunger during molding.
4. *Heat the plastic.* Set the heat control to provide the proper temperature. Some experimentation may be needed to achieve the proper temperature. Most materials inject well at 325° to 425° F.

Fig. 16-9. Laboratory Injection Press with Cast Epoxy Molds used in Unit 18

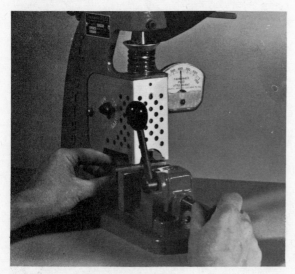
Fig. 16-10. Unit 18, Step 1 — Locking the Mold in Place

Fig. 16-11. Step 5 — Injecting the Plastic

5. *Inject the plastic.* Move the plunger control forward. This will first cause the plunger to move down, then push the nozzle against the mold, and inject the plastic. Hold the plunger down until the mold is filled. When plastic flashes around the nozzle, the mold is probably filled. See Fig. 16-11.

6. *Allow to cool.* In this machine there is no provision for cooling the mold with circulating water. If the cycle is repeated many times the mold may become warm and the plastic will not solidify. In this case, remove the mold and place it in cold water; then dry it carefully.

7. *Open the mold and eject the part.* With this machine, it is generally easier to remove the molds from the vise to eject the part. See Figs. 16-12 and 16-13. Figs. 16-14 — 16-16 show a different type of injection molding operation. The mold is made of sprayed metal and has cooling tubes cast in place. Injection is at right angles to the parting plane so that a sprue, runners, cold-slug well, and gates are part of the molding.

Fig. 16-14. **Sprayed Injection Mold Mounted with Cooling Tubes in Place** (Cerro)
Note the runner and gate system in the center.

Fig. 16-15. **Sprayed Mold in Injection Press** (Cerro)

Fig. 16-12. **Step 7 — The Molds Removed**

Fig. 16-13. **Step 7 — Sprue on Mold Part**

Fig. 16-16. **Injection Molded Part with Sprue, Cold Slug, Runners, and Gate Attached** (Cerro)

Study Questions

1. What is flash? What is a parting line and how is it related to flash?
2. Generally, where is the parting line on an injection-molded article?
3. Why must undercuts be avoided in injection-molded articles?
4. What problems are presented in molding articles with variable wall thicknesses?
5. Is fine detail on the surface of the molded article practical in injection molding? Explain.
6. What are two meanings of the term, "sprue?"
7. Describe a cold-slug well and its purpose.
8. What are runners and what is their purpose?
9. What is a gate? What function does it serve? What size should it be in relation to the runners?
10. Why is venting necessary to an injection mold? Where is it placed?
11. What means are used to remove parts from an injection mold?
12. What are the "hot side" and the "cold side" of the mold and why are they so called?
13. What materials are suitable to make injection molds? Which is best for production work?
14. What class of plastics is used with injection molding? Why?
15. Name several individual plastics that are injection molded. What is the special problem in molding nylon?
16. What are the basic components of any injection-molding machine?
17. What factors must be specified in describing an injection-molding press?
18. What two mold materials are especially suitable for injection molds for experimental work? Why?
19. What two equipment factors must be taken into account in designing molds for injection molding?

CHAPTER SEVENTEEN

compression-molding thermosets

The most common method for producing articles from *thermosetting* plastics is compression molding. Its advantage for laboratory work is that it can make use of almost any type of press capable of producing from three to fifty tons of force. Because of the extreme force needed to compression-mold, it is necessary to use very strong materials for molds.

Product Design

After the functional aspects of a product have been taken into account, the designer must be concerned with the design restrictions that are imposed by the molding technique to be used. The following sections discuss the basic design restrictions imposed by compression molding.

Dimensional Change

Molded articles will not retain the exact size and shape they possess immediately upon removal from the mold. Generally, they will shrink; uneven shrinkage will cause warpage. Factors affecting the degree of dimensional change are the plastic used, the temperature drop that takes place in cooling, and the amount that the plastic has been compressed during molding.

The designer must attempt to reduce the amount of shrinkage that takes place and to minimize its effects on the finished product.

There are several things the designer should do to reduce shrinkage and warpage. Wall thickness should be kept uniform throughout the article. As a part is removed from the mold, thin sections will cool more rapidly than thick sections with a possibility of warpage. If changes in thickness are necessary they should be made gradually. When thick and thin sections must be joined, it should be done with as large a fillet as possible. Large surfaces should be contoured slightly and reinforced with ribs if at all possible in the design.

Flash

By the nature of the process there must be some type of joint in the mold. In compression molding, the joint occurs where the mold plunger and the cavity meet. During molding, the molten plastic will flow into this joint, producing *flash*, an extra fin. After molding, flash must be removed and the surface polished. The line usually remaining on the article where the flash was removed is called a flash line.

The designer's problem is to locate the flash line so that it is easy to remove without marring the remaining surface and so that it enhances the design or at least does not detract from it. Fig. 17-1 shows sample flash lines on a product.

Undercuts

An important fact to consider in any design for a molded article is that it must be removed from the mold. Two factors must be considered in this regard, undercuts and draft.

Undercuts may be either external or internal. External undercuts are depressions on the outside of the article and internal undercuts are those on the inside. Fig. 17-2 shows the two types. It is possible to produce external undercuts, although with increased mold cost, but the production of internal undercuts is extremely impractical. If the design necessitates the use of external undercuts they can be molded with a two-piece cavity liner that is held together with a chase. Part removal requires that the entire mold be disassembled each time and an additional flash line is created. To produce internal undercuts it would be necessary to somehow collapse the mold plunger in order to remove the molded part.

Even where there are no undercuts on the surface of the article, surface tension is created which, coupled with slight shrinkage, can make removal from the mold very difficult. For this reason, it is desirable to taper the sides of the object slightly; this taper is called *draft*. With shallower parts less than one degree of draft is necessary for most plastics, while with deep-drawn articles three to four degrees may be needed. In all cases, the designer should allow as much draft as is consistent with the appearance and function of the article.

Ribs

The strength of an article can be increased by an increase in wall thickness. This adds bulk to the product and may not be consistent with the function and appearance desired. A preferable solution is often to mold ribs into the surfaces. Though generalizations for all situations are difficult, one common rule for rib dimensions is as follows: the thickness of the rib should be about half the thickness of the wall to which it is joined and the height of the rib should be about one and one-half the wall thickness to which it is joined. The edges of the ribs should be rounded and the line at which they join the wall should be generously *filleted* (a rounded inside corner).

Wall Thickness

In addition to the function and the appearance of the article, wall thickness will be dictated by the ease of molding and the strength needed during processing. The most desirable design is one that allows the plastic to flow freely to all recesses of the mold. Table 19 lists some suggested wall thicknesses for common molding compounds.

Radii and Fillets

Radii and fillets at points where the walls of an object change direction serve to distribute stresses, facilitate plastic flow, and generally make mold construction easier. Breaks commonly occur at sharp arrises rather than at rounded or filleted ones. A radius of one-quarter to three-quarters of the thickness of the wall section is recommended.

Molded articles with rounded arrises and corners are usually more attractive and the durability of the edges is increased.

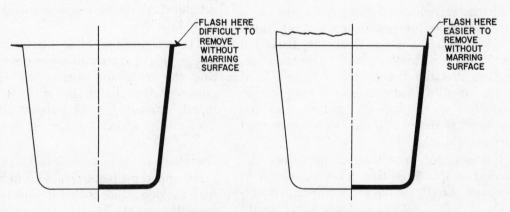

Fig. 17-1. Flash Locations in Molded Articles

TABLE 19
WALL THICKNESSES FOR MOLDED ARTICLES

Plastic	Minimum	For Small Articles	Average for Most	Large to Maximum
Phenolics				
General purpose, or flock filled	.050″	.062″	.125″	.187 to 1.000
Fabric filled	.062	.125	.187	.187 to .375
Mineral filled	.125	.125	.187	.200 to 1.000
Alkyds				
Glass filled	.040	.093	.125	.187 to .500
Mineral filled	.040	.125	.187	.187 to .375
Ureas and Melamines				
Cellulose filled	.035	.062	.100	.125 to .187
Fabric filled	.050	.125	.125	.125 to .187
Mineral filled	.040	.093	.187	.187 to .375

From **Plastics Engineering Handbook**, Third Edition, 1960.

Surface

The surface of a compression-molded article can assume any texture or luster desired. While very smooth and lustrous surfaces (which are produced by highly polished mold surfaces) are easier to remove from the mold, textured surfaces tend to hide blemishes and imperfections.

Tool Design

Types of Molds

There are at least four types of molds and many special adaptations of each. The most common basic types are flash, fully positive, semi-positive, and landed positive. While some parts could be molded in any of the types of molds, each type is especially suited to given shapes.

Flash Molds: In a flash mold there is no telescoping action between the two parts. More plastic than is required for the finished part is placed in the mold cavity. As the mold closes it starts to compress the plastic. The excess plastic flows or flashes out of the recess, blocking the remaining plastic as the mold fully closes and compresses it to its final size and shape.

This type of mold is the easiest to make and is adaptable to molding thin shapes which are quite flat. Less pressure is exerted on the plastic because it is not fully confined; the result is a less dense molding than with other

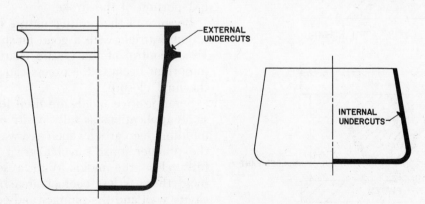

Fig. 17-2. External and Internal Undercuts on Molded Articles

mold types. It is not very satisfactory for use with plastics that have a high *bulk factor* because the uncompressed plastic must be heaped above the top of the mold cavity and may spread out of the mold very easily before full compression is reached.

In constructing a flash mold, the cavity is made the exact size and shape of the desired part. The top force is shaped exactly like the top surface required on the parts. Fig. 17-3 shows a flash mold.

Fully Positive Molds: As the name implies, there is complete and positive contact with all portions of the plastic throughout the entire mold cycle. The mold cavity is a well much deeper than the height of the part to be molded with a plunger that telescopes within the cavity. The amount of space remaining between the bottom of the plunger and the bottom of the cavity when the mold is fully closed determines the thickness of the part.

In constructing the fully positive mold, the depth of the cavity must take into account the bulk factor of the plastic molding compound. The bulk factor is the ratio of the volume of the molding compound to the volume of the molded part. The cavity must allow for the amount of plastic needed plus an additional allowance to insure that the plunger will trap all of the material.

With this type of mold, maximum pressure is exerted on the plastic because none can escape. The result is a very dense part. It is essential that exactly the proper amount of plastic be loaded into the mold. If too much is inserted the mold cannot be fully closed. If too little is inserted, the part will not be completely filled nor be of the proper density. An extremely close fit is required between the cavity and the plunger. There is a danger in this type of mold of scoring the cavity wall if plastic gets between it and the side of the plunger.

Fully positive molds are suited to molding heavy sections or products where maximum density is required. Articles with a sharp arris are readily molded this way. Positive molds are advantageous for materials with large bulk factors and with quick setting materials where leakage of the flowing plastic is not a problem.

Fig. 17-4 shows a fully positive mold.

Semi-positive molds: The semi-positive mold exhibits some characteristics of the flash mold and some of the fully positive mold. There is a telescoping action between the cavity and the plunger, but the plastic is allowed to flash until the last portion of the downward stroke. The cavity is so constructed that it and the plunger fit closely only for the last portion of the stroke.

Because of the positive nature of this mold a dense article with a good finish is possible. Exact control of the plastic charge is not as important because the excess can flash before the final closure.

Semi-positive molds are used for much the same applications as fully positive molds. For molding deep articles such as a water tumbler, the plunger must travel a great distance to fully close the mold. With a semi-positive mold there is less contact area between the cavity wall and the plunger and consequently less chance of scoring the cavity wall during

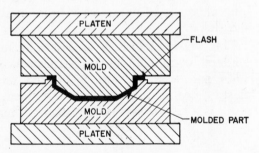

Fig. 17-3. A Flash Mold

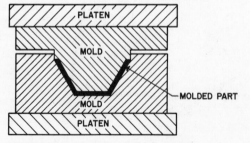

Fig. 17-4. A Fully Positive Mold

molding. Also, machining a close fit is much less difficult with a semi-positive mold. Fig. 17-5 shows a typical semi-positive mold.

Landed positive molds. The landed positive mold is a combination mold in the sense that it is like a flash mold at the bottom of the cavity of a fully positive mold. All of the plastic is contained in a cavity throughout the cycle. The plunger has a flat rim, or *land*, around its outside face that fits against another land in the mold cavity. As the plunger starts its stroke and begins compressing the material, it is allowed to flash over the lands until final closure completely compresses the plastic.

As with the fully positive mold, the proper amount of plastic must be loaded into the cavity because there is no place for the excess to go. High density and good surface finish are produced in this process because of the positive nature of the molding.

The particular use of this mold in place of a common fully positive mold is for molding shapes with a rounded edge on top. If a fully positive mold is used for this shape, the plunger must have a thin sharp arris on the end. With a landed positive mold this shape is produced by a round bottom groove in the plunger. A plunger of this design will hold up much longer in use which is especially important when the mold is made from soft materials such as brass or casting plastics.

Fig. 17-6 shows a typical landed positive mold.

Ejection Devices

Very flat and smoothly shaped molded articles may be rather easily pulled from the mold. With articles of much depth or with textured surfaces, some means of ejection from the mold is required. With some molding, the part sticks to the plunger and with others to the cavity. The ejection device is commonly some type of pin that moves against deep parts of the mold as the plunger and cavity are separated. Exact size and location must be determined by the individual part to be ejected.

Mold Materials

Production molds are usually made from highly polished, hardened steel because they are subjected to tremendous forces, sustained temperatures of 300° to 400° F., and the abrasive effects of molding compounds. For short run and experimental work, softer metals such as mild steel, brass, and aluminum can be used. The pictures in Unit 19, *How to Compression-Mold,* show a cast aluminum mold used with glass-filled polyester premix. Other mold materials such as wood, plaster, and plastics are generally not hard enough or strong enough to resist the rigors of compression molding.

Standard mold bases, ready for the machining of mold cavities, are available and simplify the problems of machining matched surfaces and placing line-up bushings and pins. Fig. 17-7 shows a sample mold base.

Materials Used

Any plastic can be compression molded. However, since thermoplastics harden by

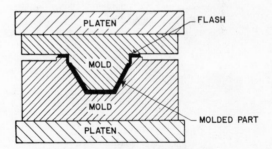

Fig. 17-5. A Semi-Positive Mold

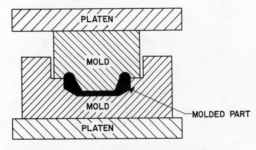

Fig. 17-6. A Landed Positive Mold

Fig. 17-7. A Standard Mold Base (Detroit Mold)

Fig. 17-8. A 50-Ton Compression Molding Press
for Laboratory Use   (Dake)

cooling and the entire mold is heated during the compression molding cycle, it is usually impractical to compression-mold thermoplastics because of the time consumed in heating and cooling the mold for each cycle. In laboratory or experimental work, however, thermoplastics may be processed in this manner.

Molding compounds are generally supplied as powders or pellets. For production, the powder is usually compressed into discs of exactly the proper amount for a given operation. The use of these discs, or *preforms* as they are called, eliminates the time-consuming weighing of materials for each charge. This partial compressing of the material also reduces the size of the loading well which is needed in the mold. Some molding compounds are supplied as premixes — mixtures of polyester resin and glass fibers are common. Under heat and pressure in the mold the putty-like premix liquifies and flows, producing a glass-reinforced molding.

The basic material of the compression molding industry is the family of phenolics. Most compression-molding procedures are described in terms of phenolics with exceptions listed for other thermosets.

Equipment

Compression molding requires some means of forcing the mold together and some method of heating the plastic and mold.

The most common method of compressing the mold is with some type of two-platen press. The platens should have some arrangement for fastening the mold halves to them to facilitate opening and closing the mold. Presses are rated according to the total force in tons that they will apply. Compression molding requires from 1000 to 3000 pounds per square inch of molding area. The capacity of the press needed can be determined from the mold area involved. Laboratory presses are usually in the five- to fifty-ton capacity range, and production presses exert pressures as high as 4000 tons or more. A laboratory

50-ton compression molding press is illustrated in Fig. 17-8.

Presses are closed hydraulically, mechanically, or pneumatically. Speed of closure is important; slow-curing plastics require a slow-closing press, while faster curing materials must be compressed more rapidly. A general purpose press should have arrangements for varying the closing speed.

Many presses open by gravity; that is, when the closing force is released, the weight of the platen, mold half, and ram causes the press to open. With parts that are difficult to eject it may be necessary to have a press with double action which opens as well as closes the press.

Since the mold must be kept at a constant temperature of 300° to 400° F. it is desirable that the press have heated platens. Some molds are cored and heating devices are inserted directly in them. Electrical heat is most convenient for laboratory presses, but steam is also used.

Preheating the plastic before placing it into the mold speeds up the molding process and also dries the plastic, preventing the formation of steam pockets. For laboratory work, an oven is satisfactory, but high-frequency electronic heaters are used for production.

When selecting a press the following specifications should be considered: pressing capacity in tons, maximum mold dimensions allowable, maximum molding stroke, maximum opening between platens, maximum and minimum closing speed, maximum and minimum pressing speed, maximum opening speed, and type of system for applying pressure.

Procedures

This section will deal with the modifications of standard tooling procedures to adapt them to compression molding of thermosets. It also outlines the actual compression-molding operation using laboratory-type equipment.

Molding Factors

To achieve the best results in molding requires the proper combination of a series of interdependent factors. Some experimentation will be necessary to determine the best combination. Start with the resin supplier's recommendations. The factors that must be considered are mold temperature, molding pressure, and curing time.

Molding Temperature: Generally, the mold temperature ranges from 270° to 380° F. Parts having very thin sections may be molded at temperatures as high as 400° F. The filler included in the molding compound affects mold temperature. Since mineral-filled compounds are better conductors of heat, they should be molded at lower temperatures than materials filled with wood flour or cellulose.

In experimental work especially, it is desirable to use as low a mold temperature as possible. With thermosets, the higher the temperature, the faster the material will set. If the temperature is too high, thin sections might solidify before the material has a chance to flow to all recesses of the cavity. This is particularly a problem with a hand-operated press where the closing time may be in excess of 15 to 30 seconds. Excessively high temperatures can also cause surface hardening (*case hardening*) with undercured cores.

Molding Pressures: In general, holding pressures are specified for both conventional and low-pressure phenolics. Preheating the molding compound reduces the pressure required. Conventional phenolics require a minimum of 3000 pounds per square inch of mold area without preheating and as little as 1000 psi with efficient high-frequency preheating. Low-pressure phenolics, properly preheated, can be molded with as little as 250 psi. The speed with which the press is closed and the depth of the molded article also affect pressures. Table 20 gives suggested molding pressures.

Curing Time: A period of time ranging from 15 seconds to five minutes may be required to allow the plastic to undergo the chemical change required for hardening. This is known as the curing time.

TABLE 20

PRESSURE FOR COMPRESSION MOLDING

Depth of Molding (inches)	Conventional Phenolic		Low-Pressure Phenolic	
	Preheated	Not Preheated	Preheated	Not Preheated
0–.75	1000– 2000	3000	350	1000
1.50	1250– 2500	3700	450	1250
2	1500– 3000	4400	550	1500
3	1750– 3500	5100	650	1750
4	2000– 4000	5800	750	2000
5	2250– 4500	**	850	***
6	2500– 5000	**	950	***
7	2750– 5500	**	1050	***
8	3000– 6000	**	1150	***
9	3250– 6000	**	1250	***
10	3500– 7000	**	1350	***
12	4000– 8000	**	1450	***
14	4500– 9000	**	1550	***
16	5000–10000	**	1650	***

From **Plastics Engineering Handbook,** Third Edition, 1960.
   **Add 700 psi for each additional inch of depth; but beyond 4″ it is desirable and beyond 12″ it is necessary to preheat.
***add 250 psi for each additional inch of depth ; but beyond 4″ it is desirable and beyond 12″ it is necessary to preheat.
   Pressures given in pounds per square inch. To determine necessary molding pressure, multiply by the area in square inches of the plunger-half of the mold.

Fig. 17-9. Unit 19, Step 1 — Molds Mounted in Compression Molding Press

Fig. 17-10. Step 7 — Placing Molding Compound in the Cavity

UNIT 19
HOW TO COMPRESSION-MOLD THERMOSETS

The following is only a generalized procedure. The equipment used, the design of the mold, and the plastic to be molded will affect the details of the process.

1. *Set up the mold in the press.* Place the assembled closed mold on the lower platen as shown in Fig. 17-9. Close the press until the platens are tight against the mold. Fasten the plunger-half of the mold to the upper platen and the cavity-half to the lower platen.

2. *Heat the mold.* Bring the mold up to the temperature recommended for molding the given plastic.

3. *Measure the plastic charge.* Determine the volume of the molded part, multiply that by the bulk factor, and add about 10 percent for flash. Some experimenting with the exact quantity will be necessary.

4. *Preheat the plastic charge.* Place the plastic charge in an open, flat pan in an oven at the temperature recommended by the supplier. In some cases this may not be necessary.

5. *Apply a release agent to all parts of the mold.* Very smooth, polished steel molds may not require a release.

6. *Open the mold.* Open the press far enough to allow the plastic to be loaded into the cavity.

7. *Charge the mold.* Place the plastic into the cavity. See Fig. 17-10.

8. *Close the mold.* Observe the speed of closing required for proper material flow, Fig. 17-11.

9. *Breathe the mold.* After the mold has been fully closed for about ten seconds, open it slightly to allow trapped gases to escape. Fully close the mold again. Some materials do not require breathing.

10. *Allow to cure.* Leave the mold fully closed long enough to allow the part to cure. Follow the supplier's instructions for curing time.

11. *Open the mold and eject the part.* See Figs. 17-12 through 17-14.

12. *Clean the mold.* It is extremely important that the mold be carefully cleaned after each cycle. Failure to do so will result in mold damage.

Note the series of pictures in Figs. 17-15 and 17-16, which show the procedure used when the mold is small enough to be removed with the molded part. The fixture used in disassembling the mold holds the bottom cavity in place while the upper portion is removed.

Fig. 17-12. Step 11 — The Press Open
Note the flash on the molded part.

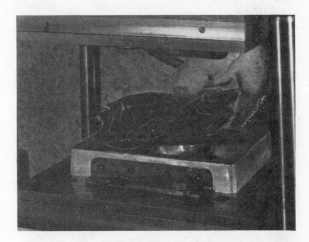
Fig. 17-13. Step 11 — Removing the Part from the Mold

Fig. 17-11. Step 8 — The Press Closed

Fig. 17-14. Step 11 — Molded Part before Trimming Flash

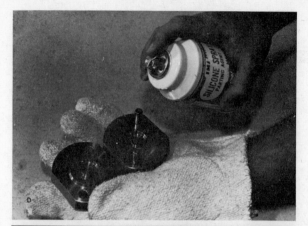

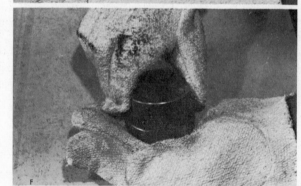

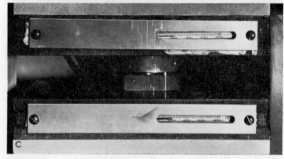

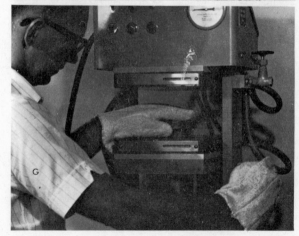

Fig. 17-15. Preparing the Mold

(A) Two halves of flash mold, molded part, and phenolic molding compound. (B) A 25-ton hydraulic laboratory compression press. (C) Mold heating in press. Platen temperature approaching 300° F. (D) Spraying mold release. (E) Charging mold with phenolic compound. (F) Assembling charged mold. (G) Placing mold into press.

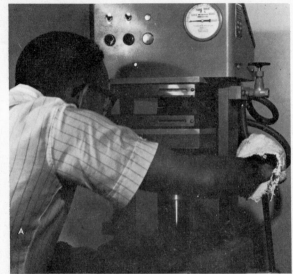

Fig. 17-16. Molding

(A) Closing the press. (B) Curing the plastic at a pressure of approximately 9,000 psi. (C) After press is opened, removing the mold and cured plastic. (D) Disassembling the mold by using a fixture. (E) Removing the molded part. (F) The mold and molded part with flash removed.

Study Questions

1. Generally, what restrictions are imposed on the design of an article by the process of compression molding?
2. What may cause warpage in a compression-molded article?
3. How is shrinkage minimized in a molded article?
4. Where will the flash line be on a compression-molded article?
5. What must the designer consider in locating the flash line?
6. What must be taken into account in design to make sure that the molded article can be readily removed?
7. What are two types of undercuts? Can they be obtained in compression molding?
8. How much draft is needed on the side of a mold?
9. What is the disadvantage of producing strength by increasing wall thickness in a molded article? What is often a better solution?
10. What generalization is used to determine desirable wall thickness?
11. Why are curves desirable where the object changes direction?
12. What is the advantage of designing an object to call for a rough surface?
13. Name four types of compression molds.
14. What is the particular advantage or use of each type?
15. Why is it difficult to use a flash mold with plastics having a large bulk factor?
16. Why is a fully positive mold so named?
17. Why is a very close measuring of plastic so necessary with the fully positive mold?
18. How is the depth of the cavity determined in a fully positive mold?
19. Why is the semi-positive mold used in some cases in preference to the fully positive mold?
20. How does the landed positive mold get its name?
21. What is the special shape that can be readily produced by the landed positive mold?
22. What part of the mold causes the finished part to be removed from the mold?
23. What materials are suitable to make molds in this process? Why are strong hard materials so essential in compression molding?
24. What class of plastics is usually compression molded? Why?
25. In what form is the plastic commonly used in compression molding?
26. What is the most common plastic processed by compression molding?
27. Essentially, what must compression molding equipment be able to do?
28. How are molds heated?
29. What specifications should be considered in selecting a compression molding press?
30. What molding factors must be considered in choosing equipment?
31. What are common molding temperatures? Pressures? Curing times?

CHAPTER EIGHTEEN

molding and casting cellular plastics

A number of plastics are available in expandable form or *foam* as they are often called. This section will be limited to a discussion of two that are of particular importance, *expandable polystyrene* and *rigid polyurethane*. Low-cost products with outstanding insulating qualities, low density, and high moisture resistance can be made with simple molds and processing equipment.

Product Design

Although polystyrene and polyurethane differ in many ways they are similar in general properties. They possess high insulating values, low density, and a resistance to the absorption of water. They exhibit low surface hardness (although this varies with the density), low compressive strength, low tensile strength, and relatively low flexural strength. Polyurethane can be compounded in a flexible form however.

In designing with the material, it is best to avoid long, thin sections. Rounded arrises are preferred to sharp ones. Spherical shapes provide increased strength. Since the weight of the material is low, it is not necessary to make articles hollow or to use thin wall sections. The designer's problem is one of making the object attractive even though it has a massive wall.

In processing it is necessary to provide at least two degrees of draft on all vertical sections and allow no undercuts. A parting line will be slightly visible but no flash need result. Parting lines should be placed so as to add to the design or go unnoticed .

Tool Design

Tools for Expandable Polystyrene

Molds for expandable polystyrene must be able to withstand temperature elevation to 275° F. and sudden cooling to 122° F., pressures up to 50 psi, and the moisture produced by condensing steam. In terms of these requirements there are several factors to keep in mind when constructing molds for this kind of work:

(1) To insure rapid heating and cooling, the walls of the mold should be *as thin as possible*.

(2) Molds should be constructed from materials that *readily conduct heat*.

(3) A *water-resistant material* should be used.

(4) The mold must *resist cracking* caused by constant temperature change.

Cast aluminum molds are commonly used to satisfy these requirements. Sheet metal molds spun from aluminum or copper are also used.

Completely closed molds are required, since the shape of the finished article is produced by containing expanding beads within a cavity. Some means of holding the mold together is needed; for laboratory work,

C-clamps or bolts are satisfactory. Special quick-locking fasteners are available also.

As with any mold, sufficient draft must be provided to allow the molded part to be removed. Usually, two degrees of draft is adequate but if more is possible in the design of the article, removal will be easier.

The parting line should be placed so as to produce no undercuts in either mold half to hamper part removal. In this type of molding no flash is produced but often a slight ridge will be visible at the parting line. The part and mold should be so designed as to take advantage of this ridge. For example, the parting line on the pail shown in Fig. 18-1 is at the rim where it provides a sharp arris and requires no trimming.

Molds must be designed so that they can be filled easily with pre-expanded beads. In some cases, the cavity of the mold can be filled when the mold is open; the other half is then attached. In designs where a long thin wall is to be molded, pressure filling of the assembled mold is necessary. In this case, the bottom of the mold can be drilled and tapped for one or more half-inch pipe plugs. These plugs will leave some markoff on the finished

part and should be placed where such markoff is not objectionable.

All mold surfaces must be as smooth as possible. Though the coarse textured appearance of the material tends to hide imperfections in the molded surface, roughness in the mold may cause difficulty in removing the part.

To allow the steam to pass through the mold and act on the beads, some type of ventilation must be provided in the mold walls. In some cases a number of $\frac{1}{32}$-inch holes can be drilled in the mold. Ordinarily, holes are needed on only one side of the mold, and since they produce small bumps in the finished part, they should be placed on surfaces where such imperfections are not objectionable. Another common ventilating device is a *core vent*, which is a small plug (about ⅜ inch in diameter) with slots cut into it. The core vent is less likely to become clogged with the expanding plastic but leaves more distinct marks on the plastic than do holes in the mold.

Tools for Rigid Polyurethane

Since the process of casting rigid polyurethane does not involve the use of steam, mold making is much simpler than for expandable polystyrene. Some heat is generated by the reaction of the foaming process but it is desirable that this be contained rather than dissipated to speed up the curing process.

For experimental work, cast-plaster molds are very satisfactory. Reinforced-plastic molds are also good and will generally last longer than plaster.

As with molds for expandable polystyrene, those for urethane must be closed. Force is produced by the expanding foam and some means of securely clamping the mold is needed. For experimental work, *C*-clamps or bolts are satisfactory.

Sufficient draft should be provided so that the molded article can be ejected from the mold. Usually two degrees of draft is sufficient. Care must be taken to insure that there are no undercuts to lock the molded article into the cavity.

Fig. 18-1. Top Edge Parting Line on Mold for a Pail of Expanded Polystyrene

The parting line should be placed to eliminate any undercuts. If the mold halves are tightly joined, no flash will result, but there will usually be a slight parting line present on the finished piece.

Vents should be provided in the mold to allow trapped air to escape. A sprue through which to fill the mold should be provided in one mold half.

All mold surfaces should be as smooth as possible. Rough surfaces are likely to cause the material to stick to the mold.

Fig. 18-2 shows a plaster mold for a duck decoy.

Materials Used

Expandable Polystyrene

Expandable polystyrene comes in the form of small hollow spheres about the size of grains of sugar. The beads are filled with a gas. As they are heated, the walls of the beads, being thermoplastic, soften and the gas expands, causing enlargement. The material will expand to as much as sixty times its original volume if unconfined. The density of the finished molding can be controlled by controlling the amount of expansion. Densities as low as one pound per cubic foot are possible with maximum expansion.

Expanded polystyrene exhibits a closed-cell structure, is an excellent thermal and electrical insulator, absorbs almost no water even when submerged, maintains excellent dimensional stability at temperatures up to 185° F., and has chemical resistance similar to styrene in other forms.

Rigid Polyurethane

Urethane foams are generally supplied for experimental work as two liquids. One component contains the *resin* and the other a *catalyst* for the resin and a *propellant* or foaming agent. When the two are mixed in the proper proportions a chemical reaction takes place which causes the material to foam, expand, and harden.

Equipment

Polystyrene Equipment

The equipment for the molding of expandable polystyrene must provide a means of producing steam under pressures of five to thirty-five pounds.

Depending upon the size of the mold used, the *pressure vessel* may be a pipe with both ends closed, a home pressure cooker, or a laboratory autoclave. For laboratory work, the latter is very convenient. Basically, an *autoclave* is a steam pressure vessel similar to a pressure cooker used in the home. While the commercial autoclave is more convenient to operate, any container that will accommodate the mold and contain the necessary steam pressure will suffice. A pressure gauge and a temperature gauge are desirable and some type of pressure-release valve is needed.

In some types of molding no separate pressure vessel is needed. The mold itself serves as the pressure vessel. In this application, a steam line is connected directly to the mold cavity. The source of steam can be a steam generator, a line from the heating system, or a hose from a pressure cooker.

Cooling can be easily done by submerging the mold in cold water. Some equipment provides for circulating cool water through

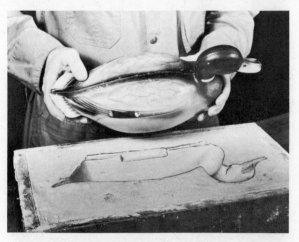

Fig. 18-2. Plaster Mold for Casting Polyurethane Foam

the mold at the conclusion of the steam cycle. Fig. 10-2 in Chapter 10 shows pictures of commercial-type equipment.

Polyurethane Equipment

No special equipment is needed for working with rigid urethane foam. An accurate scale is necessary to weigh the proper proportions of the two components. For small batches, mixing is done by hand; for large quantities, a mechanical mixer is better.

Commercial equipment is available to meter the correct amounts of foam and to spray it in place.

Procedures

Two sets of procedures are outlined. The first explains the thermal molding of expandable polystyrene and the second describes casting with chemically foamed polyurethane.

UNIT 20
HOW TO MOLD
EXPANDABLE POLYSTYRENE

1. *Pre-expand the beads.* The beads should be pre-expanded to the desired density. For experimental work, an easy method is to place the beads in a pan of boiling water. As the heat from the water surrounds the beads, they expand. The expanding beads become lighter and rise to the surface. The largest (and lightest) beads will be on top and can easily be skimmed with a cooking strainer. After pre-expansion, it is desirable to age the beads for about twenty-four hours before use.

2. *Prepare the mold.* Make sure that all steam holes are open. Spray the insides of the mold with a silicone spray mold release every eight or ten times it is used.

Fig. 18-3. Unit 20, Step 3 — Charging the Mold with Expandable Polystyrene Beads

Fig 18-5. Step 4 — Placing Charged Mold into Autoclave

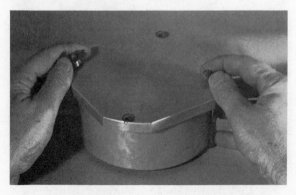

Fig. 18-4. Step 3 — Locking the Mold

3. *Charge the mold.* Fill the mold cavity with pre-expanded beads. On some types of molds the beads can simply be poured into the cavity as illustrated in Fig. 18-3; in more complex molds with long, thin wall sections it is advisable to blow the beads by using air pressure. This can be done with a spray gun like that used for flock with a pressure of 35-50 pounds per square inch. Make sure that the mold is completely filled and that the plugs are securely replaced in the filler holes. See Fig. 18-4.

4. *Expand the beads.* Place the charged mold into the autoclave, Figs. 18-5, 18-6, and raise the steam pressure to the desired amount. Usually a maximum of 35 psi is all that is required, and on many items as little as 10 to 12 psi will be enough. The pressure usually will not

need to be maintained for more than one to five minutes. Experimentation with the proper time and pressure for a particular application will be necessary.

5. *Cool the mold.* Remove the mold from the autoclave and cool it by submerging it in cold water.

6. *Eject the molded part from the mold.* Open the mold and remove the part. If the plastic expands into the steam holes, an ejection pin or plate may be necessary for removal of the part. In some cases, a jet of compressed air will dislodge the part, as illustrated in Fig. 18-7.

The mold and finished part are shown in Fig. 18-8. This is the molded holder for an eight-pack of coasters. Plans for the mold and the coasters are shown as Problem Seven in the project section at the end of the book. See page 212.

Fig. 18-6. Step 4 — Locking the Autoclave

Fig. 18-7. Step 6 — Ejecting Molded Part with Air Pressure

Fig. 18-8. Step 6 — The Mold and Finished Part

UNIT 21
HOW TO CAST
RIGID POLYURETHANE FOAM

The casting of polyurethane foam is one of the simplest molding operations. It consists of mixing two chemicals, pouring them into a closed mold, allowing the mixture to expand and fill the mold, and leaving it to cure.

1. *Prepare the mold.* Clean the mold surfaces carefully. Apply wax to all mold surfaces to insure an easy release.
2. *Measure the required amounts of the components.* Read the supplier's directions for the proper quantities to produce the correct density. Place the measured amounts in separate containers until ready to mix.
   a. Small quantities can be measured by volume with measuring spoons. Use separate spoons for each component.
   b. Larger quantities can be weighed with a scale graduated to at least quarter ounces. See Fig. 18-9.
   c. Many suppliers provide standard quantities so that the entire contents of one container is combined with that of another to produce the correct mixture.

3. *Add color to resin if desired.* The color should be thoroughly mixed with the resin before the catalyst is added.
4. *Combine the components.* The catalyst is generally thinner than the resin and is more easily poured.
5. *Mix.*
   a. Small quantities can be readily mixed with a stirring rod or spoon.
   b. Larger quantities should be mixed with a mechanical mixer such as a beater or a drill.
6. *Pour the mixture into the mold.* In many cases the mixture can be poured directly into one half of the mold. Note in Fig. 18-10 the foam beginning to rise. In others it may be poured through a sprue into the already closed mold.
7. *Close and clamp mold.* Since the expanding foam creates a good deal of pressure, hold the mold tightly together to avoid flash.
8. *Allow to foam.* If the proper quantity of foam is present, some excess should appear through the sprue and vents. Note this excess coming up through the sprue in Fig. 18-11. The reaction is exothermic and the mold will become warm as foaming takes place.

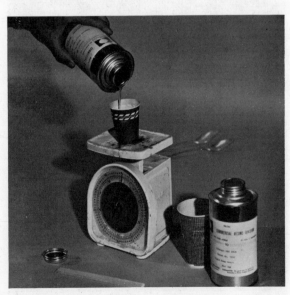

Fig. 18-9. Unit 21, Step 2 — Weighing Components

Fig. 18-10. Step 6 — Mixed Foam in Open Mold

9. *Allow to cure.* Consult the resin supplier's directions to determine curing time. Usually one hour is sufficient.

10. *Eject from the mold.* Open the mold halves and remove the part. In some cases ejection pins or plates may be necessary. Fig. 18-12 shows the finished part. See more illustrations on pages 206-7.

Study Questions

1. What two expandable plastics are treated in this chapter?
2. What are the similar properties of the two materials? How are they different?
3. What design factors must be taken into account because of the properties of the materials?
4. What temperatures must molds be able to withstand in molding expandable polystyrene?
5. What pressures are likely to be exerted on such molds?
6. What are four important factors to consider in mold design for expandable polystyrene?
7. Why are completely enclosed molds needed?
8. Where should the parting line be placed?
9. What problems of mold design are presented by methods of filling the mold? What are possible provisions for filling?
10. Why should mold surfaces be very smooth?
11. What purpose do the holes in the mold serve? What is a core vent and why is it used in preference to holes?
12. Why are molds for casting polyurethane often simpler to make than those for molding expandable polystyrene?
13. What mold materials can be used for polyurethane?
14. What are similarities in design between molds for the two plastics? What are differences?
15. In what form is expandable polystyrene supplied? What makes it foam?
16. What is a minimum density for expanded polystyrene?
17. What is the physical structure for expanded polystyrene?
18. In what form is urethane usually supplied. How does it foam?
19. What kind of heat is commonly used to expand polystyrene?
20. What are some devices that are used to heat molds for expandable polystyrene?
21. What equipment is needed to cast urethane?

Fig. 18-11. Step 8 — The Closed Mold

Fig. 18-12. Step 10 — Molded Part and Open Mold

CHAPTER NINETEEN

plastisol casting

The manufacture of one-piece, hollow, completely enclosed articles is difficult to accomplish with most plastics processes. This presents no problem with plastisol casting. Plastisols can also be used to put protective coatings on metals. Intricate shapes and undercuts can be readily produced.

Product Design

The outstanding properties of articles made from plastisols are flexibility, moderate tensile strength, excellent resistance to most chemicals, and a wide variety of color possibilities.

Because the finished product is flexible, one of the design limitations of many other processes is overcome. Articles with undercuts can be molded because the part can be collapsed to remove it from the mold or stretched to pull it from the plug.

Fine detail is readily obtainable; plastisols are liquid and will flow into any fine recess in the mold.

Hollow as well as solid objects can readily be made. Generally, a *uniform wall thickness* is easier to produce than a variable one. Nevertheless special control during processing allows a heavier buildup in various places.

Plastisols adhere well to porous surfaces but not to smooth surfaces. The adhesive properties make it possible to apply a protective coating to materials susceptible to corrosion while the lack of adhesion to polished surfaces is advantageous in stripping castings from polished molds.

If color is desired in the finished product it can be mixed with the resin before processing. Detail is easily painted on finished products.

Tool Design and Construction

Either molds or plugs can be used for processing plastisols; matched plugs and molds are not needed. Open objects can be made on plugs or with one-piece open molds. If a hollow, one-piece article is to be produced, a two-piece completely closed mold is needed. It must close tightly to reduce the size of a parting line. No draft is needed.

In deciding whether to use a plug or mold the designer is concerned with the desired location of detail on the finished product. If detail is required on the outside of the article, a mold should be used; if on the inside, a plug should be used. However, since the finished product is flexible, thin-walled objects can be turned inside out after production.

Tooling for this operation is not subjected to great stress or surface abrasion. Therefore the tooling need not possess great strength or surface hardness. The effect of *heat* is a more important consideration. Tools must withstand temperatures of 250° to 600° F. In some cases, the mold is heated after the plastisol is placed in it. Thus, the tool should be made from a material which readily conducts heat. Cast aluminum or electroformed copper are commonly used.

In laboratory work it may be desirable to heat the mold before the plastisol comes into contact with it. In this situation, a material which will hold heat should be used. Ceramic materials, casting plasters, and thermosetting plastics can be used here.

Materials Used

Plastisols, available in a variety of colors, are suspensions of vinyl resins in liquids. At room temperature the materials remain liquid, varying in consistency from water thin to thick pastes. The consistency selected depends upon the type of processing and the desired wall thickness. Some formulations are *thixotropic*, that is, they will remain on vertical wall sections without sagging or running. When heated to 300° or 350° F., plastisols become tough solids.

Equipment

Very simple equipment will suffice for laboratory work. A source of controlled heat is necessary. An ordinary cooking oven with thermostatically controlled temperatures from 250° to 550° F. is satisfactory.

For rotational casting, a device is needed that will rotate the molds in two planes at the same time.

Production equipment is available to provide automatic or semi-automatic control of all parts of the operation.

Procedures

Four operations in working with plastisols are outlined here: dip coating, dip casting, slush casting, and rotational casting. All make use of the fact that plastisols remain liquid at room temperatures but solidify when they come in contact with surfaces heated to 300°-350° F.

UNIT 22
HOW TO DIP-COAT
WITH PLASTISOLS

Dip coating consists of immersing a heated article, usually metal, into a plastisol until the desired thickness of plastic is deposited on the surface.

1. *Prepare the surface.* Plastisols do not adhere well to smoothly polished surfaces. The metal should be cleaned and coated with a sealer. Most suppliers specify a sealer, but lacquer is often used.
2. *Heat the object to be dipped.* The directions with the plastisol will indicate the temperature to be used. Commonly it is 300° to 350° F. Increased temperatures may be necessary with objects of small cross section which tend to lose their heat rapidly.
3. *Immerse the object in the plastisol for a time sufficient to build up the desired coating.* See Fig. 19-1. The heat from the

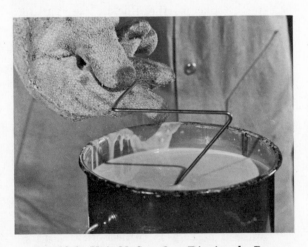

Fig. 19-1. Unit 22, Step 3 — Dipping the Part

Fig. 19-2. Step 3 — Draining Excess Plastisol

Fig. 19-3. Step 4 — The Cured Coated Part

object is transferred to the plastic causing it to solidify and adhere. The longer the object is left in the plastisol, the thicker will be the coating. If a thicker layer is desired, the partially coated object may be reheated and redipped. Fig. 19-2 shows the object being drained.

4. *Cure the resin.* In some situations the resin may be thoroughly cured by the dipping procedure. With small objects the resin may merely be gelled and not completely cured. See Fig. 19-3. Directions for curing are provided with the materials. Curing times are usually not over 30 minutes.

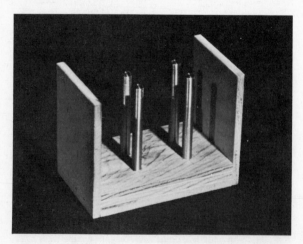

Fig. 19-4. Unit 23, Step 1 — Plug on Which Article Is Cast

UNIT 23
HOW TO DIP-CAST WITH PLASTISOLS

Dip casting is similar to dip coating except that the finished article is stripped from the plug after being cured.

1. *Make the plug.* The plug is generally the shape of the inside of the article to be made. In cases where the article is to be turned inside out after removal from the plug, the detail on the plug becomes the outside of the article. All surfaces should be smooth, true, and free of imperfections. Fig. 19-4 shows plugs to mold the caps for ends of rods and tubes.

2. *Prepare the surface of the plug.* If the surface of the plug is fairly smooth, a mold release is not needed. Where there is fine detail and rough surface to the plug, a mold release will facilitate removal of the part.

3. *Heat the plug.* Manufacturer's directions for the specific plastisol will give the necessary temperature. Commonly it is 300° to 350° F. With very thin-walled plugs which tend to lose their heat rapidly, a higher temperature may be necessary.

4. *Immerse the plug in the plastisol* as shown in Fig. 19-5. The heat from the plug causes the plastisol immediately surrounding it to solidify and adhere to the surface. The longer the plug is left in the plastic, the thicker the casting. Experience will indicate the necessary time. Usually 30 seconds to several minutes is sufficient.

5. *Cure the resin.* Where the casting is thin, it may be completely cured in Step 4. Note Fig. 19-6. In other cases, it may be necessary to cure it in an oven for 5 to 15 minutes.

6. *Strip the casting from the plug.* Compressed air may be blown between the plug and the casting or the article may be simply pulled by hand from the plug, as Fig. 19-7 illustrates. Many times the finished casting is turned inside out in removal and used that way.

Fig. 19-5. Step 4 — Dipping the Plug

Fig. 19-6. Step 4 — The Solidified Parts

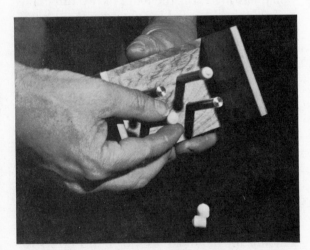

Fig. 19-7. Step 6 — Stripping Cured Parts from Plug

UNIT 24
HOW TO SLUSH-CAST WITH PLASTISOLS

Slush casting consists of pouring an excess of liquid plastisol into a heated mold, allowing the desired thickness to solidify against the mold wall, and pouring out the unsolidified resin.

1. *Make the mold.* Generally a one-piece open mold is used. See Fig. 19-8. With extreme undercuts it may be easier to remove the finished part if a two-piece mold is used.
2. *Prepare the mold.* No release agent is needed but the mold must be clean, smooth and polished.
3. *Heat the mold.* The required temperature is usually specified by the supplier. Commonly it is 300° to 350° F.
4. *Fill the mold with plastisol.* Simply pour the liquid into the cavity until it is filled as shown in Fig. 19-9.

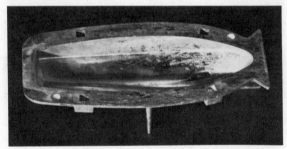

Fig. 19-8. Unit 24, Step 1 — The Mold

Fig. 19-9. Step 4 — Filling Mold with Plastisol

Fig. 19-10. Step 6 — Pouring Out Excess Plastisol

Fig. 19-11. Step 8 — Removing Part from Mold

Fig. 19-12. Step 8 — The Mold and Finished Part

5. *Allow the desired thickness to solidify against the mold.* The time necessary to accomplish this will vary with several factors such as temperature of the mold, inside area, and thickness of the mold. If the desired thickness is not built up, the mold should be reheated.
6. *Pour out the excess plastisol.* Turn the mold over, pouring the liquid material into the container for further use. Note Fig. 19-10.
7. *Cure the gelled plastisol.* In some cases no further cure will be needed while in others, the mold and gelled plastisol should be placed in an oven for 5 to 15 minutes.
8. *Remove the part from the mold.* It may be stripped by hand, as in Fig. 19-11, or blown out by compressed air between the mold and the part. Fig. 19-12 shows the mold and the finished toy boat.

UNIT 25
HOW TO ROTATIONALLY CAST PLASTISOLS

In simple slush casting, there is a tendency for the liquid plastisol to run to the bottom of the mold and build up a greater thickness there. Furthermore, an open mold is used with the result that the product must also be open. To overcome these two shortcomings, rotational casting turns the mold in two directions to force the material evenly against all parts.

Examine the shop-made rotational casting machine for plastisols in Fig. 19-13. Note the hot plate in the bottom for heat and the mounted hand drill for rotation in two planes. The mold fastened to the chuck spins on its axis, while the chuck also swings around the shaft on the big gear. The knob has been removed from the large gear and the gear is screwed to the wooden bracket. The usual end handle has been replaced by a cross handle which is used to turn the frame of the drill during the rotational process. A carriage bolt secured to the center of a small block forms a mount for the mold, as shown in Fig. 19-16. The carriage bolt is fastened in the chuck and molds can be screwed to the mounting block.

1. *Make the mold.* A completely closed two-piece mold is used—best made of cast aluminum or copper t o allow rapid heating.
2. *Prepare the mold.* No mold release is needed, but the mold should be clean and polished.
3. *Fill the mold with a premeasured amount of plastisol,* as shown in Fig. 19-14. Since any excess of uncured plastic cannot be removed from an enclosed hollow article, only the needed amount is placed in the mold. If two halves are used, the mold must be fastened together, Fig. 19-15.
4. *Place the closed mold in the rotating equipment.* See Fig. 19-16.
5. *Heat the mold as it is rotated.* The mold is generally heated after filling so that the plastic does not begin to solidify until it is rotated.
6. *Cure the plastisol.* In many cases it will be completely cured in the rotation process. In others, it will simply gell against the mold wall and must be cured for 5 to 15 minutes after rotation.
7. *Open the mold and remove the finished part.* See Fig. 19-17.

Fig. 19-14. Unit 25, Step 3 — Filling Mold with Plastisol

Fig. 19-15. Step 3 — Fastening Mold Halves Together

Fig. 19-16. Step 4 — Placing Filled Mold in Rotational Casting Machine

Fig. 19-13. Rotational Casting Machine for Plastisols

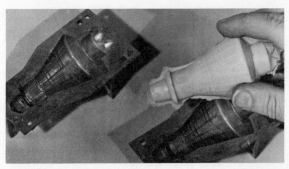

Fig. 19-17. Step 7 — Removing the Part from Mold

Study Questions

1. What shape is readily produced with plastisols that is difficult with other processes?

2. What are the general properties possessed by plastisol articles?

3. Why are undercuts possible in articles made from plastisols?

4. How are the adhesive properties of plastisols exploited in processing them?

5. Which tools are used with plastisol — plugs, molds, or matched plugs and molds?

6. How do you determine which type of tool to use?

7. To what must the tool be resistant?

8. What are plastisols?

9. In what form are plastisols used?

10. How are plastisols solidified ?

11. What equipment is needed to process plastisols?

12. What are the four methods by which plastisols are processed and what is the particular application of each?

CHAPTER TWENTY

reinforcing plastics

Probably more work has been done by the layman and homecraftsman with reinforced plastics than with any other process of the industry. Much of the so called "fiber glass" work can be done with little equipment; materials are readily available and easy to work with. Production techniques have made this also an important mass production process. Reinforced plastics products have high strength, translucent to opaque colors, and interesting fiber patterns. Many of the tools for this process are made by the same techniques as are the products themselves.

Product Design

Reinforced plastics provide colorful, tough, durable, and rigid products. They offer fine resistance to weather, chemicals, and electricity. To obtain full benefit of the advantages of this process the designer must keep in mind several considerations.

Sharp arrises and corners are difficult to produce and maintain. They are likely to be "resin-rich" areas with little reinforcement present. Curved surfaces are preferable. Also it is well to maintain uniform wall thickness in an object since gradual increases in thickness, as in tapered surfaces, are difficult to produce.

The maximum possible draft should be allowed. Although an object with a vertical wall can be removed from the tool if the cavity is not too deep, a draft of two to five degrees will greatly facilitate removal. A wall section over $\frac{1}{16}$ inch thick will be quite rigid and difficult to "spring" from an undercut mold. In most cases undercuts cannot be produced in reinforced plastics without special tooling.

Large, flat, unsupported areas are not desirable because of warpage and lack of stiffness. However ribs or corrugations can provide the necessary mechanical properties in this case.

Even though painting of the laminate is possible, a more lasting finish is produced if the color is mixed with the resin. The translucency of reinforced plastics depends upon the resin, the color, and the reinforcing material. Patterned fabrics can be embedded just below the surface to produce any color or design desired. Fiber glass cloth produces uniform screened appearance, and mat and fibers are produced in interesting random patterns.

With the proper reinforcement, these plastics can possess strength in one or more directions.

Tool Design

One favorable feature in working with reinforced plastics is the simplicity possible in the tooling. Much work is done in both the laboratory and the factory with very simple tooling, but in some production work complex and expensive molds and plugs are used.

In molding of reinforced plastics, a matched plug and mold are needed. However, more commonly a single tool, either a plug or a mold, is used. If the convex surface of the finished product must be smooth, a mold is used. If the concave surface must be smooth, a plug is used.

In making products by this process no pressure is applied to the plugs and molds nor is the tooling bent or twisted. Some heat is produced by the resin as it hardens, but since a single tool is used, there need not be any great buildup of heat. As a result, the tooling for reinforced plastics does not need great compressive strength or surface hardness. However it must be very warp resistant and have an extremely smooth and true surface.

A wide variety of materials can be used to construct the tooling. Plaster and wood, which are inexpensive and easy to modify, are used for design and developmental work. Metals are used for some production work. Perhaps the most common tooling in use is made from reinforced plastics by the same techniques as are finished products. Once the design has been satisfactorily modified in a plaster or wood tool, a plastic tool is made from it. Such tools are light in weight, tough and durable, and exhibit very smooth non-porous surfaces.

Extreme care must be exercised in making the tool surfaces smooth and true. Liquid resins reproduce exactly the surface of the mold or plug including any imperfections. Furthermore, any roughness in the surface will make it more difficult to remove the hardened resin. All surfaces must be thoroughly filled and sealed. Plaster or wood tools should be shellacked or lacquered and rubbed to a smooth non-porous surface.

Surface tension is produced as the resin hardens. To facilitate removal of the laminate, at least two degrees of draft should be provided on all vertical sections. Where possible, more draft is desirable.

Materials Used

There are four general groups of materials with which the worker in reinforced plastics must be concerned: the resins, the reinforcement, parting agents, and colors.

The Resins

Theoretically, any plastic resin can be reinforced with some other material and thus be termed a reinforced plastic. In the industry, only nine of the families of resins are actually used to some extent. These are polyesters, epoxies, phenolics, melamines, silicones, alkyds, cellulosics, vinyls, and acrylics. Of the nine, polyesters and epoxies account for all but a small fraction of the amount used. Polyesters, in turn, account for the bulk of those used but epoxies are making great gains.

The chemical nature of polyesters allows a wide variety of formulations with varying physical properties. A change in the formulation can produce end products varying from flexible to rigid. Viscosity can be controlled to produce variations from free-flowing resins to those that will adhere to vertical mold sections with no sagging or running. Heat resistance up to 500° F. can be incorporated. Often an improvement in one property works to the detriment of another property; a particular formulation should be selected for its major desired characteristic. Polyesters are supplied as clear rather thick liquids which must be catalyzed and promoted to harden at room temperatures. They are easily colored while in the liquid state.

Epoxies are considerably more expensive than polyesters. However their unusual combination of high strength, low water absorption, and minimum cure shrinkage are responsible for their ever increasing use. They too can be produced in a variety of formulations with a variety of properties. Mixing procedures are similar to those for polyesters. They are supplied as thick liquids which must be catalyzed to cure at room temperatures.

The Reinforcement

A number of materials can be used to reinforce plastic laminates. Particular materials are used to obtain specific properties, for example asbestos gives fire resistance. The most common reinforcement and the one which accounts for a major share of the use, is fibrous glass in some form.

TABLE 21
CHARACTERISTICS OF VARIOUS
GLASS REINFORCEMENTS

Type	General Description	Directionality	Glass Content	Use	Relative Cost	Relative Usage
Mats	Non-woven random matting	Non-directional	20–45%	Simple contours	Medium	Great
Rovings	Rope-like bundles of continuous strands	Unidirectional	50–70%	Preforming, unidirectional reinforcing	Low	Great
Chopped Strands	Bulk, cut strands	Non-directional	15–45%	Molding compounds	Low	Medium
Milled Fibers	Small filaments	Non-directional	2–10%	Castings	Low	Very small
Surfacing Mats	Non-reinforcing filaments	Non-directional	5–15%	Surface smoothness	High	Small
Beams	Parallel yarn matting	Unidirectional	50–80%	Cylinders	Medium	Very small
Fabrics	Many styles, finishes	Unidirectional or Bi-directional	45–65%	High performance parts	High	Great
Woven Rovings	Coarse, heavy fabrics	Bi-directional	45–65%	Boats	Medium	Medium

From "Reinforced Plastics", **Industrial Design Magazine**, October, 1958.

Glass possesses a unique combination of properties. It exhibits low specific gravity, high dielectric strength, no flammability, low thermal conductivity, chemical inertness, high mechanical strength, and dimensional stability over a range of temperatures.

For use in reinforced plastics, glass is produced in the form of fibers or filaments from .0002 inch to .0010 inch in diameter. These fibers are made into various mats and cloths much as is yarn. Each form has a particular use. Table 21 explains the forms available and their characteristics.

Parting Agents

Part of the high strength of reinforced plastics is due to the ability of the plastic resin to adhere well to the reinforcement. Resins used in reinforcing adhere well to a variety of materials. Consequently, some means must be provided to prevent the adhesion of the finished laminate to the mold or plug on which it is made. Parting agents or mold releases are used for this purpose. Four general types of release agents are used.

(1) *Films* place a thin, contour-following non-adhesive surface between the mold and the plastic. Typical materials used are cellulose, polyvinyl alcohol, and water-soluble modified styrene.

(2) *Film-forming materials* are sprayed or brushed on the mold to form thin films. Common materials in this category are methyl cellulose, cellulose acetate, and the familiar blue polyvinyl alcohol.

(3) *Lubricants* remain as liquid, non-adhesive barriers between the tool and the plastic. Typical are graphites, petroleum jelly, and sulfate esters.

(4) *Powders* place a dry non-adhesive coating on the tool. Powdered mica, oleic acid, zinc stereate, and dusting powders are used.

Colors

Polyester and epoxy resins are supplied as clear liquids. While they could be supplied in colors this is not done because it reduces the shelf life of the material. Colors are available in the form of pastes that are mixed with the resins just prior to adding the hardener. The colors are commonly metallic oxides made into pastes with a vehicle that will blend with the resin without changing its properties.

Equipment

One of the advantages of reinforced plastics work is that it can be done with no specialized equipment. For common, hand lay-up operations the only supplies needed are ordinary paint brushes or rollers, containers for mixing resins, and scissors for cutting cloth and mat.

For spray-up operations, special spray equipment is needed. Several patented systems are available. They generally consist of a two-nozzle spray gun and a means of chopping glass fibers. One nozzle sprays *catalyzed resin* and the other sprays *promoted resin*. Fed between the two nozzles is a stream of *chopped glass fibers*. All three mix at the point of impact with the mold. Spray-up equipment is available in extensive factory installations or as small, portable laboratory equipment.

Procedures

Personal Care

Several of the materials used in reinforced plastics work are skin irritants to some individuals. More likely to cause irritation are the

Fig. 20-1. Measuring with Two-nozzle Metering Device (U.S. Gypsum)

hardeners used with epoxy resins. Other irritations are possible too. Constant cleaning of hands and arms with solvents dries the skin and removes natural oils. Contact with fiber glass can result in small particles of the glass being rubbed into the skin. In isolated cases, the fumes from resins, solvents, and hardeners can cause discomfort. Extensive studies conducted by materials manufacturers have shown that ordinary care in avoiding actual contact with the resins and hardeners will eliminate almost all difficulties. A few basic rules should be followed.

(1) *Keep work area clean.* Cover benches with paper and replace it if resin is spilled.

(2) *Ventilate work area.* Open windows will often provide sufficient ventilation but, if possible, work should be done under a hood, or near an exhaust outlet to avoid breathing vapors. This also removes pungent odors.

(3) *Wear rubber gloves* to handle resins and hardeners, especially in working with epoxies. While some people will experience no ill effects from getting some resin on their fingers it has been found desirable to have this protection.

(4) *Clean hands and arms thoroughly* after working with materials. Remove any resin with denatured alcohol and then wash with soap and water. Several hand cleaners are available which contain lanolin to restore natural oils to the skin.

Mixing Resins and Hardeners

Liquid resins and their hardeners must be properly measured and mixed. There are three different ways in which the *measuring* may be done.

(1) Using premeasured amounts of resin and hardener. Most suppliers offer their resins and hardeners in separate standard units. To mix, the total quantity of hardener is added to the container of resin. If the quantity supplied is practical to use, this is a good system because it insures proper amounts of the two components. It is generally more expensive, however.

(2) Measuring proper amounts of resin and hardener from larger containers. In some cases it is desirable to purchase the materials in larger amounts. Directions for mixing are given by the supplier in terms of either weight or volume. With some resins the mixture can be varied, using the operator's experience and a knowledge of drying conditions and working time as his guide.

(3) Measuring with a metering device. For the laboratory doing much work with small amounts of resin, it is advisable to have a metering device that dispenses the proper quantity of resin and hardener through two separate nozzles. The two components are kept in separate containers and only the desired amounts of each are dispensed for use. Fig. 20-1 shows a two-nozzle metering device for measuring resin and catalyst.

Mixing can be done by hand using a spoon or paddle for small amounts. A mixer is desirable for larger amounts. The hardener must be thoroughly dispersed through the resin. Mixing for approximately *five minutes* is necessary.

UNIT 26
HOW TO HAND LAY-UP
PLASTIC LAMINATES

The simplest and most economical means of producing plastic laminates is known as hand lay-up. It consists of applying a reinforcing material to the shape of a mold and impregnating it with a resin to cause it to hold that shape. The procedure outlined here applies to the use of fiber glass cloth or mat as a reinforcing agent and polyester or epoxy resin as a plastic.

1. *Prepare the mold or plug.* A single mold or plug is used. Molds can be made from wood, plaster, plastics, or metal. Their surface should be thoroughly sealed with shellac or lacquer.
2. *Apply mold release.* Use the mold release specified by the resin supplier.
3. *Apply surface or "gel" coat.* To provide a smooth, texture-free surface on the finished laminate, first apply a $\frac{1}{32}$-inch to $\frac{1}{16}$-inch coat of resin to the mold or plug surface. With epoxies, a special surface coat resin is used; with polyesters, the laminating resin is used. If color is desired, it should be added to the surface coat before application.
   a. Measure the proper amounts of resin and catalyst. Follow the manufacturer's directions.
   b. Mix the resin and catalyst according to directions.
   c. Apply the surface coat to the entire mold or plug surface. This can be brushed, rolled or sprayed. See Fig. 20-2. Be sure to remove all bubbles.
4. *Fillet sharp corners and projections.* Prepare a putty-like mixture of resin, catalyst, and chopped glass fibers and fillet any sharp corners or thin projections. This provides added strength and reduces the possibility of resin-rich pockets during laminating.
5. *Allow surface coat to become tacky or touch-dry.* The surface coat should become dry enough that its smooth surface does not break during subsequent applications. Some manufacturers recommend that the surface coat be allowed to dry completely and then be roughened with fine abrasive paper to provide a good bond with succeeding layers.

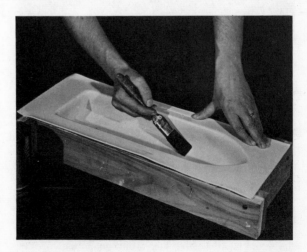

Fig. 20-2. Unit 26, Step 3 — Applying the Gel Coat

6. *Prepare reinforcing material.* Cut the necessary layers of glass cloth or mat to the desired size and shape. See Fig. 20-3. Some stretching of material is possible, but material must be cut for severe shapes. For greater strength, joints should be lapped; if uniform thickness is important, butt joints can be made. However, each layer should be joined at a different piece.

7. *Mix laminating resin and catalyst.* Follow the supplier's directions. With epoxies, a hardener is added. With polyesters, a hardener and a promoter are often added.

8. *Apply layers of reinforcement and resin.* Flow on a uniform layer of resin. Lay on the glass cloth or mat and carefully smooth it over the resin, working the resin through the material. Remove all trapped air bubbles with a brush or roller, as shown in Fig. 20-4. Apply more resin if needed but remember that the proper amount of resin is just enough to completely impregnate the cloth. It is the glass that provides the strength; excess resin weakens the part. Add succeeding layers of reinforcement and resin. It is not necessary to allow each layer to harden before the next application.

9. *Allow to harden.* Polyester and epoxy resins harden completely in one to twelve hours. Warm, dry conditions speed up the process. When the surface of the part is no longer sticky to the touch, it is hard enough to remove from the mold.

10. *Remove from mold or plug.* See Fig. 20-5. Even if a release agent has been carefully applied, there is a good deal of surface tension to resist removal. Either uniform wedging with a chisel or blowing compressed air between the mold and the laminate will cause it to release.

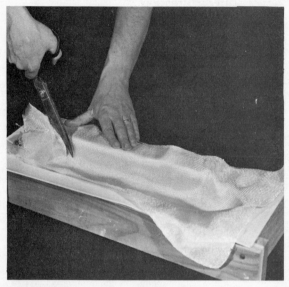

Fig. 20-3. Step 6 — Cutting Cloth to Size and Shape

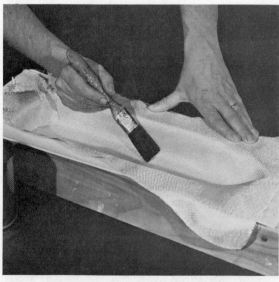

Fig. 20-4. Step 8 — Applying Fiber Glass Cloth and Resin

Fig. 20-5. Step 10 — Removing the Part from Mold

UNIT 27
HOW TO SPRAY-UP
PLASTIC LAMINATES

Spray-up and hand lay-up are similar in many respects but are different in two aspects. In this spray-up technique, the resin is applied with a spray gun instead of brush or roller and the reinforcement used is in the form of chopped glass fibers rather than cloth or mat.

1. *Prepare the mold or plug.* The same type of tooling is used in this technique as in hand lay-up.
2. *Apply mold release to all surfaces of the tooling.*
3. *Spray surface or gel coat.* Mix any desired color with the resin for the surface coat. Spray a thin even layer on all mold or plug surfaces. Use a standard spray gun with the pressure and nozzle which is appropriate to the viscosity of the resin. Note Fig. 20-6 .
4. *Spray needed coats of resin and chopped fibers.* Use the two-nozzle system to build up the desired thickness. Keep the spray gun in such a position that the spray is at right angles with the surface being sprayed. It is not necessary to allow each coat to harden before applying another. See Fig. 20-7.

5. *Roll out variations in the surface.* Go over the entire surface with a rubber roller to work out any air pockets and to smooth the surface, Fig. 20-8.
6. *Allow to harden and remove from mold or plug.* When the surface is not sticky to the touch, it can be removed from the tooling.

Fig. 20-7. Step 4 — Spraying Resin and Chopped Fibers (Rand)

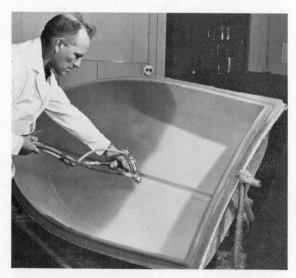

Fig. 20-6. Unit 27, Step 3 — Spraying Gel Coat on Mold (Rand)

Fig. 20-8. Step 5 — Boat Hull after Rolling Down

Study Questions

1. What is the common term applied to reinforced plastics?
2. What factors should be considered when designing an article to be made by reinforcing?
3. Why are "resin-rich" areas likely to lack strength?
4. How is color obtained in reinforced plastics?
5. Why is the tooling so simple for reinforced plastics?
6. How do you decide whether to use a plug or a mold? In what case do you use a matched plug and mold?
7. What materials can be commonly used for molds for reinforced plastics work?
8. Is fine detail practical on reinforced objects? Explain.
9. What materials are used in reinforcing?
10. What individual plastics are used in reinforcing? Which one is most common?
11. Plastics used with reinforcing are in what form?
12. Which reinforcing plastic is used where extremely high strength is needed?
13. What reinforcing agents are used? Which is by far the most common?
14. What is the principal advantage of each of the forms in which glass reinforcement is available?
15. Why are parting agents needed?
16. What are four types of parting agents?
17. What coloring materials are used?
18. What equipment is needed for reinforcing?
19. What does spray-up equipment consist of?
20. What precautions should be followed in working with reinforced plastics?
21. What are three ways to measure resin and catalyst?
22. What are the various processes by which reinforcing is done?

This part of the book contains sample projects employing applications of all the processes described in the operational section. All projects have been designed and made with laboratory and experimental equipment but they could be set up for production as well.

For each project, a working drawing is included with a diagram of the processes involved. The diagrams are in "schematic" form because the individual piece of equipment will dictate the specifics.

Detailed procedures are not given for each article. The specific steps in each operation have been outlined in the previous parts of the book and modifications may be necessary in terms of available equipment.

Each drawing indicates the process by which each part could be made. In many instances, other operations could be used; the idea behind those chosen was to provide a variety of experiences. In cases where a molded part is called for, if molding equipment is not available, the part can be machined from rod, bar, or sheet plastic.

It is hoped that these ideas will suggest others. As the student works with the various processes of the plastics industry, a vast number of other ideas will be suggested.

PART V **sample problems and projects**

PROBLEM ONE
fruit bowl

SIMPLE
THERMOFORMING

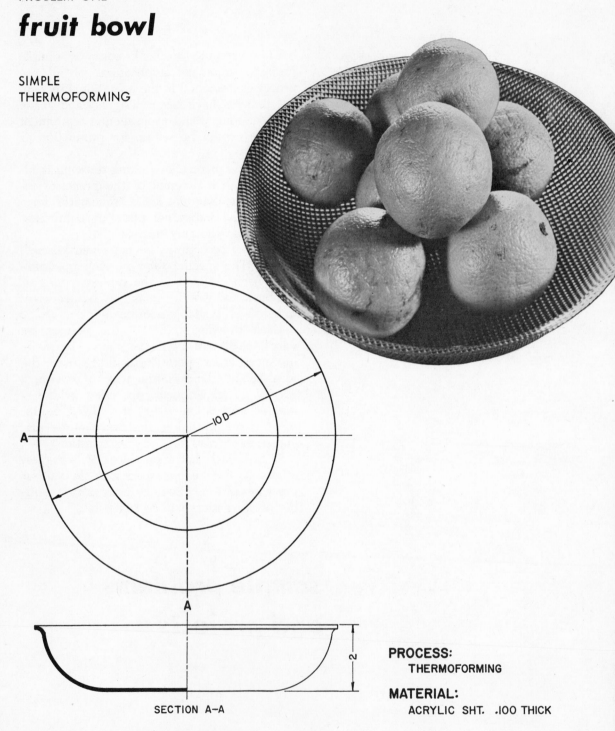

-10 D-

A ---- A

A

SECTION A-A

2

PROCESS:
THERMOFORMING

MATERIAL:
ACRYLIC SHT. .100 THICK

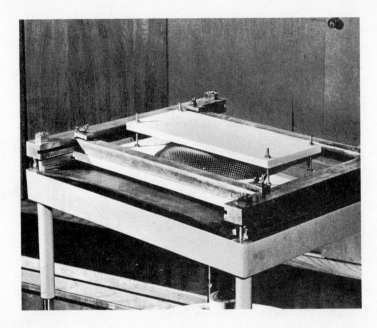

This project is made by one of the simplest applications of thermoforming, free-blowing. The form is simple to make; it is merely a circular hole in a board. The forming equipment can be very simple; a hand tire pump will provide sufficient pressure for the forming operation. Variations in size and shape are easily made. The bowl need not be circular but can be any desired form. The bowl is shown being free-blown in a laboratory press.

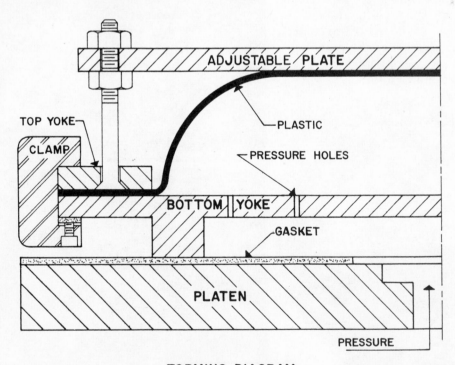

FORMING DIAGRAM

PROBLEM TWO

bowl

HAND LAY-UP
LAMINATION

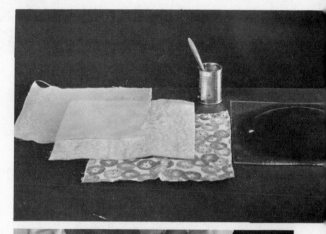

This bowl can serve as a base for a dec-orative center piece on a table. The mold can be turned from wood or screeded from plaster. A mold can even be thermoformed by much the same process as is used to make the bowl in the previous drawing. Attractive effects can be produced by laminating a piece of colored and patterned cloth just after the gel coat. Legs to raise the bowl can be machined from wood or metal.

The top photo shows the mold with a gel coat, as well as the materials used — either the glass cloth or mat can be used. The center photo shows the application of the patterned fabric, and the lower photo shows the final layer — the glass cloth and resin.

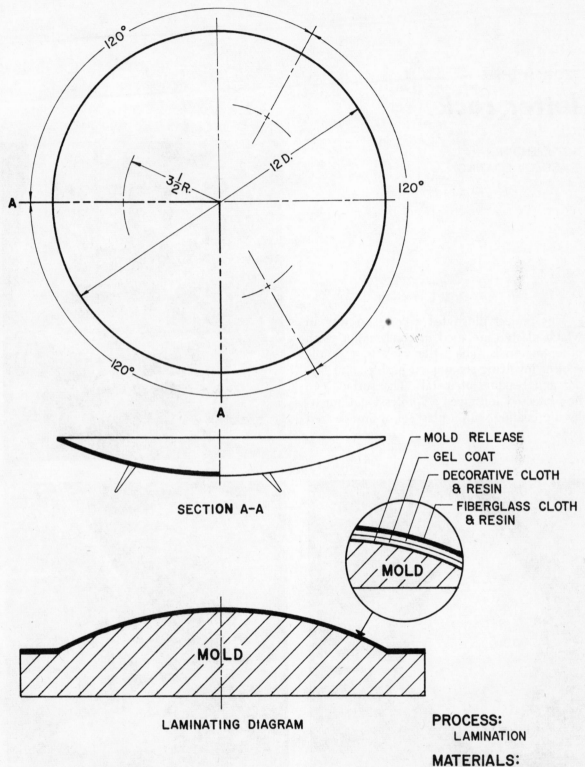

120°

120°

120°

3½ R.

12 D.

A

A

SECTION A-A

MOLD RELEASE
GEL COAT
DECORATIVE CLOTH
& RESIN
FIBERGLASS CLOTH
& RESIN

MOLD

MOLD

LAMINATING DIAGRAM

PROCESS:
LAMINATION

MATERIALS:
POLYESTER RESIN
FIBERGLASS CLOTH

PROBLEM THREE
letter rack

WIRE BENDING,
PLASTISOL COATING

This project illustrates a common way in which plastics are used in combination with other materials. The letter rack is a simple project involving some good problems in lay-out and bending of metals. The surface can be protected and given a "professional touch" by dip coating with a plastisol of any desired color.

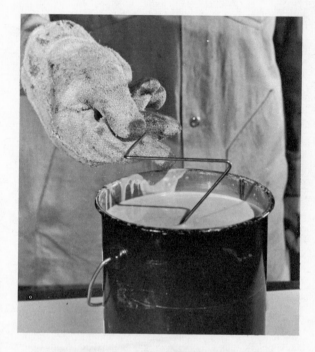

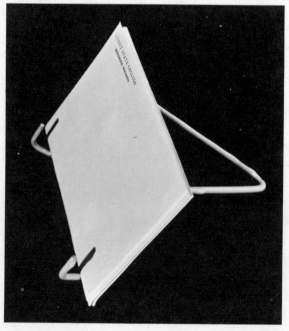

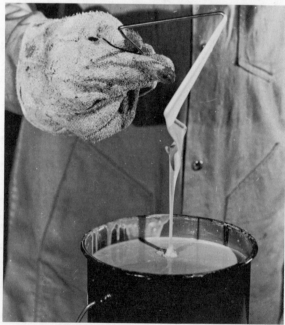

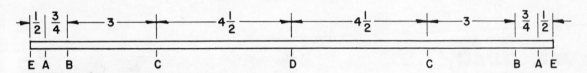

STEP NO. I: BEND LAYOUT

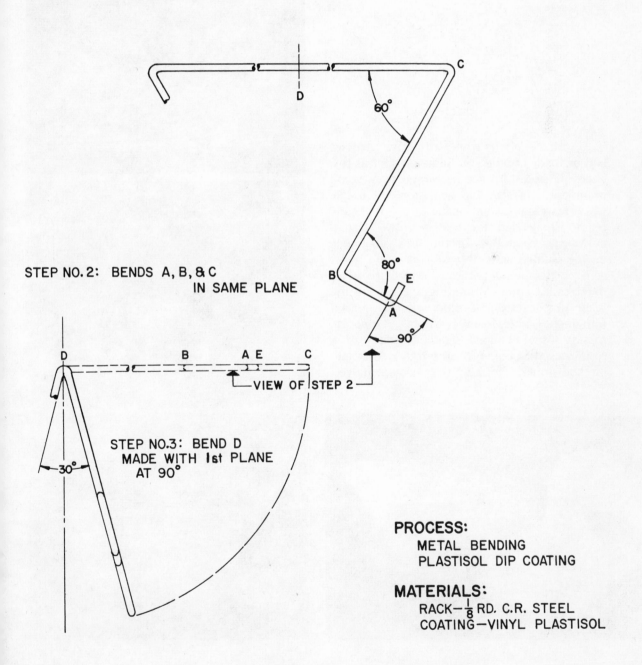

STEP NO. 2: BENDS A, B, & C
            IN SAME PLANE

STEP NO.3: BEND D
            MADE WITH 1st PLANE
            AT 90°

PROCESS:
METAL BENDING
PLASTISOL DIP COATING

MATERIALS:
RACK—$\frac{1}{8}$ RD. C.R. STEEL
COATING—VINYL PLASTISOL

PROBLEM FOUR
duck decoy

CHEMICAL
FOAMING

A variety of bouyant attractive articles can be made in much the same manner as this decoy. The pattern can be carved from wood or modeled in clay and a plaster cast made. Careful weighing and mixing of polyurethane foam are needed for best results. Mineral colors can be added, or the finished article can be painted with oil base paints.

Top: Removing pattern from cast-plaster mold half. *Center:* Measuring and mixing the resin and catalyst. *Bottom:* Resin poured into mold — note foam beginning. *Opposite, top-left:* Mold clamped together — note excess resin at sprue. *Opposite, top-right:* Alternate method — thermoforming the decoy in halves.

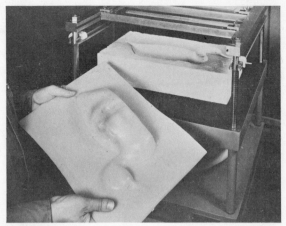

SAMPLE MODEL

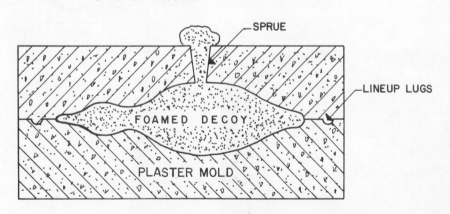

SPRUE

LINEUP LUGS

FOAMED DECOY

PLASTER MOLD

FOAMING DIAGRAM

PROCESS:
CHEMICAL FOAMING

MATERIAL:
RIGID URETHANE FOAM

PROBLEM FIVE

ice bucket

EXPANDABLE POLYSTYRENE,
MOLDING,

THERMOFORMED LID

This project is a little more complex and lends itself well to mass production. The molds for the bucket are cast from aluminum and machined in a lathe. Some type of pressure vessel, an autoclave, is needed for the expansion of the polystyrene beads. The cover is an interesting application of thermoforming on a turned-wood mold. The knob can be molded or purchased. Since the material cost is low, a number of the buckets can be made once the molds are completed. The product can be put to other uses too, such as a minnow bucket, a planter, or a cooler for picnic lunches.

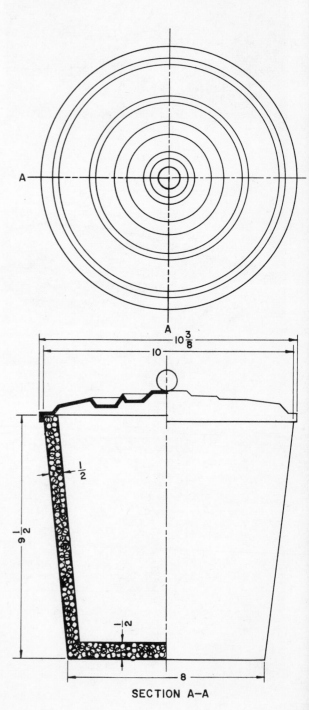

SECTION A-A

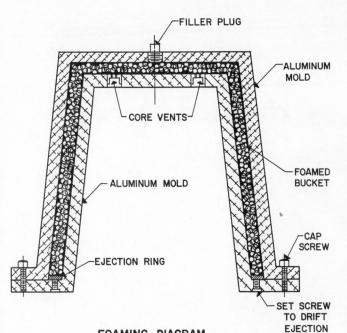

FILLER PLUG

ALUMINUM MOLD

CORE VENTS

ALUMINUM MOLD

FOAMED BUCKET

CAP SCREW

EJECTION RING

SET SCREW TO DRIFT EJECTION RING

FOAMING DIAGRAM

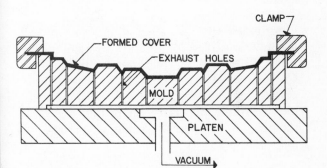

CLAMP

FORMED COVER

EXHAUST HOLES

MOLD

PLATEN

VACUUM

FORMING DIAGRAM

PROCESSES:
BUCKET—FOAMING
COVER—THERMOFORMING

MATERIALS:
BUCKET—EXPANDABLE POLYSTYRENE
COVER—STYRENE SHT. .100 THICK

PROBLEM SIX
checker board

THERMOFORMING,

PLASTISOL CASTING

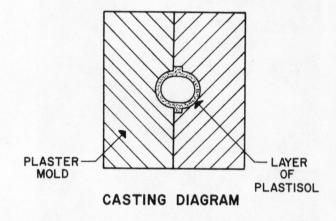

PLASTER MOLD — LAYER OF PLASTISOL

CASTING DIAGRAM

Although this is called a checker board, it can be modified for a wide variety of games such as tic-tac-toe, pom-pom pullaway, or Chinese checkers. The mold is very simply made from wood. The checkers shown are molded from plastisols but could be cast, molded, or machined from a variety of materials.

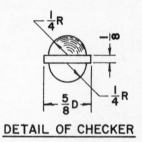

$\frac{1}{4}R$ $\frac{1}{4}R$ $\frac{5}{8}D$

DETAIL OF CHECKER

PAINT ONE HALF DIFFERENT COLOR
TO MAKE "KINGS" BY INVERTING

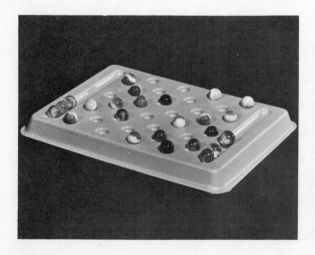

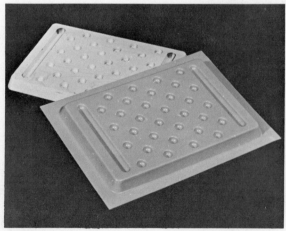

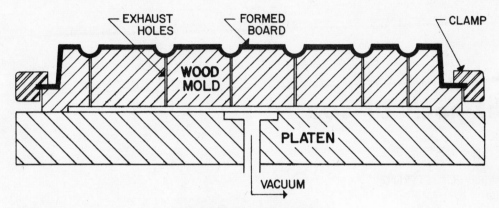

EXHAUST HOLES — FORMED BOARD — CLAMP

WOOD MOLD

PLATEN

VACUUM

FORMING DIAGRAM

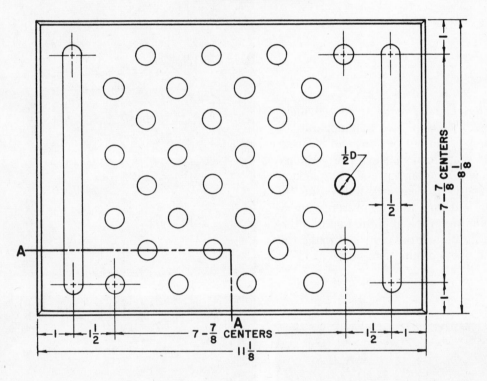

$\frac{1}{2}$D

$\frac{1}{2}$

7-$\frac{7}{8}$ CENTERS

8$\frac{1}{8}$

1

1

A —— A

1   1$\frac{1}{2}$ 7-$\frac{7}{8}$ CENTERS   1$\frac{1}{2}$ 1

11$\frac{1}{8}$

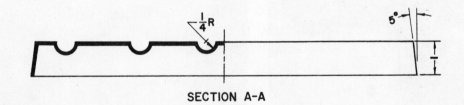

$\frac{1}{4}$R   5°

1

SECTION A-A

PROCESSES:
 BOARD—THERMOFORMING
 CHECKER—PLASTISOL CASTING

MATERIALS:
 BOARD—STYRENE SHT. .100 THICK
 CHECKER—VINYL PLASTISOL

eight-pack of coasters

THERMOFORMING,
EXPANDABLE POLYSTYRENE
MOLDING

The coasters can be made from the many small pieces of sheet plastic that accumulate in the shop. A variety of designs can be used. The finished shape can be sawed or punched with a hollow punch on a press. The package provides an attractive means of keeping the set together, and, in addition, presents an excellent machining problem in the manufacture of the mold. Low material costs can make this an excellent mass production problem.

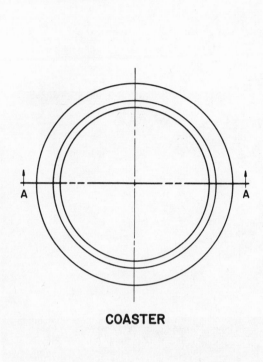

COASTER

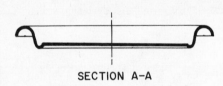

SECTION A–A

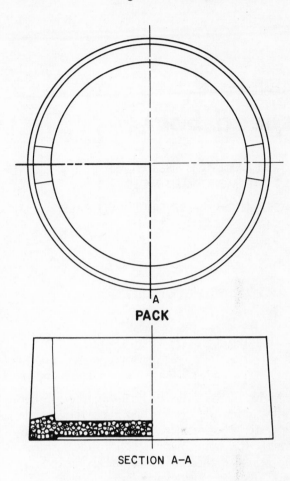

PACK

SECTION A–A

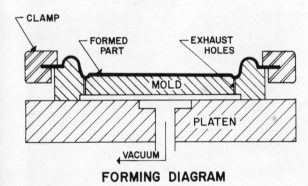

FORMING DIAGRAM

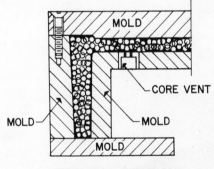

FOAMING DIAGRAM

PROCESS:
THERMOFORMING

MATERIAL:
STYRENE SHT. .030 THICK

PROCESS:
FOAMING

MATERIAL:
EXPANDABLE
POLYSTYRENE

speed boat

HAND LAY-UP OF FIBER GLASS
ON THERMOFORMED MOLD,

FABRICATION OF SEVERAL MATERIALS

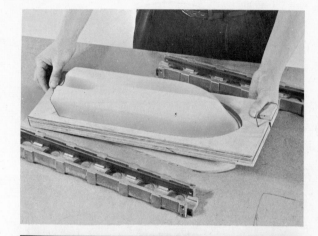

Many of the full-size boats on the market today are made from fiber glass reinforced-polyester plastics. This boat can be made in exactly the same manner. The project shows the use of a thermoformed mold backed up with plaster. Wide variations in design are possible to suit the individual.

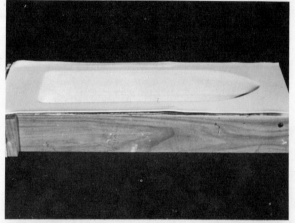

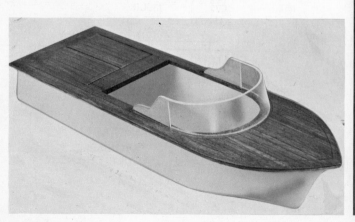

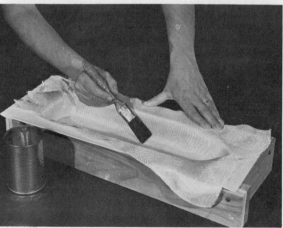

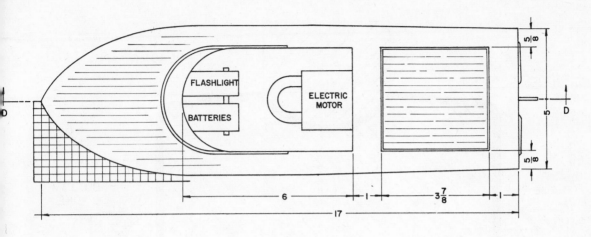

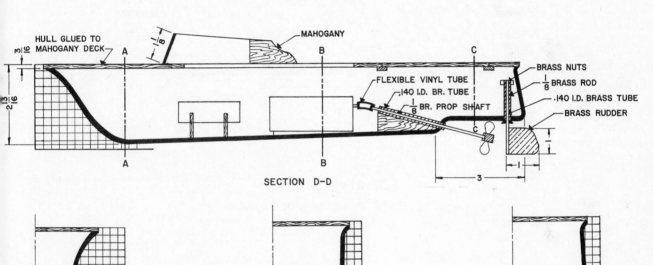

SECTION D-D

A-A   B-B   C-C

PROCESSES:
    MOLD—THERMOFORMING
    HULL—LAMINATION

MATERIALS:
    MOLD—STYRENE SHT. .100 THICK
    HULL—POLYESTER RESIN
        FIBERGLASS CLOTH

(More plans on next two pages)

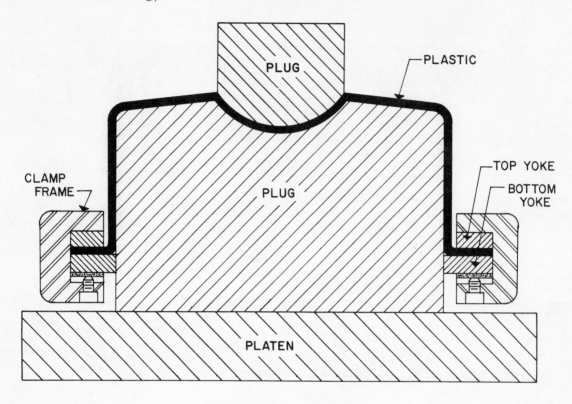

PLUG

PLASTIC

CLAMP
FRAME

PLUG

TOP YOKE

BOTTOM
YOKE

PLATEN

FORMING DIAGRAM
TO FORM PLASTIC MOLD LINER

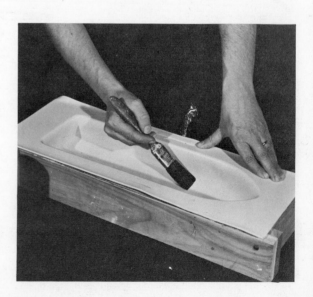

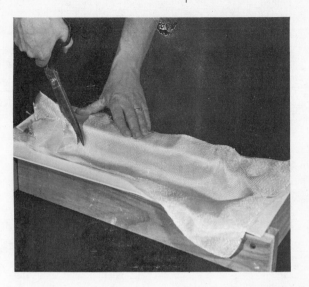

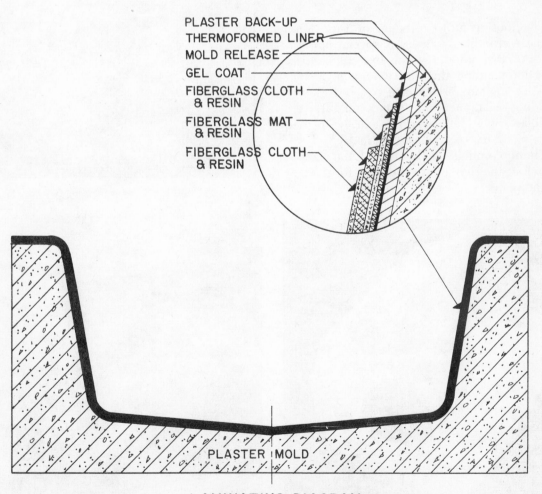

PLASTER BACK-UP
THERMOFORMED LINER
MOLD RELEASE
GEL COAT
FIBERGLASS CLOTH
& RESIN

FIBERGLASS MAT
& RESIN

FIBERGLASS CLOTH
& RESIN

PLASTER MOLD

LAMINATING DIAGRAM

PROBLEM NINE

recipe file

THERMOFORMING,
INJECTION MOLDING,
COMPRESSION MOLDING,
FABRICATION

The most complex product of this group is the recipe file. It includes special applications of thermoforming the base and cover, injection-molding the card mount, and compression-molding a knob and two bearings. If molding equipment is not available, the various knobs and bearings can be turned from metal or rod or sheet plastic.

Thermoforming the bottom of the case is shown at the right. Turn the page for the rest of the plans.

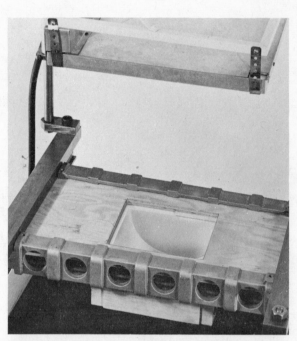

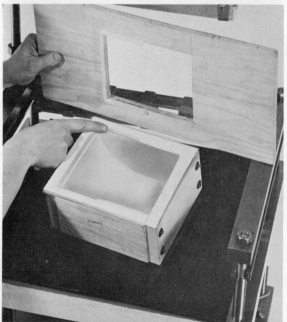

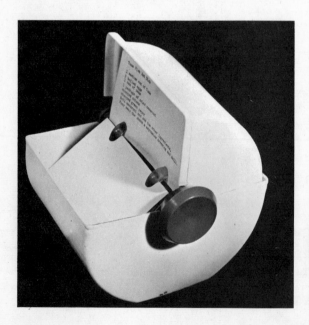

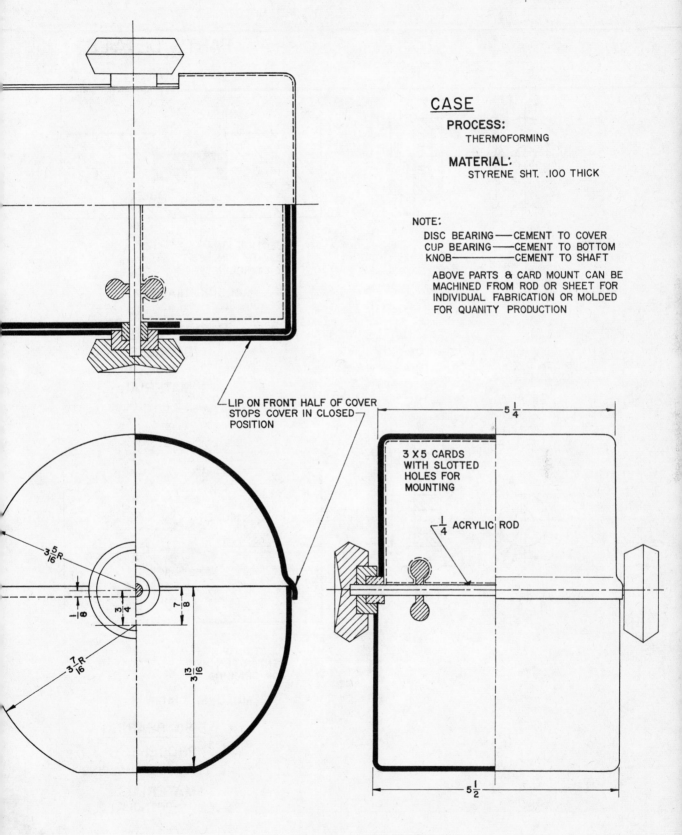

CASE

PROCESS:
THERMOFORMING

MATERIAL:
STYRENE SHT. .100 THICK

NOTE:
DISC BEARING——CEMENT TO COVER
CUP BEARING——CEMENT TO BOTTOM
KNOB————————CEMENT TO SHAFT

ABOVE PARTS & CARD MOUNT CAN BE
MACHINED FROM ROD OR SHEET FOR
INDIVIDUAL FABRICATION OR MOLDED
FOR QUANITY PRODUCTION

LIP ON FRONT HALF OF COVER
STOPS COVER IN CLOSED
POSITION

3 X 5 CARDS
WITH SLOTTED
HOLES FOR
MOUNTING

$\frac{1}{4}$ ACRYLIC ROD

$5\frac{1}{4}$

$5\frac{1}{2}$

$3\frac{5}{16}$R

$3\frac{7}{16}$R

$\frac{1}{8}$

$\frac{3}{4}$

$\frac{7}{8}$

$3\frac{13}{16}$

PARTS DETAILS

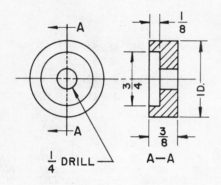

$\frac{1}{4}$ DRILL

A—A

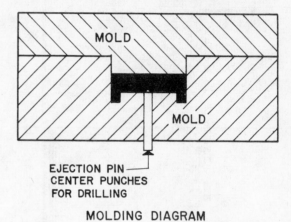

EJECTION PIN
CENTER PUNCHES
FOR DRILLING

MOLDING DIAGRAM

CUP BEARING

PROCESS:
COMP. MOLDING

MATERIAL:
PHENOLIC

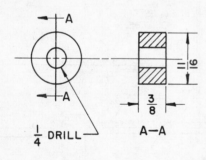

$\frac{1}{4}$ DRILL

A—A

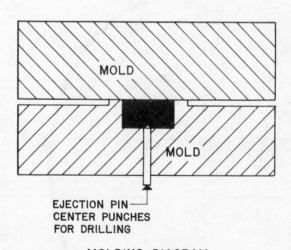

EJECTION PIN
CENTER PUNCHES
FOR DRILLING

MOLDING DIAGRAM

DISC BEARING

PROCESS:
COMP. MOLDING

MATERIAL:
PHENOLIC

PARTS DETAILS

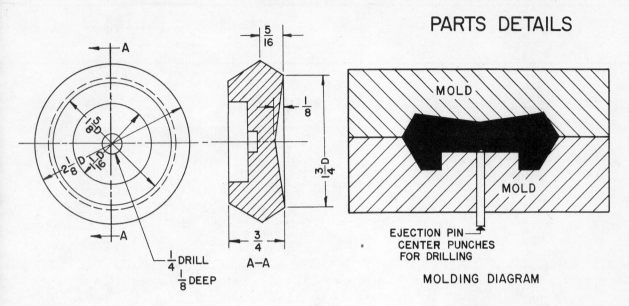

$\frac{5}{16}$

$\frac{1}{8}$

$\frac{3}{4}$D

$2\frac{1}{8}$D

$\frac{1}{16}$D

$\frac{5}{8}$D

$\frac{3}{4}$

A—A

$\frac{1}{4}$ DRILL
$\frac{1}{8}$ DEEP

MOLD

MOLD

EJECTION PIN
CENTER PUNCHES
FOR DRILLING

MOLDING DIAGRAM

KNOB

PROCESS:
COMP. MOLDING

MATERIAL:
PHENOLIC

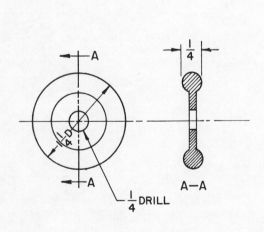

$\frac{1}{4}$

$\frac{1}{4}$D

A—A

$\frac{1}{4}$ DRILL

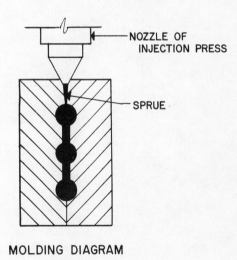

NOZZLE OF
INJECTION PRESS

SPRUE

MOLDING DIAGRAM

CARD MOUNT

PROCESS:
INJECTION MOLDING

MATERIAL:
POLYSTYRENE

appendix

Bibliography

Akin, Russell B. *Acetal Resins*. New York: Reinhold Publishing Corp., 1962.

Allcott, John V. *Plastics Today*. New York: Oxford University Press, Inc., 1960.

Ansley, Arthur C. *Manufacturing Methods and Processes*. Philadelphia: Chilton Company, 1957.

Arnold, L. K. *Plastics as Materials of Construction*. Ames, Iowa: Iowa State University, Iowa State University Press, 1958.

Bick, Alexander. *Plastics: Projects and Procedures with Polyesters*. Milwaukee: The Bruce Publishing Co., 1962.

Bjorksten, J., *et al. Polyesters and Their Applications*. New York: Reinhold Publishing Corp., 1956.

Blais, John F. *Amino Resins*. New York: Reinhold Publishing Corp., 1959.

Brenner, Walter, *et al. High Temperature Plastics*. New York: Reinhold Publishing Corp., 1962.

Butler, James. *Compression and Transfer Molding of Plastics*. New York: Interscience Publishers, Inc., 1960.

Butzko, Robert L. *Plastic Sheet Forming*. New York: Reinhold Publishing Corp., 1958.

Buyer's Guide to Plastics Materials and Machinery and Equipment for the Plastics Industry. London: British Plastics Federation, 1963.

Carswell, Thomas S. *High Polymers*. New York: John Wiley & Sons, Inc., 1947.

Cherry, Raymond. *General Plastics*. Bloomington, Illinois: McKnight & McKnight Publishing Co., 1965.

Christopher, William F., and Fox, Daniel W. *Polycarbonates*. New York: Reinhold Publishing Co., 1962.

Cook, J. Gordon. *Miracle of Plastics*. New York: The Dial Press, Inc., 1962.

Cope, Dwight. *Plastics Book*. Homewood, Illinois: Goodheart-Wilcox Co., 1957.

Dearle, D. A. *Opportunities in Plastics*. New York: Vocational Guidance Manuals, 1953.

Delmonte, John. *Metal-Filled Plastics*. New York: Reinhold Publishing Corp., 1961.

———— *Plastics Molding*. New York: John Wiley & Sons, Inc., 1952.

Dombrow, Bernard. *Polyurethanes*. New York: Reinhold Publishing Corp., 1957.

Duffin, D. J. *Laminated Plastics*. New York: Reinhold Publishing Corp., 1958.

Edwards, Lauton. *Industrial Arts Plastics*. Peoria, Illinois: Chas. A. Bennett Co., Inc., 1964.

————. *Making Things of Plastics*. Peoria, Illinois: Chas. A. Bennett Co., Inc., 1954.

Floyd, Don E. *Polyamide Plastics*. New York: Reinhold Publishing Corp., 1958.

Gibbs & Cox, Inc. *Marine Design Manual for Fiber Glass Reinforced Plastics*. New York: McGraw-Hill Book Co., Inc., 1960.

Golding, Brage. *Polymers and Resins: Their Chemistry and Chemical Engineering.* Princeton, New Jersey: D. Van Nostrand Co., Inc., 1959.

Gould, David F. *Phenolic Plastics.* New York: Reinhold Publishing Corp., 1959.

Griff, Allen L. *Plastics Extrusion Technology.* New York: Reinhold Publishing Corp., 1962.

Horn, Milton B. *Acrylic Plastics.* New York: Reinhold Publishing Corp., 1960.

Jones, David A., and Mullen, Thomas A. *Blow Molding.* New York: Reinhold Publishing Corp., 1962.

Kinney, G. F. *Engineering Properties and Applications of Plastics.* New York: John Wiley & Sons, Inc., 1957.

Kortz, H. E. *Instructions for Professional Production of Laminate and Cast Plastic Tools and Dies.* Warren, Michigan: Mainland Plastics Industries, 1958.

Kresser, Theodore O. J. *Polyethylene.* New York: Reinhold Publishing Corp., 1957.

————, *Polypropylene.* New York: Reinhold Publishing Corp., 1960.

Lappin, Alvin R. *Plastics Projects and Techniques.* Bloomington, Illinois: McKnight & McKnight Publishing Co., 1965.

Lawrence, John R. *Polyester Resins.* New York: Reinhold Publishing Corp., 1960.

Lee, Henry, and Neville, Kris. *Epoxy Resins.* New York: McGraw-Hill Book Co., Inc., 1957.

Martens, C. R. *Alkyd Resins.* New York: Reinhold Publishing Corp., 1961.

Meals, Robert N., and Lewis, Frederick M. *Silicones.* New York: Reinhold Publishing Corp., 1959.

Melville, Sir H. W. *Big Molecules.* New York: The MacMillan Co., 1958.

Morgan, Phillip (ed.). *Glass Reinforced Plastics.* New York: Philosophical Library, Inc., 1957.

Mosle, Ernest P. *Runnerless Molding.* New York: Reinhold Publishing Corp., 1960.

Narcus, Harold. *Metallizing of Plastics.* New York: Reinhold Publishing Corp., 1960.

Neumann, J. A., and Bockoff, F. J. *Welding of Plastics.* New York: Reinhold Publishing Corp., 1959.

O'Neill, J. M. *Fabricating with Formica.* Milwaukee: The Bruce Publishing Co., 1958.

Packaging with Plastics: A Progress Report. New York: American Management Association, Inc., 1959.

Paist, Walter D. *Cellulosics.* New York: Reinhold Publishing Corp., 1958.

Plastic Sheet Forming. New York: American Management Association, Inc., 1958.

Plastics Processing Industry, The. New York: The Tarnell Co., 1962.

Redfarm, C. A., and Bedford, J. *Experimental Plastics for Students.* New York: Interscience Publishers, Inc., 1960.

Resins, Rubbers, Plastics Yearbook. New York: Interscience Publishers, Inc. (published yearly).

Riley, Malcolm W. *Plastics Tooling.* New York: Reinhold Publishing Corp., 1961.

Rudner, Merritt A. *Fluorocarbons.* New York: Reinhold Publishing Corp., 1958.

Simonds, Herbert R. *Source Book of New Plastics.* New York: Reinhold Publishing Corp., 1961.

————, and Church, James M. *Concise Guide to Plastics.* New York: Reinhold Publishing Corp., 1963.

Skeist, Irving. *Epoxy Resins.* New York: Reinhold Publishing Corp., 1958.

Smith, W. Maye. *Vinyl Resins.* New York: Reinhold Publishing Corp., 1958 .

Society of the Plastics Industry. *Plastics Engineering Handbook.* New York: Reinhold Publishing Corp., 1960.

Sonneborn, Ralph H. *Fiber Glass Reinforced Plastics.* New York: Reinhold Publishing Corp., 1954.

Stannett, Vivian. *Cellulose Acetate Plastics.* New York: Chemical Publishing Co., Inc., 1951.

Steele, Gerald L. *Fiber Glass, Projects and Procedures.* Bloomington, Illinois: McKnight & McKnight Publishing Co., 1962.

Teach, William C., and Kiessling, George C. *Polystyrene*. New York: Reinhold Publishing Corp., 1960.

Thompson, G. S. *Gum Plastics*. New York: Reinhold Publishing Corp., 1958.

Turner, James O. *Plastics in Nuclear Engineering*. New York: Reinhold Publishing Corp., 1961.

Winding, C. C., and Heatt, G. D. *Polymeric Materials*. New York: McGraw-Hill Book Co., Inc., 1961.

Zade, H. D. *Heat-Sealing and High-Frequency Welding of Plastics*. New York: Interscience Publishers, Inc., 1959.

Note: The long dash indicates that the name of the author of the previous listing is repeated.

Plastics Periodicals

CANADIAN PLASTICS, 341 Church St., Toronto, Ontario, Canada.

INDUSTRIAL DESIGN, Whitney Publications, Inc., 18 E. 50th St., New York 22, N. Y.

MATERIALS IN DESIGN ENGINEERING, 430 Park Ave., New York 22, N. Y.

MODERN PACKAGING (Includes a yearly *Modern Packaging Encyclopedia*), 770 Lexington Ave., New York 21, N. Y.

MODERN PLASTICS (Includes a yearly *Modern Plastics Encyclopedia*), 770 Lexington Ave., New York 21, N. Y.

PLASTICS DESIGN AND PROCESSING, Box 148, Libertyville, Ill.

PLASTICS TECHNOLOGY, 630 Third Ave., New York 17, N. Y.

PLASTICS WORLD, 1 River Road, Cos Cob, Conn.

PROGRESSIVE PLASTICS, 481 University Ave., Toronto 2, Ontario, Canada.

SPE JOURNAL, Society of Plastics Engineers, 65 Prospect St., Stanford, Conn.

WESTERN PLASTICS, 274 Brannon St., San Francisco, Cal.

Trade Publications

BAKELITE REVIEW (quarterly), Union Carbide Corp., Plastics Division, 270 Park Avenue, New York, N. Y.

CHEMMUNIGNÉ, Atlas Powder Co., Wilmington 99, Delaware.

DOW DIAMOND (quarterly), Dow Chemical Co., Midland, Michigan.

DuPONT MAGAZINE (bi-monthly), E. I. DuPont de Nemours & Co., Wilmington 98, Delaware.

DUREZ MOLDER (monthly), Durez Plastics Division, Hooker Chemical Corp., North Tonawanda, N. Y.

FORMICA WORLD (quarterly), Formica Corp., 4614 Spring Grove Ave., Cincinnati 32, Ohio.

GOODCHEMCO NEWS (quarterly), B. F. Goodrich Chemical Co., 3135 Euchid Ave., Cleveland, Ohio.

HERCULES CHEMIST (monthly), Hercules Powder Co., Hercules Tower, 910 Market St., Wilmington 99, Delaware.

MONSANTO MAGAZINE (monthly), Monsanto Chemical Co., Lindberg & Olive St., St. Louis, Mo.

ROHM AND HAAS REPORTER (bi-monthly), Rohm and Haas Co., Washington Square, Philadelphia 5, Pa.

Films

The films listed are general or semi-technical in nature and suitable for classroom instruction. Other trade films are available for specialized purposes such as sales or technician training. Films containing advertising are not included.

KINGDOM OF PLASTICS. 10 min., sound, color. Produced by General Electric Co. Available from several state university film libraries.

The film opens with a children's guessing game in progress, where the object in question, a plastic thimble, turns out to be neither animal, vegetable, nor mineral. The film then explains the fourth kingdom, plastics. The film develops the concept of thermosetting and thermoplastic materials. Though made in 1946, the material presented is still basic.

PLASTICS: INDUSTRIAL PROCESSES AND PRODUCTS. 24 min., sound, color. Produced by Audio-Visual Center of Stout State University, Menomonie, Wis. Available for purchase from the producer or for rent from a number of state university film libraries.

A survey of principles and applications of eight basic processes of the plastics industry: compression molding, transfer molding, injection molding, blow molding, extrusion, expansion, lamination, and thermoforming. Animation is used to explain principles of the processes shown in the industrial sequences. Consumer applications of the products manufactured are depicted. Major processes and products are visually reviewed. A teacher's guide for use with the film is available from the producer. Closely follows organization of this textbook as the author was the consultant for the production of the film.

FORMING PLASTICS SHEET MATERIALS. 12 min., sound, color. Produced by Di-Acro Corporation, Lake City, Minn. Available on free-loan basis from the company.

An industrial arts instructor (the author) demonstrates the operations of mechanical stretch forming, vacuum forming, and free blowing. Sample shop projects are shown.

MOLDING PHENOLICS. 20 min., sound, black and white. Produced by the Bakelite Corporation, 30 East 42nd St., New York, N. Y. Available on free-loan basis from the company.

Although the film deals entirely with phenolics, the basic principles of molding and the various types of molds are well explained. This film deals with molding in greater depth than does PLASTICS: INDUSTRIAL PROCESSES AND PRODUCTS. It should be used in an advanced course dealing specifically with molding.

ORIGIN AND SYNTHESIS OF PLASTICS MATERIALS. 16 min., sound, black and white. Produced by the Visual Education Service of the Office of the U.S. Office of Health, Education, and Welfare. Available from a number of state university film libraries.

Describes the process by which man has developed plastics materials by an analogy with nature's methods of combining air, water, sunlight, and soil. Steps involved in actually producing the plastics materials are traced through animation and direct photography. Though produced in 1945, the basic content is still applicable.

PLASTIC TOOLING AND PATTERN-MAKING WITH EPOXICAL RESINS. 36 min., sound, color. Produced by U.S. Gypsum Co., 300 West Adams St., Chicago 6, Ill. Available on loan from the company.

Illustrates industrial tooling and pattern-making with epoxy resins. It includes: (1) how gypsum cement molds are made to produce plastic foundry patterns; (2) how a large auto hood panel is fabricated from epoxy resins for use as a checking and sub-assembly fixture; (3) how epoxy resins can be used in regular die-fabrication techniques; and (4) a graphic representation of new techniques used to fabricate original models, molds for polyester prototypes, vacuum-forming forms and other models. Somewhat technical in nature, but excellent for advanced work in plastics toolings.

A listing of special purpose films in plastics is available in *Film Catalog of the Plastics Industry,* The Society of the Plastics Industry, 250 Park Avenue, New York 17, New York.

Equipment Manufacturers

The following companies supply at least one piece of relatively small versatile equipment suitable for laboratory, design, and experimental work. A more complete list, including specifications, may be found in the *Modern Plastics Encyclopedia* for a recent year, 770 Lexington Avenue, New York, New York.

Compression or Injection Molding Presses

Dake Corp.
641 Robbins Road
Grand Haven, Michigan

Pasadena Hydraulics, Inc.
1433 Lidcombe Avenue
El Monte, California

Erie Engine and Manufacturing Co.
953 East 12th Street
Erie, Pennsylvania

F. J. Stokes Corp.
5500 Tabor Road
Philadelphia, Pennsylvania

Logan Hydraulics
4901 W. Lawrence Avenue
Chicago, Illinois

Fred S. Carver, Inc.
5 Chatham Road
Summit, New Jersey

Hull-Standard Corp.
Hatboro, Pennsylvania

Atlas Hydraulics Division
3576 Ruth Street
Philadelphia 34, Pennsylvania

Simplomatic Manufacturing Co.
4416 W. Chicago Avenue
Chicago 51, Illinois

Guy P. Harvey & Sons, Inc.
40 Spruce Street
Leominster, Massachusetts

British Machine and Foundry Suppliers
Port Washington, New York

Van Dorn Iron Works
2685 E. 79th Street
Cleveland 4, Ohio

Newbury Industries
Route 87
Newbury, Ohio

Conapac Corp.
120 East 13th Street
New York, New York

Thermoforming Presses

Di-Acro Corp.
Lake City, Minnesota

Conapac Corp.
120 E. 13th Street
New York, New York

Thermomat Co.
623 Prospect Street
Trenton 8, New Jersey

Auto-Vac Co.
105 Meadow Street
Fairfield, Connecticut

Erdco Engineering Corp.
136 Official Road
Addison, Illinois

Precision Products Co.
252 E. 16th Street
Paterson, New Jersey

Atlas Vac-Machine Corp.
1287 Clinton Avenue North
Rochester 21, New York

Plast-o-Craft Co.
391 Mulberry Street
Newark, New Jersey

Extruders

Wayne Machine and Die Co.
23 Grand Street
Garfield, New Jersey

Killion Tool and Manufacturing Co.
56 Depot Street
Verona, New Jersey

Modern Plastic Machine Corp.
64 Lakeview Avenue
Clifton, New Jersey

National Rubber Machinery Co.
47 W. Exchange Street
Akron 8, Ohio

Johnson Manufacturing Co.
Chippewa Falls, Wisconsin

Reifenhauser U.S. Sales Corp.
60 E. 42nd Street
New York 17, New York

index